RADIO COMMUNICATION SERIES

BEVERLY DUDLEY, Consulting Editor

FREQUENCY MODULATION

FREQUENCY
MODULATION

BY

AUGUST HUND

Technical Consultant, U. S. Navy Radio and Sound Laboratory.
San Diego, California

FIRST EDITION

ELEVENTH IMPRESSION

McGRAW-HILL BOOK COMPANY, Inc.

NEW YORK AND LONDON

1942

PREFACE

The purpose of this book is to present an engineering text on frequency modulation covering both basic principles and the design of commercial apparatus. The practical applications that are described follow closely good present-day engineering practice.

Frequency modulation is a new development in the art of radio, and short cuts should be used only when the features that frequency modulation stands for are not violated. The main features are high-fidelity transmission and a modulation system that avoids some of the interference otherwise occurring in the transmission by means of carrier currents.

A thorough knowledge of the principles underlying frequency modulation is essential to an appreciation of the design necessary for the apparatus.

It has been necessary to make use of Bessel functions and customary calculus, but the reader will find that the engineering applications are simple, especially when the curves and tables given in this book are used. Some of the tables and curves show at a glance the band width required for transfer networks. The applications presented can be understood without a knowledge of the derivations. Detailed numerical computations appear throughout the text and in connection with design formulas. Numerical calculations often appear step by step so that the reader not well versed in such applications should have no difficulty in understanding how to obtain a design value. To some readers such a treatment may look tiresome and lacking in unity. It should be understood, however, that the unity of the presentation lies in the method of approach in the mathematical and numerical formulation of problems that occur in the branch of FM engineering.

It has also seemed necessary to use often abbreviations such as FM, PM, and AM instead of the long expressions frequency modulation, phase modulation, and amplitude modulation. It is admitted that such abbreviations have a certain degree of abruptness, especially when used as nouns. The reader will find, however, that sentences often appear much less involved when the abbreviations are used. This is a text on a new phase of radio engineering and many novel phenomena are explained and abbreviations for expressions that occur often can, therefore, be excused when, by their use, the remainder of a sentence becomes more prominent.

It has seemed advisable to describe phenomena and features in frequency modulation as compared with customary amplitude modulation

v

and phase modulation. The latter type of modulation is by no means the same as frequency modulation although some similarities exist. Because of this comparison, the text is also a book on the basic principles of all three types of modulations.

Simultaneous occurrence of frequency modulation with either of the two other types of modulation, as well as the simultaneous action of all three types of modulation, is treated in the theoretical part of the book. This is done in order to show that an amplitude limiter can be used successfully and without producing distortion only when amplitude variations are not caused in the primary frequency-modulation stage by the same stimulus that causes the desired frequency modulation. Besides, the theory of the superposition of different types of modulations may be thought-provoking about other applications not yet in use.

The text is divided into five chapters and an Appendix. The first chapter deals with fundamental relations. It discusses noise interference and wave propagation in the upper megacycle range of carrier frequencies, which are of concern in FM systems. It will be found that the field intensity now decreases with the square of the distance to the transmitter and that we deal essentially with only a primary service area. Since many principles are discussed in this chapter, much space had to be devoted to it.

Chapter II deals with auxiliary apparatus such as frequency modulators, frequency discriminators, and amplitude limiters. Much stress has been put upon showing that the speed of electrical actions in networks, partly due to their circuit elements, plays an important part in the best design of apparatus. For this reason a section on time constants was added in this chapter. In the section on amplitude limiters, as well as in the section on preaccentuators and deaccentuators, it is brought out how such apparatus are to be designed with respect to suitable time constants. This feature can also be noted in Figs. 80 and 85, which show apparatus used in FM receivers. In FM systems the linear tube requirements are of secondary importance, but the networks between tubes have to be linear with respect to amplitude as well as phase for the entire range of carrier frequencies belonging to the particular band width.

Chapter III gives descriptions of all commercial FM transmitters manufactured in this country. The descriptions are presented in conjunction with the results found in Chap. I.

Chapter IV gives a detailed description of FM receivers. A designer should have no difficulty in applying the given networks to his particular needs. Many receiver tests are also described in this chapter.

Chapter V deals with receiver and transmitter aerials as well as with feeders such as are being used in the range of frequencies assigned to FM stations.

The Appendix gives a detailed solution for the distribution of the modulation energy in the frequency spectrum. It is the width occupied by the significant side currents in this spectrum for which the transfer networks have to be designed and not necessarily the peak-to-peak frequency swing. The Appendix gives also tables for the integral-sine, cosine, and exponential functions that are so useful in computing the reactance and resistance components of high-frequency conductors. The simple numerical application of such tables and corresponding curves likewise given in this book is described in detail in Chap. V. There is also added a table for circular, hyperbolic, and exponential functions in terms of increasing arguments expressed in radians. The corresponding angle in degrees is added in these tables in order to have a comparison for circular functions. To express such functions in terms of radian units is especially useful in engineering solutions occurring in FM problems, since the modulation index, which is the ratio of the amplitude frequency swing to the signal frequency, is numerical. The references at the end of the Appendix cover most of the current literature and are intended for readers who wish to follow up certain phases of FM engineering.

The features of this book are, therefore:

1. The text is useful for the practicing engineer as well as for classroom work.

2. A critical treatment of nearly every phase encountered in present-day FM engineering is presented.

3. The text is complete in itself.

4. All theoretical derivations are applied to present-day FM apparatus.

5. Numerically and in gradual steps, it is demonstrated how apparently difficult mathematical formulas can be readily applied to engineering solutions, by the use of either tables or curves.

6. Many explanations are given directly in the illustrations so that the figures can often be used without consulting the text.

7. The treatment is thorough and should, therefore, also be of use to the expert in the field of FM engineering.

8. Inasmuch as special design formulas often have to be employed in connection with band width and the natural speeds of networks, this text helps to bring the information on circuit design up to date.

9. The importance of servicing and maintaining FM receivers has been recognized by the inclusion of text material on useful tests and complete alignment of FM receivers.

10. Inasmuch as Chap. I presents a general theoretical treatment of amplitude, phase, and frequency modulation, this book furnishes a comparison and evaluation of the three methods of modulation.

The author is much indebted to the publishers and their editorial staff, who have encouraged such a publication from the very beginning

and made invaluable suggestions while the manuscript was being prepared.   The author is indebted to Mr. O. L. Heeger, of the Radio
Institute of California, under whose auspices lectures on frequency
modulation were given by the author to a group of broadcast engineers.
This enabled the author to find out what is actually needed in the presentation of such a publication.   Credit is also due Mr. Clyde W. Tirrell,
Navy Radio and Sound Laboratory, San Diego, Calif., who has read
the manuscript twice with respect to exposition.

The author welcomes any corrections or suggestions for improvement.

AUGUST HUND.

Santa Monica, Calif.,
    October, 1942.

CONTENTS

FREQUENCY MODULATION

In commercial alternating-current technique, distortion in a current is generally considered an undesirable by-product. In communication engineering even pronounced linear distortion is often desirable since it can be used for transmitting intelligence, as is described in this volume.

In pure mathematics, certain functions lead to an infinite series of terms, which often do not yield a very useful solution. In this volume, Bessel and other functions are made use of and yield convenient design formulas for computing the band width and other circuit properties in communication systems employing phase or frequency modulation.

CHAPTER I

FUNDAMENTAL RELATIONS AND FEATURES IN FREQUENCY-MODULATED, PHASE-MODULATED, AND AMPLITUDE-MODULATED SYSTEMS

Inasmuch as a high-frequency (h-f) current is characterized by its *amplitude, frequency,* and *phase,* it can be distorted or modulated by amplitude changes, by frequency changes, or by phase changes. We can, therefore, have amplitude modulation (AM), frequency modulation (FM), and phase modulation (PM).

It is also possible that any two of these modulations may exist simultaneously or that all three types may occur. With present-day commercial practice only one kind of modulation, say FM, is desirable in a given system. The other two, if they exist simultaneously, are undesirable by-products.

A clear understanding of all three types of modulation is necessary in order to account for undesirable superimposed modulations of either of the two undesired types. A clear understanding is also essential since, besides direct FM systems, we have a commercial transmitter system where AM produces the first side-pair modulation product. In virtue of the action of certain circuit elements, this gives rise to PM effects, and in virtue of the further action of another correcting network gives a frequency spectrum distribution as though FM were the cause. This has reference to the well-known Armstrong system of frequency modulation.

1

1. Fundamental Relations.—The general equation[1] for the instantaneous value I_t of an unmodulated sinusoidal carrier current, as shown in Fig. 1, is

$$I_t = I_m \sin \alpha = I_m \sin (\Omega t + \theta) \tag{1}$$

This represents a vector of constant length I_m rotating in a counterclockwise direction with a constant angular velocity Ω. We note that, in the general case, we have a fixed relative phase θ. Now,

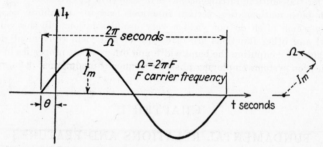

FIG. 1.—Current wave of amplitude I_m, period $1/F$ seconds and relative phase θ.

if a signal current of instantaneous value $i_t = i_m \cos \omega t$ is acting on a suitable modulator, we can affect the carrier amplitude I_m without varying either Ω or θ, thus producing AM. And if I_m and Ω are kept constant, so that the signal current varies only the relative carrier phase θ with maximum phase deviations or phase swings of $\pm\Delta\theta$, we have PM. If I_m and θ are kept constant and only the carrier frequency F, in $\Omega = 6.28F$, is varied by means of the signal current with maximum frequency deviations or frequency swings of $\pm\Delta F$, we have FM.

Referring to Fig. 2a, we note that for sinusoidal AM the carrier amplitude or carrier level I_m fluctuates periodically between the limits $I_m - i_m$ and $I_m + i_m$; i.e., the maximum carrier level deviations are $\pm i_m$ as is well known in the art. Full or 100 per cent modulation occurs when the amplitude i_m of the signal current, so to speak, "uses up" the entire carrier level I_m as the modulation takes place downward. This occurs for $I_m = i_m$ or for a modula-

---

[1] Inasmuch as in current literature on FM several different symbols are in use for the same quantities, the nomenclature adopted in this book is that used in "High-frequency Measurements," McGraw-Hill Book Company, Inc., New York. F stands for the carrier frequency since it is always larger than the frequency f of the modulating or signal current. Any measurable deviations from the carrier frequency F are denoted by ΔF. We then have $\Omega = 2\pi F$; $\omega = 2\pi f$; and $\Delta\Omega = 2\pi \Delta F$. This procedure seems logical and gives expressions that are clearer to the eye than subletters.

tion ratio of $K = i_m/I_m = 1$. If this ratio is multiplied by 100, we have the modulation expressed in per cent. A value of K larger than unity represents overmodulation and produces distortion and is therefore undesirable. Referring to Fig. 1 and to Eq. (1), we note that amplitude variations are in *quadrature* with respect to variations of the carrier frequency F and variations of the phase θ. Hence, customary types of detectors used for AM will not demodulate or detect any FM or PM currents.

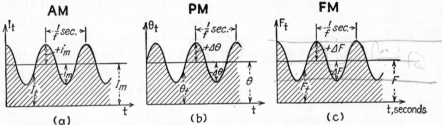

Fig. 2.—The three types of modulation. (Maximum deviations are i_m, $\Delta\theta$, and ΔF.)

With respect to PM, Fig. 2b shows that the relative phase θ is varied sinusoidally with maximum positive and negative phase swings $\Delta\theta$, which is now a phase variation and no longer a current variation i_m. In the PM generator we have, therefore, to translate a harmonic signal *current* variation into a corresponding *phase* variation. This can be readily done and is described on page 75.

In a similar way, for frequency modulation, the modulation cycle has a maximum amplitude which is now a frequency variation and is equal to the frequency swings $\pm\Delta F$. We need to have, therefore, a device in the FM transmitter that translates the harmonic signal *current* variation into a corresponding harmonic *frequency* variation. This also can be readily done in practice as is described on page 75.

Figure 2 shows another important fact, which should be especially realized when dealing with FM, whether direct or indirect.[1] This important fact is that the frequency f of the signal current, *i.e.*, the current that modulates the carrier frequency F, should not be confused with the maximum frequency excursions $\pm\Delta F$, which are caused by the signal current $i_m \cos (2\pi f)t$. As far as the signal frequency f is concerned, the signal frequency determines only the *rate* at which modulation takes place. This is

[1] By indirect FM is meant, for instance, a system like that used in the Armstrong transmitter.

true for AM and PM as well as for FM.   Hence, the signal frequency f determines only the *pitch* of the sound heard at the receiver.   Since ΔF is the maximum amplitude of the carrier frequency variation about the center frequency F, ΔF must serve the same purpose in FM as does the maximum amplitude i_m in AM.   Hence, ΔF determines the *intensity* of the transmitted signal and the *loudness* of the received signal.   Relatively small values of ΔF in an FM transmitter of fixed maximum allowable frequency excursion (*i.e.*, the largest value of ΔF that is permissible) then produce weak sounds, and the largest amplitude of ΔF, which should not be exceeded, causes the loudest sound.   For this reason the largest permissible value $\Delta F = \pm 75$ kc, as established by the requirements of the FCC, is sometimes called 100 per cent FM, although this term is quite erroneous, as will be understood from the discussion on page 15.

Inasmuch as FM occurs in quadrature to any amplitude variations, interfering amplitude modulations, such as some types of lightning flashes, will not affect FM directly.   A frequency demodulator with the reference operating point at the mid-point of its linear discriminator characteristic will not register at all such amplitude modulations at its output side.   Since FM is a variation along the *time axis* (Fig. 1), excessive undesired amplitude modulations can be avoided by amplitude limiters without diminishing the degree of FM.   This is explained in Sec. 19 in detail.

However, it can be shown (Sec. 19) that even an unmodulated superimposed interfering carrier can cause, in addition to AM, a "phase flutter," *i.e.*, an equivalent small undesirable "ΔF flutter." This flutter effect is avoided in modern engineering by using *wide-band* FM; *i.e.*, FM for which the desired maximum frequency excursions $\pm \Delta F$ are relatively large.   Hence, the desired frequency deviations will, so to speak, "override" the very small undesired equivalent frequency swings due to the flutter.

Even though in both FM and PM (see Fig. 2) the mode of variations in F or θ, respectively, seems the same, FM is different from PM as far as the actual results are concerned.   In both FM and PM generally we have not just one side-current pair, as with AM, but many side-current pairs   As will be shown, with PM the number of important side-current pairs depends only on the maximum phase deviation $\pm \Delta \theta$, but with FM the number of important side-current pairs depends on the ratio $\Delta F/f$; *i.e.*, it depends also on the pitch or frequency f of the signal to be transmitted. The energy distribution is, therefore, different for FM and for PM and, of course, also different for AM.

It should also be clearly understood (for details see page 31) that the maximum frequency deviation ΔF is *by no means always equal to half the band width* assigned to and required for FM. The actual band width approaches the peak-to-peak frequency swing $2\,\Delta F$ only for large ratios of $\Delta F/f$, which is generally satisfied by modern wide-band FM when the loudest signals are being received. Generally, the band width for which circuits have to be designed depends on the number of important side currents as well as on the signal frequency f. It should be understood that a larger number of side currents does not necessarily mean that the required band width occupies more frequency space (Fig. 13). Generally, a large ratio of $\Delta F/f$ gives many side-current pairs, but the spacing between successive side currents on each side of the true carrier F depends on the signal frequency f. Hence, if a certain ratio $\Delta F/f$ calls for 10 important side currents on each side of the mean carrier frequency F and the signal frequency f is 25 cycles per second, the required upper side-band width would be $10 \times 25 = 250$ cycles per second and the entire band width for which the networks need to be designed would be twice this value, or 500 cycles per second. However, if a 100-cycle note causes the same number of side currents (which would require in this case a larger ΔF value in order to keep the $\Delta F/f$ ratio the same as before), $10 \times 100 \times 2 = 2{,}000$ cycles per second or 2 kc would be the required total band width.

Since AM is a modulation in *quadrature* with the time axis of the carrier, and both PM and FM are modulations *along* the time axis of the carrier, we have a means for producing such time axis modulations from the customary AM, if we have the AM *carrier portion* act in *time quadrature* with the *unmodulated carrier level*. This can be readily understood from Fig. 3 where the vector *OP* denotes the carrier level I_m of the unmodulated carrier current $I_m \sin \Omega t$. When there is no modulation, this vector rotates counterclockwise with a constant angular velocity Ω. The instantaneous locus of P is a circle of radius $OP = I_m$. Suppose we have AM and at the instant shown in Fig. 3a the entire amplitude i_m of the signal or modulating current $i_m \cos (2\pi f)t$ increases the vector OP to a length OP_1. Then OP_1 rotates at this instant with the unchanged angular velocity $2\pi F$ since F is fixed for AM. Now, if a phase-shifting network causes $PP_1 = i_m$ to act perpendicularly, as in Fig. 3b, with the vector OP, then the resultant instantaneous vector OP_1 is no longer in phase with the unmodulated carrier level OP but is deviated by an angle $\Delta\theta$ from the inphase position. If the modulating vector had been $-i_m$, the resultant vector would have been OP_2 in Fig. 3b, of same length

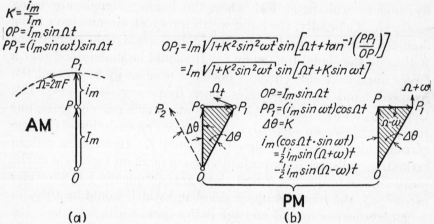

$$K = \frac{i_m}{I_m}$$
$$OP = I_m \sin\Omega t$$
$$PP_1 = (i_m \sin\omega t)\sin\Omega t$$

$$OP_1 = I_m \sqrt{1 + K^2 \sin^2\omega t}\, \sin\left[\Omega t + \tan^{-1}\left(\frac{PP_1}{OP}\right)\right]$$

$$= I_m \sqrt{1 + K^2 \sin^2\omega t}\, \sin\left[\Omega t + K \sin\omega t\right]$$

AM

$$OP = I_m \sin\Omega t$$
$$PP_1 = (i_m \sin\omega t)\cos\Omega t$$
$$\Delta\theta = K$$
$$i_m(\cos\Omega t \cdot \sin\omega t)$$
$$= \tfrac{1}{2} i_m \sin(\Omega + \omega)t$$
$$- \tfrac{1}{2} i_m \sin(\Omega - \omega)t$$

PM

(a)   **(b)**

Fig. 3.—Addition of carrier frequency component and modulation product.

as OP_1, but the angular shift $\Delta\theta$ would be in the other direction from OP. This is what occurs when the signal-current amplitude swings from $+i_m$ to $-i_m$; i.e., when $2\pi ft$ changes from 0 to 180 deg of the signal cycle. Hence, we obtain a PM with a peak-to-peak phase swing of $2\,\Delta\theta$. Therefore, the instantaneous angular velocity Ω_t is generally not equal to $\Omega = 2\pi F$ except at the moments of maximum phase deviation indicated in Fig. 3b. This means that in effect we have also "equivalent" FM since Ω_t can differ from Ω only when F undergoes equivalent variations.

Figure 3b indicates also the degree of PM since $\Delta\theta$ denotes the maximum phase excursion and is equal to $\tan^{-1}(PP_1/OP)$. For instance, for a ratio of the quadrature components of 0.5, we have approximately $\Delta\theta = 0.5$ radian, or $57.3 \times 0.5 = 28.65$ deg. With respect to the ratio PP_1/OP, which determines the maximum phase swing $\Delta\theta$, it should be understood that absolute linearity (no distortion) can exist only when this ratio is equal to the angle in radians.   This is strictly true only for small arguments of the tangent function, such as 0.2 and smaller.   This is the reason why in many practical applications in this text 0.2 is assumed as the upper limit.   Without resorting to the analysis for the 0.2 condition, we note by inspecting Fig. 3b that only for short lengths of PP_1 can we expect a PM with the entire length PP_1 as a portion of a circle.   If we have no true circle, then we have radius vectors of different lengths instead of constant OP values.   This means we have also a certain amount of AM.   Nevertheless, in practical[1] indirect FM work angles[2] not exceeding 0.5 radian or 28.65 (roughly 30 deg) are made use of.   Moreover, it should be noted that the length of vector OP_1 shown in Fig. 3b changes somewhat for such an upper limit as ± 30 deg and causes a small degree of AM, the effects of which can be avoided by means of an amplitude limiter.

Generally, the modulation vector PP_1 in Fig. 3b can make any angle differing from 90 time degrees, except 0 or 180 deg, with respect to the vector OP representing the unmodulated carrier level and still leave components that account for PM and equivalent FM effects.   But for such conditions we shall also experience more or less pronounced AM.   A system of this type may some day have values, though in present-day work where amplitude limitation is partly responsible for good FM reception, such vectorial addition of the modulation product is not advisable, nor is it efficient.

2. Basic Relations and Features for Amplitude Modulation.— Since with AM only the carrier level varies, *i.e.*, the amplitude I_m in Eq. (1), we have for the instantaneous carrier level for $K = i_m/I_m$, the relation $I_{mt} = I_m(1 + K \cos \omega t)$.   This is illustrated in[3]

---

[1] *Indirect* FM should not be confused with *equivalent* FM.   In indirect FM we have exactly the same frequency spectrum distribution as in direct FM, and hence *all* the features inherent with direct FM.   In other words a receiver would not disclose whether the received wave comes from an Armstrong transmitter using indirect FM or from a direct FM system.   This assumes that frequencies below 50 cycles are of no great interest as far as full modulation is concerned.   For equivalent FM the spectrum distribution holding for PM prevails.

[2] Such large upper limits produce about 10 per cent harmonic distortion.   According to Eq. (6) we have $f \Delta\theta$ for the equivalent carrier-frequency change.

[3] Figure 4 shows the case for $I_m(1 + K \sin \omega t) \sin \Omega t$ in order to show also equations for a sinusoidal amplitude variation.   If only AM is of interest, cosinoidal and sinusoidal amplitude effects lead to the same result, as far as the frequency spectrum is concerned.

Fig. 4. If the constant relative phase θ is ignored and the instantaneous amplitude I_{mt} is used instead of I_m in Eq. (1), there results

$$I_t = I_{mt} \sin \Omega t = I_m(1 + K \cos \omega t) \sin \Omega t$$
$$\overbrace{}^{\text{modulation product}}$$
$$= I_m \sin \Omega t + (KI_m \cos \omega t) \sin \Omega t$$
$$= \quad a \quad + \quad\quad b \quad\quad\quad\quad\quad (2)$$

showing that portion a is the original unmodulated carrier of level I_m and that portion b is the *modulation product*. It is this

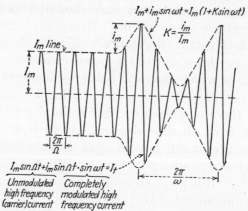

FIG. 4.—Amplitude modulation of a high-frequency current of carrier frequency $\Omega/2\pi$ by means of a signal current of frequency $\omega/2\pi$.

product which, so to speak, "handles" the signal or modulation energy. Hence, with AM the modulation energy is *entirely* in the side bands. The expansion of portion b yields

$$b = 0.5KI_m\{\sin [2\pi(F + f)t] + \sin [2\pi(F - f)t]\} \quad\quad (3)$$

It is this product that is produced at the output of a balanced amplitude modulator since the carrier portion a is balanced out or suppressed in such a modulator.

Inasmuch as the output power is proportional to the square of the respective amplitudes, we learn from Eqs. (2) and (3) and Fig. 5 that in AM for any degree of modulation K, the carrier amplitude I_m of the carrier frequency F is preserved unchanged. The *entire modulation energy* is added in the side bands only. Matters are entirely different for FM where it can even happen that the amplitude of the carrier frequency F disappears entirely or that a certain side-band pair or several of them completely vanish. Another important fact with AM is that in Eq. (2)

the term a and the modulation product are in phase with each other since both terms are governed by one and the same sine function, namely, $\sin \Omega t$. Another important feature with AM is that the evaluation of the modulation product b in Eq. (3) into two components of frequencies $F - f$ and $F + f$, respectively, shows that the lower as well as the upper side currents both have *positive* signs before the sine function. If these side currents are compared with the first side-current pair for FM (consult page 39), this will lead to a method by means of which the degree of FM can be found experimentally with the aid of a superimposed

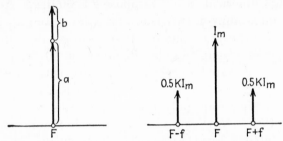

Fig. 5.—Carrier frequency amplitude I_m and respective side-frequency amplitudes $0.5KI_m$.

known AM. Furthermore, it gives a means for finding experimentally whether only true FM prevails or whether undesired AM also exists and to what extent it plays a part.

3. Fundamental Relations and Features for Phase Modulation. With PM the carrier level I_m, as well as the frequency $F = \Omega/6.28$ of Eq. (1), remains constant, but the relative phase θ undergoes changes. Hence θ is no longer fixed, but we have to deal with an instantaneous value θ_t, which, according to Fig. 2, for sinusoidal deviations is $\theta_t = \theta + \Delta\theta \sin \omega t$. Since in this case the maximum-phase offswing $\pm\Delta\theta$ corresponds to the amplitude $\pm i_m$ in case of AM, we can refer it to the original phase θ or phase level of the unmodulated carrier, just as i_m was referred to the original carrier level I_m by means of the factor $K = i_m/I_m$. Doing this with PM, we can represent the ratio $\Delta\theta/\theta$ by the degree of modulation factor K_p. The factor K_p indicates to what extent and portion of θ the phase is periodically advanced and retarded during the signal cycle of frequency f. Unlike the AM case, the phase degree factor K_p can be larger than unity. As a matter of fact, hundreds and even thousands of degrees of maximum phase excursions or phase deviations $\Delta\theta$ are desirable, especially if we think in terms of equivalent wide-band FM. This is important since, as we shall learn later on, periodic and other *phase* variations can be translated into *equivalent frequency* variations.

Using the factor K_p in the expression for the instantaneous phase, we have

$$\theta_t = \theta \left(1 + \frac{\Delta\theta}{\theta} \sin \omega t\right) = \theta(1 + K_p \sin \omega t) \tag{4}$$

At this point it is stressed that the fixed *relative phase* θ in Eq. (1) as well as in Eq. (4) is only a reference datum; *i.e.*, it has nothing to do with phase modulation. This will be readily understood from the following numerical case. Suppose θ is 30 deg. Assume that the periodic maximum off swings or phase deviations are $\Delta\theta = \pm 40$ deg. Hence, the carrier phase advances once during the signal cycle of frequency f an angular distance of 40 deg and retards during the same signal cycle to the other extreme position of minus 40 deg with respect to the fixed phase θ of the unmodulated carrier. It is, therefore, only the variable phase excursions that bring about PM. Now, suppose that the maximum phase deviation is still ± 40 deg, but that θ or the fixed relative phase is 90 deg. Then the unmodulated carrier has the form $I_m(\sin \Omega t + 90°)$ or $I_m \cos \Omega t$. This means only that the unmodulated carrier current indicated in Fig. 1 starts with maximum amplitude I_m, instead of with the much smaller instantaneous value I_t as indicated in the figure. This assumed carrier current is, therefore, only a cosine current as far as the reference ordinate axis is concerned. It is still of the same fundamental wave shape. Generally, modulations with such slow variations as correspond to audio frequencies will include very many cycles of the high-frequency current which is modulated. Hence, if this so-called "cosine wave" is phase modulated by means of a maximum sinusoidal deviation of ± 40 deg, the same degree of PM must occur as above. For this reason, it is correct to assume that, as far as PM is concerned; the value of θ in Eq. (1) stands only for the variable portion of the phase. Then we have for PM the formula for the instantaneous value of the modulated carrier current

$$I_t = I_p = I_m \sin (\Omega t + \Delta\theta \sin \omega t) = I_m \sin \alpha \tag{5}$$

where it must be realized that only the second term $\Delta\theta \sin \omega t$ in the expression for α brings about modulation. The term $\Omega = 2\pi F$ is not changed in the case of PM.

Nevertheless, something happens in regard to the *instantaneous* value of the *equivalent* frequency. This will become clear if we realize that $I_m \sin \alpha$ is still a vector of constant length equal to the unmodulated carrier level I_m. It still rotates in the conventional counterclockwise direction. However, as it tries to rotate with the constant angular velocity $\Omega = 6.28F$, the phase advances and retards or, so to speak, "flutters" forward and backward within the maximum deviation limits of $\pm\Delta\theta$, which for the foregoing numerical example would be ±40 deg. If these phase deviations swing through an angular distance of ±360 deg in $1/f$ sec, we should "wobble" over ±1 cycle around the true carrier frequency F. There would be, therefore, a gain of 1 cycle and a loss of 1 cycle and the net effect would still be F cycles per second as far as the carrier frequency F is concerned. Hence, the mean carrier frequency or the complete number of carrier cycles during complete signal-cycle periods, referred to a time interval of 1 sec, remains the same. However, the *equivalent instantaneous frequency* F_t of the modulated carrier current does *not* remain the same in the case of PM.

The value of α includes the phase flutter and denotes the arc in radians or the corresponding angle in degrees through which the rotating vector I_m moves in t sec. Therefore $d\alpha/dt$ must be the instantaneous angular velocity $\Omega_t = 2\pi F_t$ and $\Omega_t/(2\pi)$ must be the apparent instantaneous frequency F_t due to PM and due to the fixed frequency F. This yields

$$F_t = \frac{1}{2\pi}\frac{d\alpha}{dt} = \frac{\Omega}{2\pi} + \frac{\omega\,\Delta\theta}{2\pi}\cos\omega t$$
$$= F + \underbrace{f\,\Delta\theta\,\cos\omega t} \qquad (6)$$
$$\text{change in instantaneous}$$
$$\text{frequency due to PM}$$

Figure 6 illustrates what occurs in PM. The line OA denotes the position of the unmodulated carrier current vector of length I_m. If sinusoidal PM prevails, this vector flutters or oscillates about the mean position OA located midway between the extreme positions OB and OC. At the same time the entire XY coordinate system spins counterclockwise with the constant angular velocity $\Omega = 6.28F$. As already discussed, the symbol F in the expression $\Omega = 6.28F$ stands for the center or mean carrier frequency; *i.e.,* it stands for the number of carrier frequency cycles for one com-

plete signal frequency cycle when referred to a time interval of
1 sec. Since, according to Fig. 2, sinusoidal $\Delta\theta$ deviations prevail,
the vector OA moves toward the OB position at a rate determined
by the signal frequency f. At the extreme position OB the vector
must stand still, at least for an instant. The vector immediately
afterwards starts to retard its phase; *i.e.*, it starts moving clockwise with respect to the uni-
formly rotating reference axis
after having moved counterclockwise just before reaching the
extreme position OB. Hence, the
extreme position OB is a position
where no phase modulation takes
place at all and the true carrier
frequency F must prevail at that
instant. The vector OB moves
then clockwise over the original
position OA and toward the other
extreme, which is position OC.

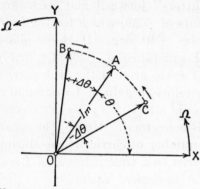

Fig. 6.—θ is fixed relative phase and $\Delta\theta$
maximum phase swing.

When reaching this position, the vector has to change over to a
counterclockwise rotation. Hence, the true carrier frequency F
must also exist for position OC.

The *fastest* change in the speed of the vector during this phase
flutter must, therefore, occur at the position OA, which would be
the correct position for the carrier frequency vector if no PM
existed. It is the *change* in this rotational speed that accounts for
the *equivalent* instantaneous carrier frequency change. In Eq.
(6) the change $f\,\Delta\theta\cos(2\pi f)t$ is caused by the time rate $d\alpha/dt$; *i.e.*,
it is caused by the apparent angular velocity of the resultant rota-
tion. By resultant rotation is meant the rotation of the XY
coordinate system with constant angular velocity Ω plus the
phase-flutter effect. Hence, we must have alternately instantaneous frequency maxima and minima in the position OA since
the oscillation of the vector about the mean position OA due to
PM causes the instantaneous equivalent carrier frequency to
increase and decrease. It is important to realize that, on account
of the time rate $d\alpha/dt$, a *sinusoidal*, PM causes a *cosinoidal* equivalent FM. These sinusoidal and cosinoidal functions have similar
shapes but *different amplitudes*. However, the shape similarity
does not hold at all when rectanguler, triangular, or other wave

shapes bring about modulation. Figure 7 shows this for the case where triangular phase swings cause PM. Along the ascending portion 1-2 of the phase deviation display, the time rate of the phase excursion is constant. Therefore, the equivalent frequency excursion ΔF, *i.e.*, the instantaneous frequency deviation from the true carrier frequency F, must also be constant and along the horizontal flat top 1-2 in the derived ΔF characteristic. All other portions of the derived ΔF performance are then self-evident.[1]

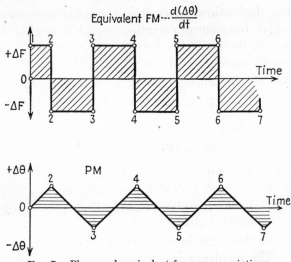

FIG. 7.—Phase and equivalent frequency variations.

The statement just made about wave shapes for sinusoidal PM entails another important fact, which is brought out in Eq. (6). It will be noted that the variable portion in the instantaneous modulated carrier frequency F_t, due to sinusoidal PM, is dependent not only on the maximum phase deviation $\Delta\theta$, which causes equivalent FM, but also on the *signal frequency f*. This equation shows that for signal frequencies of higher pitch, the equivalent frequency shift is larger than it is for frequencies of lower pitch, since the maximum frequency shift is $\pm f\,\Delta\theta$. That such a condition must exist can be noted directly from Fig. 6. For larger values of the signal or modulating frequency f, the speed of the phase flutter from A to B, back over A to C, forward again to B,

---

[1] For other illustrations consult "High-frequency Measurements," pp. 369, 373; "Phenomena in High-frequency Systems," p. 148, McGraw-Hill Book Company, Inc., New York.

and backward to C, etc., is larger than for smaller values of f. This states that for a *fixed maximum phase swing* $\pm\Delta\theta$, *more equivalent FM occurs for audio frequencies of higher pitch.*

4. Relations and Features for Frequency Modulation.—In FM systems, modulation is brought about by changing the carrier frequency F in the term $\Omega = 6.28F$ of Eq. (1). This means that the carrier level I_m and the phase θ are kept constant. Since in Sec. 3 we found that a sinusoidal PM of the form $\Delta\theta \sin \omega t$ caused an equivalent FM of form $f \Delta\theta \cos \omega t$, it is convenient to initiate (as far as the derivation[1] of certain formulas is concerned) FM by a cosinoidal frequency variation as is indicated in Fig. 2. We then have a deviation variation $\Delta F \cos \omega t$, if ΔF stands for the maximum frequency excursion from the true carrier frequency F. This gives the instantaneous carrier frequency value

$$F_t = F + \Delta F \cos \omega t \tag{7}$$

and the corresponding angular velocity

$$\Omega_t = \Omega + \Delta\Omega \cos \omega t \tag{8}$$

Hence, we may again assume a revolving vector of constant length equal to the carrier level I_m, but rotating counterclockwise with an instantaneous angular velocity Ω_t. This would give an instantaneous current value $I_t = I_m \sin \alpha$, where α denotes the arc in radians or the angle in degrees passed through by the vector I_m in 1 sec. The resultant instantaneous angular velocity in the presence of FM then is $\Omega_t = d\alpha/dt$ and $\alpha = \int_0^t (\Omega + \Delta\Omega \cos \omega t) \, dt = \Omega t + \dfrac{\Delta\Omega}{\omega} \sin \omega t$. The instantaneous value $I_t = I_f$ for FM then is

$$I_f = I_m \sin \left[\Omega t + \frac{\Delta F}{f} \sin (2\pi f)t \right] \tag{9}$$

[1] With respect to the discussion on pp. 64, 66 it should be understood that not in all cases can we arbitrarily assume cosinoidal or sinusoidal ΔF functions, whatever function (in this case $\Delta F \cos \omega t$) we choose for the derivation. The reason for this is that we bring about FM by changing certain circuit elements (for instance, a condenser transmitter is part of the circuit capacitance), or we reflect out-of-phase currents back into the frequency-determining oscillator branch and by phase balance bring about reactance modulations. Hence, the cause and the final action in the frequency-determining branch will tell only which function brings about variation in the carrier frequency. But in above derivation we are interested only in an expression of the modulation product, or products if several occur, and only with respect to the frequency spectrum distribution of the equivalent currents.

It should be noted that the amplitude of the variable term is now controlled by both the maximum frequency deviation ΔF as well as by the signal frequency f since the ratio $\Delta F/f$ is the equivalent phase amplitude. This can be understood if Eq. (9) is compared with the standard form given in Eq. (1), since $\theta = \beta \sin \omega t$ for $\beta = \Delta F/f$. Hence, FM causes also equivalent PM with an instantaneous phase θ_t. This fact is of importance and is described on page 33.

Since for FM the maximum frequency swing $\pm \Delta F$ has the same relation to the unmodulated carrier frequency F as had the signal amplitude i_m (Fig. 2) to the unmodulated carrier level I_m, we may call the ratio $\Delta F/F = K_f$ the modulation degree. It expresses what portion of the unmodulated carrier frequency F is modulated by the maximum frequency deviation ΔF. If this ratio is multiplied by 100, we have the expression for the percentage of FM. It was already mentioned on page 4 that $\Delta F = \pm 75$ kc, which is the present-day FCC ruling for maximum permissible frequency deviation, is by no means 100 per cent FM. Also it is not correct to state, as is often done, that in case of FM the degree of modulation can be "pushed" indefinitely. The theoretical maximum value that can be reached is the one for which the *entire* carrier frequency F is, so to speak, "used up" by the negative frequency swing $-\Delta F$, *i.e.*, for $\Delta F = F$. This does not, of course, consider distortion, since for such an extreme and severe modulation condition it would hardly be possible to design a reliable linear modulation system. It would require that chains of networks, not only pertaining to the actual modulator but also including frequency multipliers, would have to be designed for a corresponding band width of $2F$ for full-band transmission.

It should be clearly understood that Eq. (9), which can be written also as

$$I_f = I_m \sin \left(\Omega t + \frac{K_f F}{f} \sin \omega t \right)$$

is only the *outcome* of the instantaneous value I_t of the FM current. Equation (7), as well as the corresponding variation in Fig. 2, is the *cause* of FM. Hence, as far as the cause is concerned, it is comparatively easy in case of FM to translate a signal current $i_m \cos \omega t$, or a corresponding voltage, into corresponding frequency swings. If we compare the modulation degree factor $K_p = \Delta\theta/\theta$

in case of PM (consult Eq. 4) with the FM case now under consideration, we may think at first sight that an indefinite extension of the modulation degree K_p would be possible since K_p is normally many hundred, if not thousand, times larger than unity.[1] The relative phase θ has nothing to do with PM and we can imagine phase advances and retardations of thousands of degrees during the signal-cycle period. But Eq. (6) shows what the theoretical limitation is. In that equation the equivalent FM has an amplitude $f \Delta\theta$ and, when this amplitude is equal to the fixed carrier frequency F of PM, the limit is reached. For such a condition the entire carrier frequency F is, so to speak, being used up or canceled if $-f \Delta\theta$ acts. The attaining of this theoretical limit would give rise to great practical difficulties, at least with our present-day means, since a linearity of circuit response over such a wide frequency band ($2F$ for the full band width) could hardly be accomplished. In addition, this degree of modulation would require the entire frequency spectrum from the carrier frequency F down to zero cycles per second, even if only the lower side band were used.

For PM it must be further noted that the equivalent FM and, therefore, also the degree of equivalent FM, but *not* of PM, increases with the signal frequency f even though the $\Delta\theta$ swing is kept constant.

5. Side Current Distribution in Frequency Modulation and Phase Modulation.—Equations (5) and (9) show that as far as the mathematical expressions for the instantaneous values of an FM as well as of a PM current are concerned, they are similar and have the common form

$$I_t = I_m \sin (\Omega t + \beta \sin \omega t) \tag{10}$$

where

$$\beta = \left\langle \begin{array}{ll} \dfrac{\Delta F}{f} & \text{for FM} \\[2mm] \Delta\theta & \text{for PM} \end{array} \right\} \tag{11}$$

Equation (10) is the result of a signal $i_m \cos (2\pi f)t$ modulating a carrier $I_m \sin (2\pi F)t$ and the substitutions given in Eq. (11) give correct results as far as the frequency spectrum is concerned.

---

[1] For AM the corresponding factor K can never exceed the value of 1; for FM the corresponding factor $\Delta F/F = K_f$ can theoretically never be larger than 1.

Whether the time function of the β term in Eq. (10) has a minus value, or whether it is a sinusoidal or a cosinoidal function, is a matter of how the particular modulation is produced. This is discussed on page 66.

The solution of Eq. (10) is possible by means of Bessel functions of the first kind (for mathematical details consult the Appendix). Since Eq. (11) for the modulation index β holds for numerical values of $\Delta\theta$ in radians (which is numerical), and also for the ratio $\Delta F/f$, we have the same solution, as far as mathematical expressions are concerned, whether we deal with FM or with PM. For a maximum frequency swing $\Delta F = \pm 75$ kc and a signal frequency $f = 15$ kc, we have a β value of 5; for a maximum phase swing of $\Delta\theta = \pm 286.5$ deg[1] we also have $\beta = 5$. The solution of Eq. (10) leads to the *spectrum distribution*

$$I_t = I_m\{J_0(\beta)\sin\Omega t + J_1(\beta)[\sin(\Omega + \omega)t - \sin(\Omega - \omega)t]$$
$$+ J_2(\beta)[\sin(\Omega + 2\omega)t + \sin(\Omega - 2\omega)t]$$
$$+ J_3(\beta)[\sin(\Omega + 3\omega)t - \sin(\Omega - 3\omega)t]$$
$$+ J_4(\beta)[\sin(\Omega + 4\omega)t + \sin(\Omega - 4\omega)t]$$
$$+ \ldots \ldots \ldots \ldots \ldots \ldots$$
$$+ J_n(\beta)[\sin(\Omega + n\omega)t$$
$$+ (-1)^n\sin(\Omega - n\omega)t]\} \quad (12)$$

if ΔF, as well as the highest signal frequency f, is small compared with the center or mean frequency F. This is satisfied in commercial practice since F is in the megacycle range (for instance, 45 Mc); ΔF is at most ± 75 kc, and the largest f is at most 16 kc. That the application of this formula is simple will be seen from the numerical examples that follow.

This solution is very important as far as circuit design is concerned since its numerical evaluation gives the required band width that the circuits must handle. It shows, for instance, that theoretically an infinite number of side currents of frequencies $F \pm f$, $F \pm 2f$, $F \pm 3f$, $F \pm 4f$, etc., besides a current of carrier frequency F, are possible. Since a spectrum current, whether of center or carrier frequency F or any upper or lower side current, can play only a *practical* part when its amplitude is relatively significant with respect to the unmodulated carrier level I_m, the first step is to find the respective amplitudes of the carrier and the side currents.

[1] One radian is 57.3 deg since 6.28 radians are 360 deg.

The amplitude of the carrier frequency F is $I_m J_0(\beta)$. The value of β is found from Eq. (11), as already shown in the previous numerical case, where $\beta = 5$. For the FM case where the maximum frequency excursion ΔF is ± 75 kc and the modulating or signal frequency f is 15 kc, the carrier amplitude is $I_m J_0(5) = -0.1776 I_m$. This amplitude is only 17.76 per cent of the unmodulated carrier amplitude I_m. Hence, for an unmodulated carrier level of 100 amp, the spectrum distribution will show at the center frequency F an amplitude of 17.76 amp. We shall find further that, for both FM and PM, symmetrical frequency distribution around the carrier or center frequency F occurs. This means, for instance, that the amplitude of the upper side current of frequency $F + 3f$ has *exactly the same value* as the amplitude of the corresponding lower side current of frequency $F - 3f$. For the previous numerical example, the amplitude of these side currents has the value $I_m J_3(5)$. Since $J_3(5)$ has a numerical value of 0.3648, the amplitude, which is $3f = 3 \times 15 = 45$ kc below or above the carrier frequency F, is only 36.5 per cent of the unmodulated carrier level I_m.

We note already two essential differences between AM and FM from this numerical case. One is that many side currents are possible in FM. The other is that the frequency spectrum distribution of the modulation energy in FM is such that the energy is not entirely in the first pair of symmetrical side currents as it is with AM. In general, it is spread over several side currents including the carrier current of frequency F. A third difference is that for AM the equal amplitudes for the only possible side-current pair of respective frequencies $F - f$ and $F + f$ can *never* become larger than $0.5 I_m$, since for 100 per cent amplitude modulation $K = 1$ and the side-current amplitudes are, according to Fig. 5, equal to $0.5 K I_m$.

Moreover, from this numerical example, we note that for FM the spectrum equation (12) shows that for $\beta = 5$ the center-frequency amplitude is only 17.76 amp. Yet the symmetrical amplitudes of the third side-current pair, 45 kc below and 45 kc above the center frequency F, are as much as 36.5 amp; *i.e.*, these amplitudes are *larger* than the carrier-frequency component.

Since the side-current distribution equation (12) holds for both FM and PM, *exactly* the same numerical results for the respective amplitudes in the spectrum would hold for PM with a maximum phase swing of $57.3 \times 5 = 286.5$ deg. Hence, equal values of the modulation index β, whether due to PM or to FM, yield the same spectrum distribution.   In spite of this fact there is a *great* difference between FM and PM, since it is not only the value of β that counts but also the cause that produces this value.   This can be readily understood from Eq. (11).   For PM, the value of the modulation index is equal to the maximum phase deviation $\Delta\theta$. Hence, for a fixed maximum phase swing it does not matter whether a 50-cycle signal or a 15-kc signal modulates the phase of the carrier current.   In either case we shall have the *same number* of important side-current pairs with the corresponding amplitudes.   However, for instance, for the tenth upper and lower side current in the 50 cycles per second signal frequency case, the same amplitude pair is $10 \times 50 = 500$ cycles per second above or below the carrier frequency F; for the 15-kc signal it is 150 kc above and below the carrier frequency F.   Hence, the latter case refers to a much wider pass-band width.   This is discussed further in Sec. 7.

In the case of FM matters are different, since the modulation index β is directly proportional to the maximum frequency swing ΔF, which causes the FM, and *indirectly proportional* to the signal frequency f.   For ΔF fixed at a value of ± 75 kc, we find for a 15-kc signal frequency an index $\beta = 5$.   This causes in Eq. (12) approximately eight important side currents on each side of the carrier or center frequency F, and, therefore, a band width of $8 \times 15 = 120$ kc on each side of the carrier frequency.   But for a 50-cycle hum modulation, the value of the index becomes very large if the same ΔF value (as used in commercial practice for the upper limit) is preserved and β is equal to 1,500.   As will be shown, we have then an almost continuous spectrum distribution with essentially 1,500 side currents on each side of the carrier frequency and, therefore, a total band width of essentially $2 \Delta F = 150$ kc.   Hence, in the case of FM, the *number of important side currents is larger for the lower frequencies* in the signal band than it is for the higher pitch signals, even though ΔF is kept constant for all signal frequencies f.

6. Application of Bessel Tables and Bessel Curves.—Since to evaluate Eq. (12) it is necessary to obtain the values of the various Bessel factors, $J_0(\beta)$ for the amplitude of carrier frequency F, $J_1(\beta)$ for the amplitudes of frequencies $F - f$ and $F + f$, $J_2(\beta)$

for the side-current pair of frequencies $F - 2f$ and $F + 2f$; $J_3(\beta)$ for the next side-current pair of frequencies $F - 3f$ and $F + 3f$, etc., some useful tables and curves are given here as well as in the Appendix. The curves, although not accurate enough for many calculations, have the advantage of showing directly the variation of the amplitude values for FM and PM. The tables give more accurate results and a means for plotting certain curves so that graphical interpolation is possible. In the Appendix are formulas from which Bessel factors can be computed.

TABLE I*

β	$J_0(\beta)$	$J_1(\beta)$	$J_2(\beta)$	$J_3(\beta)$	$J_4(\beta)$
0	1.0000	0	0	0	0
0.1	0.9975	0.0499	0.00124		
0.2	0.99	0.0995	0.00498	0.00017	0.0000042
0.3	0.9776	0.1483	0.01117		
0.4	0.9604	0.1960	0.0197	0.0013	0.000067
0.5	0.9385	0.2423	0.0306		
0.6	0.912	0.2867	0.0437	0.0044	0.000331
0.7	0.8812	0.329	0.0589		
0.8	0.8463	0.3688	0.0758	0.0102	0.001009
0.9	0.8075	0.4059	0.0946		
1.0	0.7652	0.4401	0.1149	0.0196	0.002477
1.2	0.6711	0.4983	0.1593	0.0329	0.005023
1.4	0.5669	0.5419	0.2073	0.0505	0.009064
1.6	0.4554	0.5699	0.257	0.0725	0.014995
2.0	0.2239	0.5767	0.3528	0.1289	0.03399
2.4	0.0025	0.5202	0.4311	0.1981	0.064307
2.8	−0.2601	0.3391	0.4783	0.2728	0.10667

*$J_0(\beta)$, $J_1(\beta)$, $J_3(\beta)$, and $J_4(\beta)$ are the factors by means of which the carrier level I_m has to be multiplied.

Table I gives the successive amplitude factors by which the unmodulated carrier level I_m is to be multiplied in order to obtain the magnitude of any particular current in the frequency spectrum. It is just as easy to read the values from such tables and to apply them as it is to use trigonometric tables. For instance, for a maximum frequency swing of $\Delta F = \pm 20$ kc and a 10-kc signal frequency, we find that $\beta = \Delta F/f = {}^{20}/_{10} = 2$. Table I discloses that $J_0(\beta) = 0.2239$ is the value of the factor by which I_m has to be multiplied in order to obtain the magnitude of the component of the center frequency F. The value of $J_1(\beta) = J_1(2) = 0.5767$ when multiplied by I_m gives the amplitude of either the first upper side current of frequency $F + 10$ kc or the amplitude of the first lower side current of frequency $F - 10$ kc. It does not matter what the value of the carrier or center frequency F is, as long as

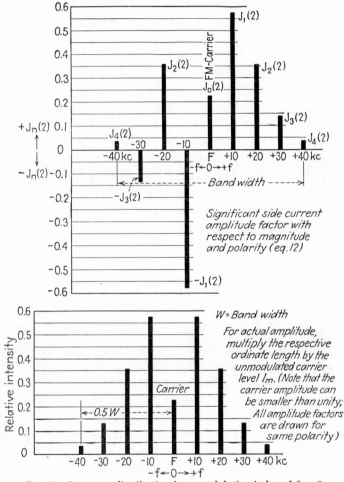

FIG. 8.—Spectrum distribution for a modulation index of $\beta = 2$.

it is large enough to accommodate the FM. The succeeding values in the $\beta = 2$ line of Table I, then, are the factors that give the relative intensities of the successive side currents more remote from the carrier frequency F. Inasmuch as all amplitudes are obtained by multiplying these Bessel factors by the same value, namely I_m, the magnitudes of the factors determine *directly* the relative intensities of the side-current pairs in the useful frequency spectrum. It is, therefore, correct if we plot only the Bessel values as shown in Fig. 8. Any other amplitudes farther away from the carrier frequency F than those shown have only a theoretical significance. The total band width is, therefore, 80 kc; *i.e.*, it is *much wider* than the peak-to-peak frequency swing $2 \Delta F = 2 \times 20 = 40$ kc. It should be clearly understood that it is the *number of important side currents* and their corresponding frequencies that *count in determining the required band width.* It is not necessarily the peak-to-peak frequency swing $2 \Delta F$ that causes the FM.

It must be admitted that without the preceding theoretical speculations it would hardly be possible to approach or to guess such design formulas as are presented in this publication. The assumption of such a relatively small frequency deviation as ± 20 kc, as used in the foregoing numerical example, is by no means out of place as far as practical applications are concerned. The ± 75 kc standard set by the FCC refers only to the *maximum* permissible swing above or below the carrier frequency F. The ± 20-kc case in the example refers simply to a less intense FM; *i.e.*, it refers to a sound probably weaker than the average loudness.

Bessel curves, as shown in Fig. 9, lead to even quicker speculations and are just as easy to apply as is the table of values. The $J_0(\beta)$ curve gives again the respective amplitude factors for the modulated component of the carrier frequency F for various values of the index β. It has already been mentioned that, unlike AM, we have in FM as well as PM a spectrum distribution of the *modulation energy* (proportional to the square of the spectrum amplitudes), which also affects the amplitude of carrier frequency F. Figure 9 shows this fact plainly. For the case when *no* FM exists there can be no frequency swing, *i.e.*, $\Delta F = 0$ and, therefore, $\beta = 0$. For $\beta = 0$, there exists only one Bessel factor, namely, $J_0(0) = 1$. The amplitude factor for the first side-band pair starts out with zero value and, therefore, no first side-band pair is possible. All other Bessel curves, such as $J_2(\beta)$ and $J_3(\beta)$, also start with zero values for zero values of β (shown in other curves but not in Fig. 9).

The $J_0(\beta)$ curve, as well as all other Bessel curves, resembles damped wave trains; *i.e.*, they *intersect* the zero or β axis. These points of intersection are of importance. For instance, this happens for $\beta = 2.4048, 5.5201, 8.6537, 11.7915, 14.931, 18.071,$

21.212, 24.353, 27.494, 30.635, etc., for the $J_0(\beta)$ curve determining the amplitude for the carrier frequency F. Hence, if the ratio of maximum frequency swing ΔF to the signal frequency f assumes such values as already given for β, the carrier amplitude must disappear altogether.

This leads to an experimental method for determining the maximum frequency deviation ΔF since the β values for which the carrier amplitude vanishes is known from the above values.

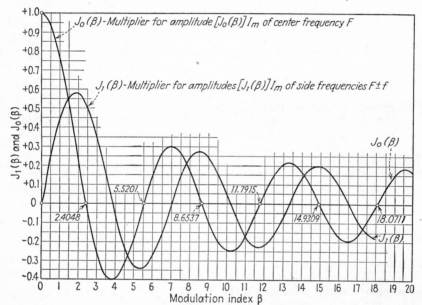

FIG. 9.—Bessel curves by means of which the magnitude or the amplitude of center frequency F and of respective side frequencies $F \pm f$ can be computed.

The signal frequency f is also known. The two curves of Fig. 9 show also that with increasing values of β the modulated carrier amplitude decreases at first toward zero. Then it becomes negative and more negative, decreases again its negative value, and becomes zero again for $\beta = 5.5201$. Then it builds up again to increasing positive amplitudes, etc. At the same time the amplitude of the first side-current pair also undergoes changes determined by the $J_1(\beta)$ curve. Table II gives the amplitude factors for β values up to 12 and for a spectrum distribution up to the fifteenth side-current pair, since $J_{15}(\beta)$ stands for the multiplier of the unmodulated carrier level I_m for the side currents of frequencies $F - 15f$ and $F + 15f$. For instance, the multiplier for the eleventh side-current pair for a modulation index of $\beta = 3$ is $J_{11}(\beta) = J_{11}(3) = 0.00000179$. Hence, this is a side-current pair that cannot play a practical part. Table II is very useful. In places where no values are given, the values are zero, or practically so.

TABLE II.—BESSEL FACTORS UP TO THE FIFTEENTH SIDE CURRENT PAIR AND FOR A MODULATION INDEX β UP TO 12

β	$J_0(\beta)$	$J_1(\beta)$	$J_2(\beta)$	$J_3(\beta)$	$J_4(\beta)$	$J_5(\beta)$	$J_6(\beta)$	$J_7(\beta)$
1	0.7652	0.4401	0.1149	0.0196	0.0025	0.00025	$0.0^4 21$	$0.0^5 15$
2	0.2239	0.5767	0.3528	0.1289	0.034	0.00704	0.0012	$0.0^3 175$
3	−0.2601	0.3391	0.4861	0.3091	0.1320	0.04303	0.0114	$0.0^2 255$
4	−0.3971	−0.066	0.3641	0.4302	0.2811	0.1321	0.0491	0.0152
5	−0.1776	−0.3276	0.0466	0.3648	0.3912	0.2611	0.131	0.0534
6	0.1506	−0.2767	−0.2429	0.1148	0.3576	0.3621	0.2458	0.1296
7	0.3001	−0.0047	−0.3014	−0.1676	0.1578	0.3479	0.3392	0.2336
8	0.1717	0.2346	−0.133	−0.2911	−0.1054	0.1858	0.3376	0.3206
9	−0.0903	0.2453	0.1448	−0.1809	−0.2655	−0.05504	0.2043	0.3275
10	−0.2459	0.0435	0.2546	0.0584	−0.2196	−0.2341	−0.0145	0.2167
11	−0.1712	−0.1768	0.139	0.2273	−0.015	−0.2383	−0.2016	0.0184
12	0.0477	−0.2234	−0.085	0.1951	0.1825	−0.0735	0.244	−0.1703

β	$J_8(\beta)$	$J_9(\beta)$	$J_{10}(\beta)$	$J_{11}(\beta)$	$J_{12}(\beta)$	$J_{13}(\beta)$	$J_{14}(\beta)$	$J_{15}(\beta)$
1	$0.0^7 94$	$0.0^8 525$	$0.0^9 2631$	$0.0^{10} 12$	$0.0^{12} 5$			
2	$0.0^4 222$	$0.0^5 25$	$0.0^6 25$	$0.0^7 23$	$0.0^8 19$			
3	$0.0^3 493$	$0.0^4 844$	$0.0^4 1293$	$0.0^5 179$	$0.0^6 228$			
4	$0.0^2 403$	$0.0^3 94$	$0.0^3 195$	$0.0^4 37$	$0.0^5 624$			
5	0.01841	$0.0^2 552$	$0.0^2 1468$	$0.0^3 351$	$0.0^4 763$			
6	0.05653	0.0212	$0.0^2 696$	$0.0^2 205$	$0.0^3 545$			
7	0.128	0.0589	0.02354	$0.0^2 833$	$0.0^2 266$			
8	0.2235	0.1263	0.0608	0.0256	0.0096	0.0033		
9	0.3051	0.2149	0.1247	0.0622	0.0274	0.0108	0.0039	
10	0.3179	0.2919	0.2075	0.1231	0.0634	0.0297	0.012	0.00451
11	0.225	0.3089	0.2804	0.201	0.1216	0.0643	0.0304	0.013
12	0.0451	0.2304	0.3005	0.2704	0.1953	0.1201	0.065	0.032

These factors multiplied by I_m yield the various spectrum amplitudes.

Figure 10 shows a very convenient form of presenting Bessel functions for use in estimating the required band width for circuit design. The curves are drawn for a constant modulation index β; the ordinate intersections with the respective curves give directly the multiplier $J_n(\beta)$, where n stands for the order of side-current pair.   For $n = 0$, we have only one current, of carrier frequency F. When, for instance, the $J_6(\beta)$ ordinate, *i.e.*, the multiplier for the amplitudes of frequencies $F - 6f$ and $F + 6f$, is of interest, it will be seen directly, without resorting to the more accurate Table II or to tables in the Appendix, that for ratios of $\Delta F/f$, as well as maximum phase swings of $\Delta\theta$, smaller than about 3, the number of

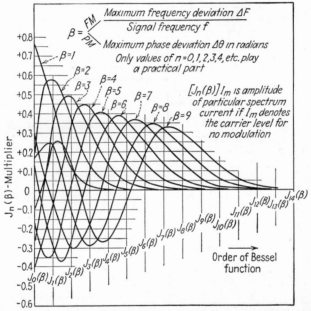

FIG. 10.—Curves for fixed modulation index β with respect to the order n in the function $J_n(\beta)$.   (By means of these curves the band width can be read off directly.)

significant side currents can never exceed six side-current pairs. A value of $\beta = 3$ causes practically a band-pass width of $2 \times 6f$, since six upper and six lower side currents play a practical part. A value of $\beta = 2$ requires only a band width of $2 \times 5f$, where f is the frequency of the signal current, *i.e.*, the current that modulates the carrier.   Further details will be given in Sec. 7.

Figure 11 gives a practical example of how the Bessel factors are used.   This example is for a case where the modulation index β is 10.   From our theory we know now that it does not matter whether we deal with the deviation ratio $\Delta F/f = 10$ in case of FM, or with a maximum phase deviation $\Delta\theta = 10$ radians or 573 deg in case of PM.   This is strictly true as far as the number of *important side currents* that play a part and as far as the respective *relative amplitudes* of these side currents are concerned.　But it should be understood that for PM the spectrum distribution of Fig. 11 holds for all signal frequencies as long as the maximum phase swing $\Delta\theta$ that *causes* the PM is kept fixed.　It is to be under-

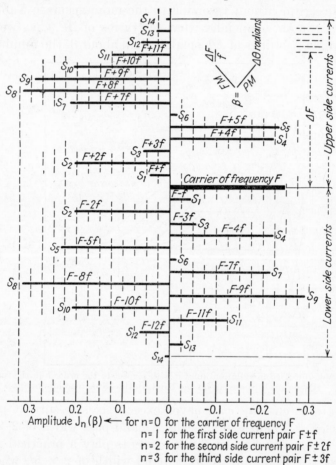

Fig. 11.—Amplitudes of significant currents in the frequency spectrum for $\beta = 10$.　(Note above distribution holds for both FM and PM.)

stood, however, that for a 50 cycles per second signal current the frequency spacings between consecutive spectrum currents is 50 cycles per second wide, just as for a 15-kc modulating current this spacing becomes 15 kc wide.　For FM, however, the distribution of Fig. 11 holds for the entire signal-frequency range only if the maximum frequency deviation ΔF that *causes* the FM changes *directly* with the signal frequency f, otherwise the deviation ratio $\Delta F/f$ cannot remain equal to 10. Hence, the maximum frequency deviation ΔF indicated in Fig. 11 is correct only for a definite value of the signal frequency f. For instance, for a 15-kc modulation frequency, ΔF would have to have a value of 150 kc in order to render $\beta = 10$, while for a 1,000-cycle note ΔF would have to be only 10 kc.

As far as the method of construction of the frequency distribution of Fig. 11 is concerned, use Table II and look at the various values on the $\beta = 10$ line. This line is especially marked in Table II for the sake of this numerical example. These values in succession are: -0.2459 for the carrier frequency F is the multiplier for I_m; 0.0435 for frequencies $F - f$ and $F + f$; 0.2546 for the next side-current pair of frequencies $F - 2f$ and $F + 2f$; etc. Table II shows that it is of no use to go much farther than to 14 side currents on each side of the carrier frequency since the amplitudes of additional side currents will be negligibly small. Hence, the band width for the modulation index $\beta = 10$ is $2 \times 14f$. This means that for a 15-kc signal the band width would be $28 \times 15 = 420$ kc; for a 1,000-cycle note it would be only 28 kc. We see already that the *highest modulating frequency requires more frequency space* as far as circuit design is concerned. For this reason a maximum deviation ratio $\Delta F/$(highest signal f) is chosen equal to 5 in modern transmitter design. Assuming 15 kc as the highest signal frequency, this value of 5 will give a maximum frequency swing equal to $5 \times 15 = 75$ kc. Hence, for the most severe band-width condition of $\beta = 75/15 = 5$, we find from the $\beta = 5$ curve in Fig. 10 that the curve creeps into the zero reference axis between the $J_8(\beta)$ and the $J_9(\beta)$ ordinates, but closer to the $J_8(\beta)$ ordinate. It does not matter how close it is since, according to Eq. (12), the ninth side-current pair must follow the eighth side-current pair as fractional side-current frequencies do not exist. The $\beta = 5$ curve in Fig. 10 shows only a small value for the eighth side-current pair and a value of practically zero for the ninth side-current pair. Hence, we have only eight side currents on each side of the carrier frequency F; therefore, we have a band width of $2 \times 8 \times f = 16 \times 15 = 240$ kc.

The transfer networks have to be designed for this frequency band width, whether they are located in the transmitter or in the receiver. Hence, the *i-f* stages in a receiver have to pass such a frequency band. This is also required for the input network of the discriminator (for details, page 78), but not for the discriminator or slope characteristic of the demodulator or FM detector. The reason for this is that the slope characteristic of the demodulator translates FM into AM and, hence, depends like the FM transmitter, i.e., the modulator unit of the transmitter, only on the maximum value of the frequency deviation ΔF. Hence, theoretically, we require a slope characteristic that can handle the peak-to-peak frequency swing for the condition of maximum deviation, which is $2 \times 75 = 150$ kc. Since the degree of linearity of a slope detector decreases at the upper and lower ends of the slope characteristic, it seems best to design the slope for somewhat more than 150-kc linearity.

That the maximum deviation ratio 75/15 takes care of the most severe condition, as far as the band width and the entire f range are concerned, can also be seen from the following analysis. Suppose we assume a 5-kc signal, then the value of $\beta = {}^{75}\!/_{5} = 15$. From the Bessel factors given in the Appendix, we find that at most 20 side currents on each side of the carrier can play a part. Hence, a frequency space of only $2 \times 20 \times 5 = 200$ kc is required. For the lower signal-frequency range, very large β values are obtained, resulting in, as a matter of fact, almost a continuous spectrum. For these low signal frequencies the band width becomes essentially equal to the peak-to-peak frequency swing, which is 150 kc.

7. Numerical Speculations on Frequency Swing, Equivalent Phase Swing, and Band Width.—An account has just been given of why a maximum frequency swing of ± 75 kc was chosen. Besides, the good feature exists that such a large swing can override undesirable phase flutter and its equivalent frequency flutter.

It is now of interest to learn how the peak-to-peak FM swing, i.e., the value of $2 \Delta F$, is related to the actual significant frequency distribution. We shall again do this for PM and FM. Figure 12 illustrates the case for PM and Fig. 13 the case for FM. For both figures the same amplitude scale was used throughout, as well as the same frequency scale. This permits, then, a direct comparison of the two. In Fig. 12 three cases are compared, but all cases are for one and the same maximum phase deviation of 5 radians or $5 \times 57.3 = 286.5$ deg. Only the significant side-current amplitudes are shown, which were obtained as described in Sec. 6. We note that for a 10-kc modulating frequency, the spectrum width required comes out as 160 kc; for a 5-kc signal this width is reduced to 80 kc; for a 1,000-cycle note the required width is only 16 kc.

Since with PM the modulation index β is equal to the value of the maximum phase swing $\Delta\theta$ which *causes* the PM, the corresponding side-current amplitudes for the upper, middle, and lower distributions shown in Fig. 12 are all alike. They have exactly the same magnitude regardless of the value of the signal frequency f. Hence, for PM and for *fixed* $\Delta\theta$ swing, we have *just as many side currents for the higher tones as for the lower tones*. However, the highest desired signal frequency requires the widest band width, just as was already found for the case of FM. Since we preserve the same number of side currents as well as the same relative magnitudes, all that happens is that for the lower signal frequencies the *energy spectrum is more crowded together*. This means that a band-pass network can be used more efficiently. By efficient use of a band-pass network is meant that the frequency space is more filled up with amplitudes that convey the signal. As far as the band-pass network design is concerned, this concentration of energy in a narrow band does not play a part. It is the width of the pass band, not the energy in a given width, that affects the problem of designing a filter.

With respect to Fig. 13, a constant frequency swing ΔF equal to 50 kc was assumed. In order to permit a clear representation, only cases down to a signal frequency $f = 2.5$ kc are illustrated in Fig. 13. Otherwise too many side currents would have appeared. Since for FM the signal frequency affects the value of the modulation index β, if ΔF that causes the FM is fixed, we have *more side currents* for the lower tones than for the higher ones. The filling up of the frequency space is due not so much to crowding the spectrum together as to an *increase in the number of significant side currents as the signal frequency is lowered*. As a matter of fact, the so-called "crowding together" of the frequency spectrum is limited. The limit is reached when the total band width due to significant side currents becomes equal to the peak-to-peak frequency swing, *i.e.*, equal to $2 \Delta F$. This occurs for large ΔF swings in the lower signal-frequency range. The higher the signal frequency, the more the actual band width required exceeds the peak-to-peak swing that causes it.

It is now of interest to learn what happens when small β values occur.   The representations to the right of Fig. 14 show what we may expect.   These Bessel factors for the multiplier of the normal carrier level I_m used to obtain the amplitude of the carrier fre-

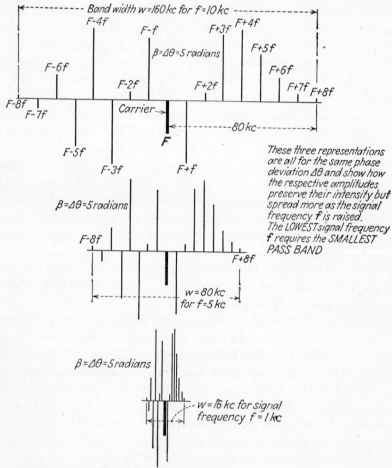

Fig. 12.—Current distribution for phase modulation of fixed maximum phase swing. $\Delta\theta = 5$ radians.

quency F, the amplitude of the first side-current pair of frequencies $F - f$ and $F + f$, the amplitude of the second side-current pair of frequencies $F - 2f$ and $F + 2f$, and the amplitude of the third side-current pair of frequencies $F - 3f$ and $F + 3f$ are again drawn to exactly the same amplitude scale.   The β scale is also the same so that a direct comparison of the curves is possible.

It will be noted that the multiplier for the modulated carrier amplitude of frequency F, which is $J_0(\beta)$, starts out with unity value; *i.e.*, its value is unity for $\beta = 0$ for which value of β neither FM nor PM can exist. The multiplier for the first pair of side-current amplitudes, which is $J_1(\beta)$, starts out with zero value.

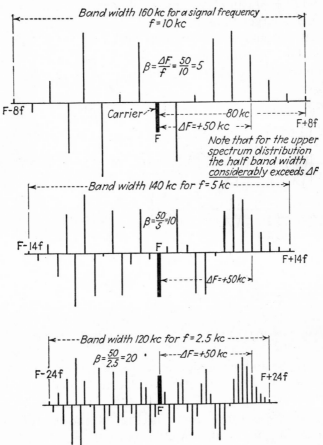

FIG. 13.—Amplitude distribution of the component currents in frequency modulation for different modulation index $\beta = \Delta F/f$.

The reason for this is that $J_1(\beta) = -d[J_0(\beta)]/d\beta$. Hence, for a portion of the $J_0(\beta)$ curve where the curve progresses horizontally, the rate of change with respect to β must be zero. Moreover, it is seen that for the second side-current pair the multiplier $J_2(\beta)$ slides into the β axis, for practical purposes at least, for values of β somewhat larger than zero. This is still more the case for the multiplier $J_3(\beta)$.

The representation to the left of Fig. 14 shows that the higher the order of the side-current pair, the larger the value of β has to be before the multiplier causes an appreciable amplitude of the particular side currents of that order.   For instance, the amplitudes for the eighth side-current pair corresponding to frequencies $F - 8f$ and $F + 8f$ can play a practical part only when the modulation index β is larger than 3.   Hence, any other still higher orders of side currents, such as $F \pm 9f$, $F \pm 10f$, or $F \pm 11f$, will have still less noticeable amplitudes for β values smaller than 3.   The $J_{16}(\beta)$ curve indicates that side currents of frequencies $F - 16f$ and

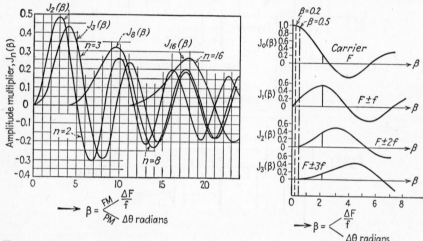

Fig. 14.—Relative spectrum current amplitudes change with the value of the modulation index β.

$F + 16f$ and the following side currents of respective frequencies $F \pm 17f$, $F \pm 18f$, $F \pm 19f$, etc., for β values smaller than about 11, for all practical purposes do not exist.   Hence, in the case of FM, such curves as those shown in Fig. 14 and curves shown at other places in this publication or plotted from tables, give a ready means of determining at sight how many side currents have to be taken into account; i.e., what band width the various circuits must be designed to handle.

It should be borne in mind again that with FM the maximum frequency deviation ΔF that causes the FM by no means always predicts the correct band width.   However, the maximum deviation ratio $\Delta F/f_{max}$ for a fixed upper ΔF limit will do this, since it causes the largest frequency spectrum spread.   On the other hand, with PM the maximum phase deviation limit $\Delta\theta$ gives

TABLE III.—ESTIMATING BAND WIDTH

$\dfrac{\Delta F}{f}$, radians*	Carrier frequency and successive significant side currents expressed in percentage of the unmodulated carrier level I_m†	Required band width	Maximum equivalent phase shift, degrees $\Delta\theta = 57.3\dfrac{\Delta F}{f}$
0.01	100; 0.5	$2f$	0.573
0.02	99.99; 1	$2f$	1.146
0.03	99.98; 1.5	$2f$	1.719
0.04	99.96; 2	$2f$	2.292
0.05	99.94; 2.5	$2f$	2.87
0.1	99.75; 4.99	$2f$	5.73
0.2	99.00; 9.95	$2f$	11.46
0.3	97.76; 14.83	$2f$	17.19
0.4	96.04; 19.6	$2f$	22.92
0.5	93.85; 24.23; 3.1	$4f$	28.7
1.0	76.52; 44.01; 11.49; 1.96	$6f$	57.3
2.0	22.39; 57.67; 35.28; 12.89; 3.4	$8f$	114.6
3.0	26.01; 33.91; 48.61; 30.91; 13.2; 4.3; 1.14	$12f$	171.9
4.0	39.71; 6.6; 36.41; 43.02; 28.11; 13.21; 4.91; 1.52	$14f$	229.2
5.0	17.76; 32.76; 4.66; 36.48; 39.12; 26.11; 13.1; 5.34; 1.84	$16f$	287
6.0	15.06; 27.67; 24.29; 11.48; 35.76; 36.21; 24.58; 12.96; 5.653; 2.12	$18f$	343.8
7.0	30.01; 0.5; 30.14; 16.76; 15.78; 34.79; 33.92; 23.36; 12.80; 5.9; 2.3; 0.8	$22f$	401.1
8.0	17.17; 23.46; 11.3; 29.11; 10.54; 18.58; 33.76; 32.06; 22.35; 12.63; 6.1; 2.6; 0.96	$24f$	485.4
9.0	9.03; 24.53; 14.48; 18.1; 26.55; 5.5; 20.43; 32.75; 30.51; 21.49; 12.47; 6.2; 2.73; 1.1	$26f$	515.7
10	24.59; 4.35; 25.46; 5.83; 21.96; 23.41; 1.45; 21.67; 31.79; 29.19; 20.75; 12.31; 6.34; 2.9; 1.2	$28f$	573
12	4.8; 22.34; 8.5; 19.51; 18.25; 7.3; 24.37; 17.03; 4.5; 23.04; 30.05; 27.04; 19.53; 12.01; 6.5; 3.2; 1.4	$32f$	687.6
15	1.4; 20.51; 4.2; 19.40; 11.92; 13.05; 20.61; 3.45; 17.40; 22; 9; 9.99; 23.67; 27.87; 24.64; 18.13; 11.62; 6.6; 3.5; 1.66	$38f$	859.5
18	1.34; 18.8; 0.75; 18.63; 6.96; 15.54; 15.6; 5.1; 19.59; 12.28; 7.3; 20.41; 17.62; 3.1; 13.16; 23.56; 26.11; 22.86; 17.06; 11.27; 6.7; 3.7; 1.9; 0.9	$46f$	1031.4
21	3.7; 17.11; 2.02; 17.50; 2.97; 16.37; 10.76; 10.22; 17.57; 3.2; 14.85; 17.32; 3.3; 13.56; 20.08; 13.21; 1.2; 15.05; 23.16; 24.65; 21.45; 16.21; 10.97; 6.77; 3.86; 2.05; 1	$52f$	1203.3
24	5.6; 15.4; 4.34; 16.13; 0.3; 16.23; 6.4; 13; 14.04; 3.6; 16.77; 10.33; 7.3; 17.63; 11.8; 3.9; 16.63; 18.31; 9.3; 4.3; 16.19; 22.64; 23.43; 20.31; 15.5; 10.7; 6.8; 3.99; 2.2; 1.1	$58f$	1375.5

* Holds also for $\beta = \Delta\theta$.

† First number denotes the percentage amplitude of carrier frequency F; second number is the percentage amplitude for side frequencies $F - f$ and $F + f$; the third number holds for frequencies $F \mp 2f$; etc.

directly a means for estimating the correct band width. This limiting phase excursion is directly the value of β and does not change with the variation of the signal frequency f. Table III shows what occurs when the β value is changed over wide ranges. All amplitude values are given as positive quantities, since the purpose of this table is only to determine the required band width for a particular $\Delta F/f$ ratio. The polarity of the various Bessel factors is, therefore, of no concern. The significant amplitudes shown are so chosen that the side currents for which the amplitudes are less than 1 per cent of the unmodulated carrier level I_m are neglected. This is quite conservative from an engineering point of view.

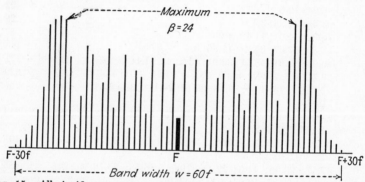

FIG. 15.—All significant spectrum amplitudes are drawn with the same polarity in order to show how the spectrum energy due to modulation is spread towards each side of the carrier of frequency F.

Examination of Bessel tables will show that the greater the value of the modulation index β, whether due to $\Delta F/f$ or to $\Delta\theta$ radians, the more side currents play a part. The modulation energy moves, so to speak, farther out on each side of the carrier frequency F. This gives a ready means of estimating where to stop with important side currents. For instance, for $\Delta F/f = 24$, we obtain the spectrum distribution of Fig. 15. Note that the largest side-current amplitudes occur near the edges of the pass band. Hence, it is only necessary to read off, for a certain value of β, the consecutive Bessel factors or amplitude multipliers until the very largest factor is reached. After this it is necessary only to continue reading off the following consecutive Bessel factors until, say, only 1 per cent of the unmodulated carrier level I_m is reached. Since all factors are multiplied by one and the same carrier level I_m, the unmodulated carrier level in terms of the

Bessel values is unity. This is the largest value that can ever occur since it holds for $\beta = 0$ and happens for $J_0(0) = 1$. If we are satisfied with significant terms, above 5 per cent of the unmodulated carrier level I_m, then we stop reading off values when the 5 per cent limit is reached.

The frequency band width in Table III is obtained by counting the number of significant side currents. For the value $\beta = 12$ we note that there are, in addition to the carrier frequency term of 4.8, 16 side currents on each side of the carrier frequency F. Hence, if f is the frequency of the current that modulates in FM, the required band width is $32f$. Following up the successive band widths in Table III, we note that there is a definite progression so that we can use this table for estimating any band width for values of $\Delta F/f$ or $\Delta\theta$ that are not given in this table but are within its range. For instance, a modulation index of 15 gives, according to this table, a frequency spread of $38f$, and a modulation index of 12 gives a spread of only $32f$. Hence, a value of $\beta = 14$ must lie somewhere between these two values. Good interpolation is obtained if we plot $\Delta F/f$ against band width. There are only two places in this table where the progression of additional important side currents shows more than a proportional increase. One such place occurs for $\beta = 7$. The reason for this is that for this value of modulation index β a side current was included that had a value of only slightly less than 1 per cent. It is the extreme significant side current shown with a value of 0.8 per cent. Because such an addition of one extra Bessel factor means two extra side currents, this will increase the apparent band width by $2f$. This side-current pair could have been neglected. The reason why side-current pairs below 1 per cent cannot have much effect is because the modulation power in each side current is proportional to the square of its amplitude.

Table III shows also that for *small* values of $\Delta F/f$, we have *only one* significant side-current pair, as for AM. The amplitude of the center or carrier frequency F is then essentially equal to the unmodulated carrier level, or at least practically so, for all values of $\beta \leqq 0.2$. This fact can also be seen from inspection of the Bessel curves given in Fig. 14. This leads, then, to a further simplification[1] of Eq. (12) since only the J_0 and the J_1 factors for these small values of β play a practical part.

[1] See p. 37.

The last column of Table III gives the values of the equivalent maximum phase swing in degrees. The values in the $\Delta F/f$ column are also maximum phase swings in radians. Hence, this table can be used for PM also.

We have, therefore, the formula

$$\Delta\theta = 57.3 \frac{\Delta F}{f} \quad \text{deg} \tag{13}$$

For $\Delta F = \pm 75$ kc, with $f = 15$ kc as the highest useful audio frequency to be transmitted, we find from Eq. (13) that the maximum equivalent phase deviation is $\Delta\theta = \pm 286.5$ deg. For the lowest useful audio frequency of $f = 50$ cycles per second, we have $\Delta\theta = \pm 86,000$ deg. This is a very large value of phase deviation if PM has to be instrumental in producing equivalent FM with large equivalent frequency swings. This difficulty can be overcome by causing PM with maximum phase swings, which are $\Delta\theta' = \Delta\theta/f$ and which have, therefore, all the features of FM. Fortunately, we have also methods available for multiplying the phase swings and, therefore, also the equivalent frequency swings. Methods are also available whereby the frequency swing can be multiplied much more than is the carrier or center frequency F itself.[1]

It is now an easy task to compute the degree of phase shift multiplication needed if indirect FM is used in a transmitting system. If we have to deal with indirect FM where the maximum phase excursion is never to exceed 0.5 radian or 28.65 deg, a phase swing multiplication of $86,000/28.65 = 3,000$ times is required for a signal frequency of $f = 50$ cycles per second and a maximum frequency deviation of $\Delta F = \pm 75$ kc. For the highest desired signal frequency of $f = 15,000$ cycles per second, a multiplication of only $286.5/28.65 = 10$ times is required. This shows why, with indirect FM designed for small distortion (about 10 per cent or somewhat less), it is the *lowest audio frequency* to be transmitted that determines the *order* of the deviation frequency multiplication required, if the maximum value of ΔF is fixed. For this reason, a value of $f = 50$ cycles per second is about the lowest signal frequency that can be handled with full ± 75-kc frequency swings, unless still higher multiplications than those brought out above are resorted to.

[1] See p. 121.

Generally, we can compute the value N of the required deviation frequency multiplication from the relation

$$N = \left\langle \begin{array}{ll} \dfrac{\Delta F}{f\,\Delta\theta} = p & \text{if } \Delta\theta \text{ is in radians} \\[3mm] 57.3p & \text{if } \Delta\theta \text{ is in degrees} \end{array} \right\} \tag{14}$$

and where ΔF and f are expressed in the same units, *i.e.*, both are in cycles per second or both are in kilocycles. For $\Delta\theta = 0.5$ radian, $\Delta F = \pm 75$ kc, and $f = 60$ cycles per second, the phase swing multiplication must be $N = 75,000/(60 \times 0.5) = 2,500$ fold.

8. Useful Formula for Small Modulation Index.—We have just seen that for β values equal to and smaller than 0.2, we have essentially only *one* significant side-current pair, as for AM. This holds true for both FM and PM. From trigonometric tables it is known that for such small arguments, *i.e.*, for values of 0.2 radian and smaller, the sine function becomes essentially equal to the value of the argument in radians and the cosine function becomes essentially equal to unity. This fact becomes clear if we realize that 0.2 radian corresponds to 11.46 deg and that smaller values than 0.2 radian correspond to still fewer degrees. For an argument of 0.2 radian, $\cos \beta = \cos 11.46$ deg $= 0.98$, which is practically unity; values smaller than 0.2 radian approach even closer to unity. For small arguments, $\sin \beta = \beta$, if β is numerical, *i.e.*, expressed in radians, and for $\sin 11.46$ deg, we find the value 0.1987, which is essentially equal to the argument 0.2.

Equation (10) shows that for both FM and PM, we have the expression $I_m \sin (\Omega t + \beta \sin \omega t)$ for the instantaneous modulated current. Putting $\Omega t = x$ and $\beta \sin \omega t = y$, we have the solution $I_m \sin (x + y) = I_m(\sin x \cos y + \cos x \sin y)$. But $\cos y = \cos (\beta \sin \omega t) = 1$ for β values equal to 0.2 and smaller and $\sin y = \sin (\beta \sin \omega t) = \beta \sin \omega t$ for such small values of β. We do not need, therefore, to use Bessel functions for such cases and have

$$I_m \sin (\Omega t + \beta \sin \omega t) = I_m(\sin \Omega t + \cos \Omega t \cdot \beta \sin \omega t)$$

Hence, if we compare this result with the case of AM taken from Eq. (2), we find for the instantaneous modulated current

$$I_t = \left\langle \begin{array}{ll} I_m(\sin \Omega t + \beta \sin \omega t \cos \Omega t) & \text{for FM or PM} \\[3mm] I_m(\sin \Omega t + K \cos \omega t \sin \Omega t) & \text{for AM} \end{array} \right\} \tag{15}$$

This relation explains why Armstrong uses a 90-deg phase shifter[1] in his indirect FM transmitting system. The Armstrong system, described in the applied part of this book, uses a balanced amplitude modulator, which produces only the modulation product since the carrier is suppressed. The 90-deg phase shift of the modulation product is necessary since this product is a cosine carrier function for either FM or PM but is a sine carrier function for AM. The 90-deg phase shift is caused by a proper plate load in the modulator. The FM effect is produced in the Armstrong system by applying a signal voltage that has a magnitude inversely proportional to the signal frequency f. This means that the amplitude modulation factor K in Eq. (15), for the conditions existing in the output branch of the balanced modulator, is no longer equal to the *original* signal level i_m divided by the unmodulated carrier level I_m, but is equal to $(i_m/f)/I_m$. The constant of proportionality is taken as unity for this explanation. This relation is expressed in terms of currents instead of in terms of the corresponding voltages effective in the balanced modulator. Each case accounts for the same value of K.

Since such an ingenious application holds only for small β values, as the foregoing derivation shows, the indirect FM, produced after the 90 time degrees phase-shifted modulation product is combined with the unmodulated carrier, is only very narrow[2] band FM. A large frequency deviation multiplication is to follow in order to satisfy the requirements of modern wide-band FM.

From Eq. (15) and its assumption of a small β value, it should be realized that only a small equivalent PM is instrumental (11.46 deg or less) in producing the desired result. Hence, if schemes

---

[1] That for FM as well as PM the modulation product must be at a phase angle of 90 deg with respect to the unmodulated carrier frequency term is due to the fact that we affect modulation in quadrature, if compared with AM.

[2] At most, only 30-deg equivalent phase fluctuation, which is somewhat more than discussed in connection with Fig. 3. It should be understood that after combination of the modulation product in time quadrature with the unmodulated carrier, we have actually all the features of direct FM in this case. The effect produced is not $\Delta\theta$ as would be the case for $K = i_m/I_m$, but is $\Delta\theta/f = \beta$. This has exactly the same form as $\Delta F/f = \beta$ and, hence, the modulation index β has not only the same numerical value as for FM but also the same $1/f$ effect behind it. The spectrum distribution is, therefore, as for actual or direct FM for the entire signal-frequency range. It should be also understood that for a *certain* signal frequency, FM and PM can have the same spectrum distribution but *not* for the entire signal-frequency range.

are used that give considerably larger phase excursions, then the 90-deg phase-shift method in its present-day form cannot lead to distortionless modulation[1] and another scheme than that employed in the Armstrong transmitter must be used.

There is more to be studied in the results of Eq. (15). Expand the modulation product into the two side components (upper and lower side currents of respective frequencies $F + f$ and $F - f$) and compare these side currents with the case of AM. We find that, for $\beta \leq 0.2$, the respective modulation products b when expanded are

$$
b = \begin{cases}
\beta(\cos \Omega t \sin \omega t) = 0.5\beta[\sin (\Omega + \omega)t - \sin (\Omega - \omega)t] & \text{for FM} \\
\\
K(\sin \Omega t \cos \omega t) = 0.5K[\sin (\Omega + \omega)t + \sin (\Omega - \omega)t] & \text{for AM}
\end{cases}
$$

Hence, for $\beta \leq 0.2$ we have the important spectrum currents

$$
I_t = \begin{cases}
I_m(\sin (2\pi F)t + 0.5\beta\{\sin [2\pi(F + f)t] \\
\qquad\qquad - \sin [2\pi(F - f)t]\}) & \text{for FM} \\
\\
I_m(\sin (2\pi F)t + 0.5K\{\sin [2\pi(F + f)t] \\
\qquad\qquad + \sin [2\pi(F - f)t]\}) & \text{for AM}
\end{cases} \tag{16}
$$

where $\beta = \Delta F/f$ in this case.[2] The relation for FM can also be directly obtained from the general spectrum solution (12) for $\beta \leq 0.2$. For such a small modulation index, Eq. (12) simplifies to a carrier of frequency F and amplitude $[J_0(\beta)]I_m$, and only one side-current pair of respective frequencies $F \mp f$ with both amplitudes equal to $[J_1(\beta)]I_m$. Table I shows that for $\beta = 0.2$ we have an amplitude factor $J_0(0.2) = 0.99$, which is practically unity; hence, $J_0(0.2)I_m = I_m$ in Eq. (12). Table I shows also that $J_1(0.2) = 0.0995$, which is essentially 0.1 or practically equal to 0.5β, since $\beta = 0.2$; hence $J_1(0.2)I_m = 0.5\beta I_m$. This holds even more closely for β values smaller than 0.2.

[1] On account of the explanations given in connection with Fig. 3 and the assumptions used in the derivation of Eq. (15).

[2] Even though Eq. (10) holds for PM also, it is important to realize this is true only as far as its application to Eq. (12) for the side currents is concerned, at least generally so. As is brought out on p. 66, we can compare relations like the above only when the relations are based on the actual conditions that caused the particular type of modulation. In Eq. (16) the FM as well as the AM take these conditions into account.

Equation (16) is important since it shows that for a modulation index $\Delta F/f = 0.2$, or smaller, FM behaves exactly like AM as far as the spectrum distribution is concerned. In addition, we can row consider the modulation index β as equivalent to a modulation factor. The amplitude of the carrier current of frequency F, whether due to FM or to AM, *remains* equal to the carrier level I_m. We also note that practically all of the modulation energy for FM exists only in the side bands. Even though for AM the modulation energy rests likewise in the only and first side-current pair, Eq. (16) shows that for AM both the upper and the lower side currents are characterized by *positive* amplitudes, which

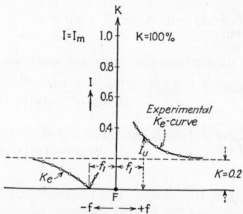

Fig. 16.—Experimental curves for the first side-current pair of frequencies $F - f$ and $F + f$ (for different signal frequencies f).

are the same and equal to $0.5KI_m$. But, for FM, the amplitude of the side frequency $F + f$ is *plus* $0.5\beta I_m$; the amplitude of side frequency $F - f$ is *minus* $0.5\beta I_m$. Hence, when FM and AM act simultaneously, there must be a signal frequency f_1 for which $\beta = \Delta F/f_1$ becomes equal to K and the lower side current vanishes. This is indicated in Fig. 16. Since, according to Eq. (16), on the upper side-band side both AM and superimposed FM effects are additive, the effective upper side-current amplitude is no longer $0.5KI_m$, as would be expected if AM only were present, nor $(0.5\Delta F/f_1)I_m$ as would be expected if pure FM prevailed. But we find an effective upper side-current amplitude $I_u = 0.5KI_m + 0.5\beta I_m$, which expression can also be written as $I_u = 0.5K_eI_m$ if the effective modulation factor for the upper side band is taken as $K_e = K + \beta$. For the lower side band it would be $K_e = K - \beta$

Hence, at this particular modulating current of frequency f_1, we have *automatic lower side-current suppression*, as far as a side frequency $F - f_1$ is concerned.

In Fig. 16 the unmodulated carrier level I_m is assumed equal to unity. Hence, the respective side-current amplitudes for various signal frequency values are given by the respective K_e characteristics. Such a superposition of two kinds of modulations is generally not desirable since the lower side-current amplitude characteristic behaves differently from the upper side-current amplitude. In other words, it is essential that we avoid a parasitic modulation of the undesired type. It is true that a detector of AM by itself does not respond at the output side to FM. But when, as is shown in Fig. 16, the effective modulation factor K_e has, so to speak, "all the characteristics of AM" then the AM detector will respond accordingly. This will produce distortion at its output and, therefore, a-f distortion. For useful FM acting with parasitic AM, we must realize that any FM-AM translator is not exactly immune to AM. All demodulators must depend on some function of the amplitude; otherwise they could not give zero output when zero amplitude is impressed. Fortunately, this is of no practical consequence, since we use at least one stage of amplitude saturation, or limitation as it is called, ahead of a frequency discriminator. This limits the amplitude applied to the discriminator enough to cut out variations of amplitude.

In connection with Fig. 3, it was already mentioned that even the geometrical quadrature addition of the modulation product with the unmodulated carrier produces, besides the desired PM, also amplitude variations; *i.e.*, it produces undesirable superimposed AM. But by "clipping off," the by-product of AM is avoided in succeeding stages. *Limiters* are therefore *essential apparatus* in FM work. Whatever undesirable AM is produced in a transmitter should be corrected right in the transmitter and, if possible, right at the place where it sets in. In a receiver, two limiter stages seem desirable. They should precede the discriminator.

Since the K_e curve of Fig. 16 on the lower side-band side passes through zero at a critical modulation frequency $f = f_1$, we have a means for finding either the value of K, if the value β for FM is known, or the modulation index β if the condition of AM is known. Since the critical frequency f_1 can be determined, for instance, by means of the calibration of a beat frequency oscillator, we can find then also the value of the maximum frequency excursion ΔF. For the critical frequency f_1, the determinations just described are based on the equality $K = \Delta F/f_1$ when the lower side current vanishes. Consider FM as the desired type of modulation. If we find by means of a search-current method[1] that the lower side-current amplitude disappears[2] at a frequency $f_1 = 4$ kc and the maximum frequency excursion is known to be $\Delta F = \pm 0.8$ kc, then we have a modulation index $\beta = 0.8/4 = 0.2$ and the unde-sired AM has a modulation factor K of 20 per cent.

It should be noted that this experimental method applies also for cases where the modulation index has almost any value[3] since according to the distribution equation (12) instead of the factor 0.5β we have to take the associated Bessel factor $J_1(\beta)$ into account. The first lower side current disappears for a $\beta = \Delta F/f_1$ value which makes $J_1(\beta) = 0.5K$ instead of $\beta = K$.

On the other hand, if the degree of AM is known, that is, if AM is the desired modulation and $K = 0.2$ as in Fig. 16 and the lower side-current amplitude disappears at a frequency of 150 cycles per second, we have $\Delta F/f_1 = \Delta F/150 = 0.2$. Hence, in this case the maximum frequency swing ΔF, due to parasitic FM, would be ± 30 cycles per second. For the case where a 10-kc signal frequency causes disappearance of the first lower side-current amplitude, we would have a maximum frequency swing $\Delta F = \pm 0.2 \times 10,000 = \pm 2$ kc. If larger β values than 0.2 exist for parasitic FM, the above relation for which $J_1(\beta)$ is equal to $0.5K$ is to be used in the computation. Larger values will, however, be unlikely to occur for parasitic modulations since a network would normally not be so poorly designed.

9. Three Types of Modulation.—As to AM, it is evident that the instantaneous value of the carrier frequency F remains constant. Since an FM as well as a PM current has the form $I_m \sin (\Omega t + \beta \sin \omega t)$ for the instantaneous current value, the argu-

---

[1] Consult "High-frequency Measurements," pp. 116–126, 377–381.

[2] For simultaneous FM and AM only the first lower side current disappears at the critical frequency f_1, but *never* the amplitude of carrier frequency F. Therefore, we should never use, in the method for determining ΔF by means of Bessel curve intersections (see p. 86), the intersection of the $J_1(\beta)$ curve since the zero amplitude condition could be entirely or partly due to a parasitic superimposed AM, instead of to the disappearance of the $J_1(\beta)$ value.

[3] For details see p. 70.

ment in the parenthesis must denote the instantaneous angular velocity Ω_t. The instantaneous frequency F_t of the carrier frequency is $\Omega_t/(2\pi)$ or

$$F_t = \frac{1}{2\pi} \frac{d(\Omega t + \beta \sin \omega t)}{dt} = F + \frac{\omega\beta}{2\pi} \cos \omega t.$$

where for FM we have $\beta = \Delta F/f$ and for equivalent FM, *i.e.*, PM, we have $\beta = \Delta\theta$. Therefore,

$$F_t = \left\{ \begin{array}{ll} F + \Delta F \cos \omega t & \text{true FM} \\ \\ F + f\,\Delta\theta \cos \omega t & \text{PM (which is equivalent FM)} \end{array} \right\} \quad (17)$$

showing again that for PM the equivalent frequency swing depends, even for a fixed maximum phase swing $\Delta\theta$, on the signal frequency f also, since the equivalent maximum frequency excursion is $f\,\Delta\theta$. At this point it should be understood that an FM-AM *translator* will respond to either PM or FM voltages as far as the a-f effects in the AM output[1] current are concerned. For this reason, distortion in FM receivers often can be due to undesirable PM effects. It is of utmost importance, therefore, that transfer networks, especially those used in the i-f stages, be designed for a linear phase shift with respect to all frequencies concerned in the band width.

Figure 17 shows AM in comparison with FM. The modulation cycle can be readily seen in the AM representation. The line density in the representation for FM (similar to sound rarefactions and condensations) indicates the modulation cycle. The respective spectrum distributions show that in the case of AM the modulation energy never affects the amplitude of carrier frequency F, while for FM the modulation energy is spread over the *entire* frequency spectrum. This is, of course, also true for PM since for a particular signal frequency f we have, according to Eq. (17), a maximum frequency deviation $f\,\Delta\theta$, which can have the same order as a true frequency swing ΔF. In FM and in PM, the modulation effect on the amplitude of carrier frequency F always causes a decrease in this amplitude, even though extremely

---

[1] In commercial frequency discriminators the output gives usually the a-f current. This means that *inherent* amplitude demodulation takes place in the discriminator. Hence such a discriminator should actually be called an FM-AM audio converter. For such discriminators the audio current at the output terminals is due to either FM or PM affecting the input of the discriminator.

small for small values of β: The $J_0(\beta)$ curve has a value equal to unity only for $\beta = 0$, *i.e.*, only in the *absence* of modulation. The larger the value of the modulation index β, the more side currents appear and the greater the tendency to spread the modulation energy toward the side currents more remote from the center current of frequency Γ.

Figure 18 compares all three types of modulations with respect to the instantaneous carrier level, carrier frequency, and carrier phase. This figure also shows how equivalent phase shifts take

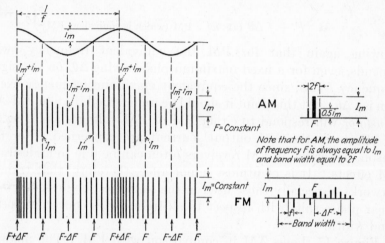

Fig. 17.—Comparison of AM with FM (note that for FM the modulation energy spreads all over the significant frequency spectrum while for AM the amplitude of center frequency is as for no modulation).

place in accordance with variations of the amplitude of the signal current in the Armstrong system.

With both FM and PM a true instantaneous and an equivalent instantaneous carrier frequency exist (Eq. 17). It is necessary, therefore, that the number of cycles per second be kept constant: otherwise the center or mean frequency will drift and will *not* be equal to the frequency F assigned to the carrier. A mean frequency drift is undesirable because the entire frequency spectrum around it, with all the important side currents, would drift with the drift of the mean frequency F. This would give more or less overlap with adjacent FM channels, even though small guard spectra exist between adjacent channels. It should be realized at this point that in FM no primary oscillator could be used with a stabilized frequency F; otherwise we could not change the frequency directly during the modulation cycle and produce FM. But with PM the frequency can be stabilized since the *equivalent* frequency change is due to phase fluctuations.

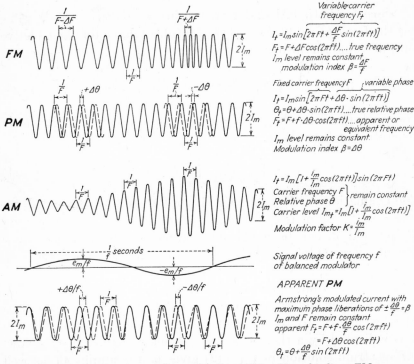

FIG. 18.—Comparison of direct FM, direct PM, AM, and indirect FM.

With respect to the effective current value I of a modulated current, we have according to Eq. (1), the formula

$$I = \sqrt{\frac{1}{2\pi} \int_0^{2\pi} I_m^2 \sin^2 (2\pi F t + \theta) \, dt} \qquad (18)$$

For AM we have instead of I_m the value $I_m(1 + K \cos \omega t)$ and the fixed relative phase θ is neglected since it has nothing to do with AM. Making these substitutions, we have

$$I = \sqrt{\frac{1}{2\pi} \int_0^{2\pi} I_m^2 (1 + K \cos \omega t)^2 \sin^2 \Omega \, dt} = \frac{I_m}{1.41} \sqrt{1 + 0.5K^2} \quad (19)$$

in contrast with the value $I_m/1.41$ for the unmodulated carrier.[1]

[1] For details consult "High-frequency Measurements," pp. 361–362.

Even though it looks evident that for pure FM, as well as for PM which gives equivalent FM, the effective value is the same as for the unmodulated current, it may be of interest to understand the proof of it.

Since for both FM and PM, the instantaneous current value has the form $I_m \sin [2\pi F t + \beta \sin (2\pi f)t]$, we have for the effective current value the formula

$$I = \sqrt{\frac{1}{2\pi} \int_0^{2\pi} I_m^2 \sin^2 [2\pi F t + \beta \sin (2\pi f)t] \, dt} \qquad (20)$$

For any type of signal current and any type of modulation, we have generally the formula

$$I = \sqrt{\frac{1}{2\pi} \int_0^{2\pi} I_t^2 \, dt} \qquad (21)$$

The evaluations of Eq. (20) for either PM or FM, depending on whether $\beta = \Delta\theta$ or is equal to $\Delta F/f$, are laborious. Fortunately, the evaluation can be made very simple if only harmonic component currents play a part, even though they may have no integer relationship with respect to each other.

We know from alternating-current theory that the fundamental and all higher harmonics in a distorted current wave are added geometrically to obtain the effective resultant current value as is indicated by a thermoelectric ammeter, for instance. Now, our spectrum solution in Eq. (12) gives us the amplitude as well as the frequency of all the sinusoidal currents. Even though not in harmonic relationship, we have also to deal with geometrical addition if we want to find the effective current value. In this manner involved integration, as indicated in Eqs. (20) and (21), is avoided. Since in Eq. (12) the amplitudes of the different spectrum currents denote maximum amplitude values, these values must be divided by 1.41 in order to obtain the corresponding effective component values. Therefore, we have for the effective value of an FM or PM current

$$I = \frac{I_m}{1.41} \sqrt{J_0^2(\beta) + 2J_1^2(\beta) + 2J_2^2(\beta) + 2J_3^2(\beta) + \cdots} \qquad (22)$$

where $\beta = \Delta F/f$ for FM, or $\beta = \Delta\theta$ radians for PM. The numerical value will then take care of the degree of the respective modulation. The factor 2 appears in all Bessel factors belonging to the side-current pairs since, for instance, for the first side-current pair an effective value $J_1(\beta)I_m/1.41$ of frequency $F - f$ has to be added *geometrically* to the effective component value $J_1(\beta)I_m/1.41$ of frequency $F + f$ in order to account for the resultant effective current of the entire pair. The addition has to be made geometrically (square root of the sum of the squares) since these two components are of *different* frequencies.

Now with a knowledge of the value of β, Bessel tables or curves show how many terms have to be used and the effective value I can be computed quickly. For instance, for a value of $\beta = 0.2$ we have only the first side-current pair in addition to the current of carrier frequency F. Hence $I = I_m/1.41 \sqrt{J_0^2(0.2) + 2 \times J_1^2(0.2)} =$ $(I_m/1.41) \sqrt{1 + 2 \times 0.1^2} = (I_m/1.41) \sqrt{1.02}$. Since, according to Table I, the exact values of $J_0(0.2) = 0.9975$ and $J_1(0.2) = 0.0995$, we note that $I = I_m/1.41$. This result could also be obtained from Eq. (16), which shows that for $\beta \leq 0.2$ we have $I = (I_m/1.41) \sqrt{1 + 2 \times 0.5^2 \beta^2}$ or $I = I_e \sqrt{1 + \frac{1}{2}\beta^2}$ where I_e denotes the effective current value of the unmodulated carrier. We see that $1 + \frac{1}{2}\beta^2 = 1.02$ as above. If no approximations had been made, *i.e.*, if all side currents, even the smallest ones, had been taken into account, the result would have been exactly equal to unity. Hence, we see that such a checkup will disclose whether we have missed important side currents.

Suppose that we have a case where the modulation index is $\beta = 5$. This is, for instance, the value for the maximum deviation ratio for wide-band FM since for $\Delta F = \pm 75$ kc and the highest signal frequency $f_{max} = 15$ kc this β value obtains. Our Bessel tables show that about eight side-current pairs play a part. The tables give the following values: $J_0(5) = 0.1776$, $J_1(5) = 0.3276$, $J_2(5) = 0.0466$, $J_3(5) = 0.3648$, $J_4(5) = 0.3912$, $J_5(5) = 0.2611$, $J_6(5) = 0.131$, $J_7(5) = 0.0534$, and $J_8(5) = 0.0184$. All values are written down without respect to polarity since it is not needed here. The sum under the square-root sign of Eq. (22) then becomes $J_0^2(5) + 2J_1^2(5) + 2J_2^2(5) + 2J_3^2(5) + 2J_4^2(5) + 2J_5^2(5) + 2J_6^2(5) + 2J_7^2(5) + 2J_8^2(5) = 0.0315 + 0.214 + 0.0044 + 0.266 + 0.306 + 0.136 + 0.0342 + 0.0056 + 0.00068 = 0.99838$, which is again essentially unity.

For FM as well as PM, the effective current reading should be the same as the value of the unmodulated carrier current, unless

the network in which the reading is taken or the network that
carries the FM or PM current cannot pass without amplitude,
frequency, or phase discrimination all the important side currents.
The ammeter method can, therefore, be used to test the pass-band
property of FM and PM networks.   If a different current reading
is obtained for no modulation or for any degree of FM or PM, the
network requires a better design.   But an increase of current,
when measured with an rms ammeter, may be due to superimposed
parasitic AM.   To find out whether this is the case, the method
described on pages 40 and 63 should be employed before correcting a transfer network.

Equation (19) has exactly the same form for FM and PM when
$\beta \leq 0.2$, if the amplitude modulation factor K is replaced by the
modulation index β.   Nevertheless, there is a great difference
between this expression with K and when β is used instead of K.
This is due to the fact that β can be used only for values of $\beta = 0.2$
or smaller.   For such values of β, Eq. (19) yields an effective
modulated current value that is essentially equal to the effective
value of the unmodulated current for AM, FM, and PM.   For
values of β larger than 0.2, the index β should not be used in Eq.
(19).   However, the equation is correct with K values for any
possible value of K.   For instance, $K = 1$ means that $i_m = I_m$ or
that 100 per cent AM exists and Eq. (19) would yield an effective
current value that is 1.2247 times larger than the effective value
of the unmodulated carrier current.

Since in the spectrum distribution for large values of β most
of the modulation energy spreads toward the side frequencies
farthest away from the carrier frequency F, it is seen that sharp
cutoffs are required in the band-pass design of FM networks.
It is true that for the smaller values of β not so many side currents
occur.   But with a fixed maximum value of $\Delta F = \pm 75$ kc the
smaller values of β occur only for the highest desired signal frequency.   This frequency is usually taken as 15 kc.   Hence, even
though not so many important side currents occur, on account of
the large value of the signal frequency f, the *band spread* becomes
widest for these small values of β when the highest permissible
modulation degree is being used.   Inasmuch as we have to deal
with all the important signal frequencies, it is the value of $\Delta F = \pm 75$ kc and the value of $f = 15$ kc that determines the required
band width.   If a sharp cutoff band-pass network cannot eco-

nomically be designed, the network should be designed for a band-pass region sufficiently wide so that the essential band width required by the spectrum distribution is properly accommodated. Such an additional band width is, in addition, favorable in regard to the signal-to-noise ratio.

10. Addition of Modulation Products.—In the case of AM, the unmodulated carrier level is equal to the amplitude I_m of the unmodulated carrier current. For FM, the unmodulated or normal carrier level is the carrier frequency F, which is also often called the mean or center frequency. Even though for PM we could call a certain fixed phase θ the normal level, we may also here refer to the carrier frequency F as the normal level since we have in effect equivalent frequency deviations about the fixed carrier frequency F.

At this point it may be of value to realize that a different instantaneous frequency F_t in case of FM means that the *fixed* carrier frequency F has *changed* to a value that at the instant t is F_t. For PM, which causes equivalent FM, the fixed carrier frequency F remains *fixed* but the PM reflects, so to speak, a superimposed carrier frequency deviation on the fixed value of F. In equivalence this gives also an apparent instantaneous frequency F_t, which differs from F. In each case, *i.e.*, for FM as well as PM, the variations about the mean frequency F are registered at the output of a frequency discriminator since this device responds to frequency swings.[1]

In connection with Fig. 5, for AM it has been seen that the modulation product b is *always* in phase with the normal carrier level a, which is equal to I_m. Hence, in AM we have only to deal at any instant with algebraic *additions*, $a + b$, or *subtractions*, $a - b$, depending on whether the magnitude $KI_m \cos \omega t$ in the

---

[1] We have, therefore, a parallel with the actions of a coil when used over a wide frequency range. A coil remains a coil, but in equivalence it acts above its natural resonance like a condenser since the coil capacitance action outweighs the inductive action. It takes then a small coil with little distributed capacitance to tune to a still higher frequency. With PM we still have the fixed F no matter how much degree of PM exists, but as far as the equivalent frequency deviations about the fixed F and their effect on the discriminator are concerned, it would require an FM deviation of the same ΔF but instantaneously in exact opposition to neutralize the frequency-variation effect due to PM. In other words, the equivalent variation $f \Delta \theta \cos \omega t$ has to be opposed by a true carrier-frequency change $-\Delta F \cos \omega t$ and such that at any instant of the modulation cycle, $\Delta F_t = f \Delta \theta_t$. This can be readily done for one particular frequency but only with a corrective network for the entire band.

term for b is positive or negative at the particular instant. The multiplier $\sin \Omega t$ in the b term of Eq. (2) shows only that the modulation product is in phase with the unmodulated carrier component.

We have also learned in connection with Fig. 3 that, when a modulation product is *added geometrically*, we produce generally both PM and AM, depending on the angle that the vectors make with respect to each other, as well as on the relative magnitude of b with respect to a. Just as with AM, the largest absolute magnitude that b can ever have depends on the degree of modulation that causes this product. If a and b are secured from the same source by first separating b from a and then shifting the phase either of b or of a by 90 time degrees, the largest magnitude of b is obtained when $b = a$. In Fig. 5 this occurs for 100 per cent modulation ($K = 1$) and for $\omega t = 0$, 180, 360, 540, etc., deg, where 180, 540, etc., refer to negative b values; *i.e.*, they refer to instants when no current at all exists for 100 per cent modulation. But if the modulation product is obtained from a secondary source, such as a balanced modulator, and the unmodulated portion a is obtained from a carrier-frequency source that is not modulated, any ratio of b/a can be physically realized. However, generally the length of the b vector should not be longer with respect to the length of the a vector than to be practically a portion of a circle of radius a. If this condition is met, we have only PM effects and practically no harmonic distortion.

For either FM or PM we can express Eq. (12) as

$$I_t = I_m\{\underbrace{J_0(\beta) \sin \Omega t}_{a} + \underbrace{[2J_1(\beta) \sin \omega t] \cos \Omega t}_{b_1}$$
$$+ \underbrace{[2J_2(\beta) \cos 2\omega t] \sin \Omega t}_{b_2} + \underbrace{[2J_3(\beta) \sin 3\omega t] \cos \Omega t}_{b_3}$$
$$+ \underbrace{[2J_4(\beta) \cos 4\omega t] \sin \Omega t}_{b_4} + b_5 + b_6 + b_7 + \cdots \} \quad (23)$$

Hence, for any value of the modulation index β, we have as many modulation products b_1, b_2, b_3, etc., as there are significant side-current pairs. On account of the alternate $\sin \Omega t$ and $\cos \Omega t$ multipliers for the modulated amplitude $J_0(\beta)I_m$ of carrier frequency F, the first modulation product b_1, the second modulation product b_2, etc., we have to deal with the geometric additions $a + b_1 + b_2 + b_3 + b_4 + b_5 + b_6 + \cdots$ in order to obtain the vector of the resultant current I_t at any instant. The addition is, therefore, in quadrature between consecutive modulation products or modulation factors b_1, b_2, b_3, etc., as well as with respect to the vector a of carrier or center frequency F.

It should be clearly understood that for either FM or PM, which differ in the spectrum solution only in that for FM the index $\beta = \Delta F/f$ and for PM the index $\beta = \Delta\theta$, the amplitude of the carrier frequency F is also affected for such quadrature modulations, i.e., modulations along the time axis. This is especially so for large values of β. However, it is not due to any one component modulation product, but to the effect of all the modulation products belonging to the respective side-current pairs. In other words, the modulation energy distributes itself over all of the frequency spectrum that is of practical importance. For the larger values of β so much energy is diverted toward the side bands on each side of the carrier frequency F that a carrier amplitude $J_0(\beta)I_m$, which is smaller than I_m, results; i.e., this diverting of energy to the side bands even takes along some of the normal carrier power. As a matter of fact, the energy distribution in the important spectrum portion of the spectrum due to noise or other erratic interference is not so effective as the energy distribution resulting from FM or PM in producing a response in the demodulator of a proper type of receiver. Hence, the desired intelligence in FM or PM will, so to speak, "outweigh" any noise that causes random energy distributions. The Bessel energy distribution is, therefore, one of the outstanding features of FM as compared with AM. These features are, of course, also true for PM.

The simplest application of Eq. (23) occurs when $\beta \leq 0.2$ since then only the a and b_1 vectors have significant values. We have then a simple vector addition in quadrature, as shown in Fig. 3. From Table I we note that for such β values the Bessel factor $J_0(\leq 0.2)$ is essentially equal to unity. Hence, the length of vector a is equal to I_m. Now if we take the case for $\beta = 0.2$, we find $J_1(0.2) = 0.0995$, which is essentially equal to 0.1, or 0.5β. The length of the vector representing the modulation product b_1 is then $b_1 = 2J_1(0.2)I_m \sin \omega t = 0.2I_m \sin \omega t$. As a matter of fact, the formula $b_1 = \beta I_m \sin \omega t$ holds for all β values smaller than 0.2 and Bessel tables are not needed. The only significant modulation vector b_1 has then an absolute length

$b_1 = 0.2I_m$ at the instant of time when $\omega t = 90$ deg; *i.e.*, at the instant when the modulation cycle just reaches the first positive maximum frequency excursion $+\Delta F$ in case of FM. Hence, as shown in Fig. 3, we add to the vertical vector a of length $a = I_m$, the vector b_1 of length $b_1 = 0.2I_m$ in time quadrature and along the positive direction. Now if we assume that the time is such that ωt is equal to 225 deg, then $\sin 225 = -\sin 45 = -0.7071$ and $b_1 = -0.707 \times 0.2I_m = -0.14142I_m$. Hence, the vector b_1 of length $-0.14142I_m$ is to be added, in quadrature and in the negative direction, to vector a, of length I_m. Since $J_0(0.2)$ is strictly equal to 0.99 and $J_1(0.2) = 0.0995$, we find for $\omega t = 90$ deg that $a = 0.99I_m$ and $b_1 = 0.199I_m$ and that for $\omega t = 225$ deg the exact value of $b_1 = -0.7071 \times 0.199I_m = -0.1406I_m$. For $\omega t = 0, 180, 360, 540$, etc., deg the modulation term b_1 vanishes and only the term $a = 0.99I_m$ remains to account for I_t. The resultant value or vector corresponding to I_t has, for the instant when $\omega t = 90$ deg, the value $I_{90} = I_m \sqrt{0.99^2 + 0.199^2}$, which is essentially equal to I_m. For $\omega t = 225$ deg we have $I_{225} = I_m \sqrt{0.99^2 + 0.1406^2}$, which is again essentially equal to I_m. This means that for the entire signal cycle of frequency f, the resultant current has the constant amplitude level I_m. The small differences between the actual square-root values and the theoretical value of unity is caused by the fact that the less significant terms were neglected in obtaining the square-root values. These differences become still more pronounced for somewhat higher β values if we add only the first modulation vector b_1 in quadrature with a, since actually the vector b_2 should be included also. The effect of neglecting the higher modulation products for $\beta = 0.5$ radian or $0.5 \times 57.3 = 28.65$ deg in PM is that during the signal or modulation cycle the resultant vector $\sqrt{a^2 + b_1^2}$ fluctuates for different ωt values and we have a small degree of AM in our calculations.

Suppose we have now to take into account more modulation products due to a larger value of β, such that more side-current pairs play an important part. Matters are then no more difficult, as the following numerical example and the vector diagram of Fig. 19 will show. The successive quadrature addition of a, b_1, b_2, b_3, b_4, etc., for significant b terms satisfies the relation $I_t = I_m \sin (\Omega t + \beta \sin \omega t)$. This holds for respective spectrum distributions for either FM or PM, depending on whether $\beta = \Delta F/f$ or $\beta = \Delta \theta$. Hence, all resultant current vectors for various values of time must have essentially the same absolute length and be equal to I_m since the foregoing expression causes a circular trace. The spectrum equation (23) also must yield a circle of radius I_m if sufficient modulation products are included. The resultant vector I_m then spins around with an instantaneous angular velocity Ω_t which is equal to $6.28[F + \Delta F \cos (2\pi f)t]$ in case of FM; for PM it is equal to $6.28[F + f \Delta \theta \cos (2\pi f)t]$, where $\Delta \theta$ is to be expressed in radians; i.e., it must be numerical. Hence, in each

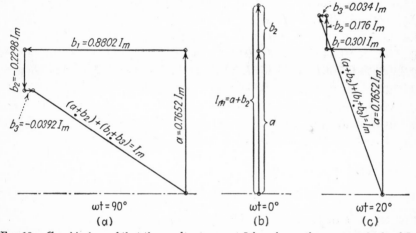

Fig. 19.—Graphical proof that the resultant current I_t has always the same carrier level I_m.

case the resultant current vector spins around with the apparent constant angular velocity $6.28F$, but at the same time it is exposed to angular velocity increase and decrease "flutters" at the signal-frequency rate. The instantaneous angular velocity deviations from the mean constant angular velocity $6.28F$ are given by $6.28 \, \Delta F \cos \omega t$ for FM and by $6.28f \, \Delta \theta \cos \omega t$ for PM, where $\omega = 6.28f$.

Assume a modulation index $\beta = 1$. Table I shows that for this case three significant modulation products play a part. Hence, the magnitude of the resultant current vector is $\sqrt{(a + b_2)^2 + (b_1 + b_3)^2}$, since successive quadrature additions must be made. Therefore, the odd terms are in phase, just as the even terms, a, b_2, b_4, b_6, . . . are in phase.

At this point it is of importance to realize that the polarity of the Bessel factors plays a part since a negative Bessel value will cause opposite polarity of the vector to be added. Of course, the harmonic modulation function ωt also affects the polarity.

From Table I the Bessel factors are $J_0(1) = 0.7652$, $J_1(1) = 0.4401$, $J_2(1) = 0.1149$, and $J_3(1) = 0.0196$. Hence, according to Eq. (23), the current of carrier frequency F has, at any time of the modulation cycle, a constant scalar value $J_0(1)I_m = 0.7652I_m = a$. For the first modulation product we have the *instantaneous* scalar value $b_1 = 2J_1(1)I_m \sin \omega t = 0.8802I_m \sin \omega t$. For the second modulation product we have the *instantaneous* scalar value $b_2 = 2 \times 0.1149I_m \cos 2\omega t = 0.2298I_m \cos 2\omega t$. For the third modulation product we have the *instantaneous* scalar value $b_3 = 0.0392I_m \sin 3\omega t$. Hence, at an instant of time, when $\omega t = 20$ deg, for example, we have $a = 0.7652I_m$; $b_1 = 0.8802I_m \sin 20$ deg $= 0.8802 \times 0.342I_m = 0.301I_m$; $b_2 = 0.2298I_m \cos 40$ deg $= 0.2298 \times 0.766I_m = 0.176I_m$; and $b_3 = 0.0392I_m \sin 60$ deg $= 0.0392 \times 0.866I_m = 0.034I_m$.

We have, therefore, the vector addition shown in Fig. 19c, which by graphical construction confirms the value of the resultant as equal to I_m. We can also find the resultant from

$$\sqrt{(a + b_2)^2 + (b_1 + b_3)^2}\, I_m = I_m \sqrt{0.9412^2 + 0.335^2}$$
$$= I_m \sqrt{0.997} = I_m.$$

For $\omega t = 0$ deg, we have the case of Fig. 19b and the values $a = 0.7652I_m$, $b_1 = 0$, $b_2 = 0.2298I_m$, and $b_3 = 0$. We obtain, therefore, a resultant current value $a + b_2 = 0.7652I_m + 0.2298I_m = 0.995I_m$, which is again essentially equal to I_m. For $\omega t = 90$ deg we have the vector display of Fig. 19a and the following computations: $a = 0.7652I_m$, $b_1 = 0.8802I_m$, $b_2 = -0.2298I_m$, and $b_3 = -0.0392I_m$. Therefore, $a + b_2 = 0.7652I_m - 0.2298I_m = 0.5354I_m$ and $b_1 + b_3 = 0.8802I_m - 0.0392I_m = 0.841I_m$. Hence, the resultant current is $I_m \sqrt{0.5354^2 + 0.841^2} = I_m \sqrt{0.992}$, which is likewise essentially equal to I_m, as should be the case. Hence, the number of modulation products chosen shows that essentially no undesired AM effects will be superimposed if the band-pass networks will accommodate or pass the three side-current pairs, since the carrier level remains essentially constant and equal to I_m.

From these numerical speculations some important conclusions may be drawn. For modern commercial wide-band FM, for the highest signal frequency at full permissible ΔF swing, the β value is equal to about 5. According to Table III, for $\beta = 5$ we have eight significant side-current pairs; that is, eight modulation products, and can expect more or less pure FM. When indirect FM is produced by means of only one modulation product, the corresponding modulation vector should never be permitted to reach a maximum value large enough to produce a β value exceeding a value of 0.2. If, as in some commercial work, β values as high as 0.5 radian are tolerated, the small superimposed AM should be "clipped off" with an amplitude limiter. It is true that even in modern direct FM the value of $\beta = 5$ for the highest signal frequency of about 15 kc holds only for the maximum permissible modulation condition in the final stages of an FM transmitter, since at least a several fold frequency multiplication is employed after the so-called "primary" FM is effected. The frequency multiplication is customarily accomplished with ordinary receiver tubes, as far as their power rating is concerned at least. Hence, the *primary* ΔF swing is not ± 75 kc, but is as many times smaller as the value of the frequency swing multiplication factor. For an eightfold frequency multiplication the primary ΔF swing is, therefore, only 75/8 kc and the corresponding β value for a maximum frequency deviaton ratio of 5 is only 5/8 for the primary FM. Hence, the circuit design requires more band width after the swings are multiplied, since β increases accordingly on account of an increase in the value of ΔF. The value of f in the expression $\beta = \Delta F/f$ cannot change with the frequency multiplication, since it accounts only for the speed with which the ΔF swings occur, and controls the pitch of the sound heard at the receiver. For weaker modulation degrees, *i.e.*, for less intense intelligence transmission, the β value becomes smaller. Then the number of corresponding side currents produced can surely be accommodated, since the band width is designed for the maximum deviation ratio 75 kc/15 kc = 5.

11. Effects When Two Types of Modulations Are Present.—It
is not uncommon to have AM associated with PM or FM. The reason for this is that any circuit reactions may produce undesirable PM, even in circuit elements between the antenna and the last power stage. Any reactive back actions on the master oscillator of an AM system will cause direct FM effects unless the source of the carrier frequency is perfectly stabilized. In connection with Fig. 3, as well as in the discussion in Sec. 10, it was noted that undesirable AM effects may appear in FM or PM systems unless these effects are clipped off. It is now of interest to examine what happens when two types of modulation occur simultaneously in a system.

In another publication[1] the general solution for the instantaneous value of a modulated current when two types of modulation are present simultaneously is given. If we neglect the constant phase in Eq. (23) of this reference, we have the simplified general solution

[1] "High-frequency Measurements," p. 376, Eq. (23).

$$I_t = I_m \overbrace{(1 + K \sin \omega t)}^{M_1} \overbrace{[\sin (\Omega t + \beta \sin \omega t)]}^{M_2}$$

$$= I_m \sum_{-\infty}^{+\infty} \Big(J_n(\beta) \sin (\Omega + n\omega)t$$

$$- 0.5 K J_n(\beta) \cos \{[\Omega + (n + 1)\omega]t\}$$

$$+ 0.5 K J_n(\beta) \cos \{[\Omega + (n - 1)\omega]t\} \Big) \quad (24)$$

The driving voltage in a load circuit coupled to an AM source causes a h-f current flow in that circuit, which is directly proportional to the induced driving voltage. Experience has shown that tanks as well as open-circuit loads[1] may cause a certain phase shift in the modulated current flow, which, in turn, means that this phase shift must be also a linear function of the driving voltage. For a sinusoidal modulating voltage, the phase θ in Eq. (1), as well as its amplitude I_m, must also vary sinusoidally. Hence, in Eq. (1) instead of I_m we have the sinusoidal amplitude variation $(1 + K \sin \omega t)I_m$ and instead of θ we have the sinusoidal phase variation $\Delta\theta \sin \omega t$. The equation for the resultant current then reads

$$I_t = I_m(1 + K \sin \omega t) \sin (\Omega t + \Delta\theta \sin \omega t)$$

Since, in PM, the maximum phase swing $\Delta\theta = \beta$, Eq. (24) applies.

This equation shows that we have now two modulation operators: M_1, which causes AM, and M_2, which causes PM. The expression $I_t = M_1 M_2 I_m$ shows that, as far as the envelope or amplitude contour of the doubly modulated current is concerned, the term M_2 can have no effect on the contour. M_2 causes quadrature actions only; *i.e.*, it causes effects along the time axis of the modulated current wave, but no effects along and parallel to the amplitude axis. These statements are correct for the load circuit, but matters are different at the reception end. Equation (24) shows that the complete modulation energy is no longer in the first and only modulation product, as in case of pure AM, but is all over the significant frequency spectrum if undesired PM is also present. Hence, all networks, including the antenna branch, have to be designed to accommodate the wider required frequency spectrum. Since the term M_2 in the spectrum solution of Eq. (24) causes quadrature effects as far as the various h-f currents resulting from the spectrum distribution are concerned, the rotating

[1] A transmitter antenna is, for instance, an open-circuit load.

vector representing the instantaneous position of the twofold modulated current I_t will no longer spin around at a steady rate. It will change in length according to the AM and will at the same time experience periodic to-and-fro phase flutters.

The expansion of Eq. (24) is simple. We have only to write down terms for $n = 0$, ± 1, ± 2, ± 3, etc., and find for the Bessel functions, expressed in B terms as $J_0(\beta) = B_0$, $J_1(\beta) = B_1$, $J_2(\beta) = B_2$, . . . , $J_n(\beta) = B_n$, the expansion

$$
\begin{aligned}
I_t = I_m[& B_0 \sin \Omega t - 0.5 K B_0 \cos (\Omega + \omega)t + 0.5 K B_0 \cos (\Omega - \omega)t \\
& + B_1 \sin (\Omega + \omega)t - 0.5 K B_1 \cos (\Omega + 2\omega)t + 0.5 K B_1 \cos \Omega t \\
& + B_2 \sin (\Omega + 2\omega)t - 0.5 K B_2 \cos (\Omega + 3\omega)t \\
& + 0.5 K B_2 \cos (\Omega + \omega)t \\
& + B_3 \sin (\Omega + 3\omega)t - 0.5 K B_3 \cos (\Omega + 4\omega)t \\
& + 0.5 K B_3 \cos (\Omega + 2\omega)t \\
& + B_4 \sin (\Omega + 4\omega)t - 0.5 K B_4 \cos (\Omega + 5\omega)t \\
& + 0.5 K B_4 \cos (\Omega + 3\omega)t \\
& + \quad . \quad . \quad . \quad . \quad . \quad . \quad . \quad . \quad . \quad . \quad . \\
& + B_{-1} \sin (\Omega - \omega)t - 0.5 K B_{-1} \cos \Omega t \\
& + 0.5 K B_{-1} \cos (\Omega - 2\omega)t \\
& + B_{-2} \sin (\Omega - 2\omega)t - 0.5 K B_{-2} \cos (\Omega - \omega)t \\
& + 0.5 K B_{-2} \cos (\Omega - 3\omega)t \\
& + B_{-3} \sin (\Omega - 3\omega)t - 0.5 K B_{-3} \cos (\Omega - 2\omega)t \\
& + 0.5 K B_{-3} \cos (\Omega - 4\omega)t \\
& + B_{-4} \sin (\Omega - 4\omega)t - 0.5 K B_{-4} \cos (\Omega - 3\omega)t \\
& + 0.5 K B_{-4} \cos (\Omega - 5\omega)t \\
& + \quad . \quad . \quad . \quad . \quad . \quad . \quad . \quad . \quad . \quad . \quad . \quad]
\end{aligned}
\qquad (25)
$$

Since $B_{-1} = J_{-1}(\beta)$, $B_{-2} = J_{-2}(\beta)$, $B_{-3} = J_{-3}(\beta)$, $B_{-4} = J_{-4}(\beta)$, and generally $J_{-n} = (-1)^n J_n$, we have $B_{-1} = -B_1$, $B_{-2} = B_2$, $B_{-3} = -B_3$, and $B_{-4} = B_4$.

We have, therefore, for the carrier frequency $\Omega/6.28$, the term

$$
\text{Carrier-frequency component} = (B_0 \sin \Omega t + K B_1 \cos \Omega t) I_m \qquad (26)
$$

Hence, the magnitude $B_0 I_m$ acts along the amplitude direction, as indicated by the sine function, and the amplitude $K B_1 I_m$ acts in quadrature with it, as indicated by the cosine function. The resultant vector of carrier frequency F experiences, therefore, an instantaneous phase shift of $\theta_t = \tan^{-1} (K B_1/B_0)$ and has an absolute instantaneous length of $I_m \sqrt{B_0^2 + K^2 B_1^2}$.

There is no difficulty in the practical application of this formula. Assume a maximum phase swing of ± 10 radians, which would be very pronounced undesired PM, and assume that the desired AM causes a modulation effect that has a modulation depth of 20 per cent, then $\Delta\theta = \beta = 10$ and $K = 0.2$. Table II, gives $B_0 = J_0(10) = -0.2459$, $B_1 = J_1(10) = 0.0435$. The amplitude of the carrier frequency is, therefore,

$$I_m \sqrt{(-0.2459)^2 + (0.2 \times 0.0435)^2} = 0.2598 I_{m/2.03 \text{ deg}}$$

since $\tan \varphi = 0.2 \times 0.0435/(-0.2459) = -0.0354$ and $\varphi = 2.03$ deg. The minus sign for the B_0 value means only that at this instant the amplitude component $B_0 I_m$ due to PM is negative; *i.e.*, it is downward if we draw the spectrum distribution and call an upward spectrum amplitude positive, as is customary.

Since, for the particular phase-modulation index of 10 selected for this example, the J_1 term has a very small value compared with the value of the J_0 term, the AM hardly affects the amplitude that would exist for pure PM at the mean carrier frequency F.

Hence, the undesired PM will cause a spectrum distribution such that we have no longer the value of I_m at frequency F that would exist for pure AM.

If a modulation index had been chosen only a very little larger, say $\beta = 11$, then Table II would have given $B_0 = -0.1712$ and $B_1 = -0.1768$; *i.e.*, almost equal values exist resulting in a considerably different value for the carrier frequency amplitude than that which would exist either for pure PM or for pure AM.

As involved as the component equation (25) may seem, it is rather easy to separate terms. It is only necessary to group terms of the same frequency, divide this much smaller group into terms governed only by the sine function, add up all the absolute values, and draw the sum along, say, the vertical axis of a coordinate system. The remaining portion consists only of cosine terms, the absolute values of which are again added but drawn along the horizontal reference axis of the coordinate system. The hypotenuse is, then, the resultant current component in the spectrum distribution. Its absolute length is the amplitude of the particular spectrum current and its direction is a measure of the equivalent phase angle due to parasitic PM. Doing this, for instance, for the upper side current of frequency $(\Omega + \omega)/6.28$, we find the side-current vector by expressing all $\sin(\Omega + \omega)t$ terms as j terms with respect to the real $\cos(\Omega + \omega)t$ terms.   The expression

$$\underset{\cdot}{I}_{F+f} = [0.5K(B_2 - B_0) + jB_1]I_m$$

is then the outcome and yields the amplitude of the first upper side current for PM + AM as

$$I_{F+f} = I_m \sqrt{[0.5K(B_2 - B_0)]^2 + B_1^2} \qquad (27)$$

with a phase angle

$$\tan^{-1}\left[\frac{0.5K(B_2 - B_0)}{B_1}\right]$$

It is seen that here the Bessel factor B_0, which actually belongs for pure PM to the carrier-frequency amplitude, also affects the first side current on either side of frequency F.   It is further seen that the Bessel factor B_2, which for pure PM belongs to the second side-current pair, enters likewise into the first side-current pair. Physically speaking, this shows that superimposed AM has the effect of *cross-spectrum distribution*.

Consider again the numerical example used in connection with the current of carrier frequency F.   We find in Table II that $B_2 = J_2(10) = 0.2546$ and have for the upper side current of frequency $F + f$, the relation

$$I_{F+f} = I_m \sqrt{[0.5 \times 0.2(0.2546 + 0.2459)]^2 + (-0.0435)^2}$$
$$= 0.164 I_m$$

Hence, we also obtain in this particular case for the upper side current of frequency $F + f$ essentially the value $0.1768I_m$, which holds for pure PM.   This is not generally true, being a mere coincidence in this case.   With respect to the first lower side current of frequency $(\Omega - \omega)/6.28$, we find in the same way the side-current vector

$$\underset{\cdot}{I}_{F-f} = [0.5K(B_0 - B_2) - jB_1]I_m$$

and its absolute amplitude value is

$$I_{F-f} = I_m \sqrt{[0.5K(B_0 - B_2)]^2 + B_1^2} \qquad (28)$$

This leads to exactly the same value as for the upper first side current [Eq. (27)].   Hence, for AM + PM we have *one and the same amplitude value* for $F \pm f$.

The modulation product of the first side-current pair can be found by collecting from Eq. (25) all the terms for $(\Omega - \omega)t$ and $(\Omega + \omega)t$ functions and proceeding as follows: With the substitution $(\Omega + \omega)t = \alpha$, $(\Omega - \omega)t = \gamma$, $B_1 = B$, and $0.5K(B_2 - B_0) = A$, we have for all $F \pm f$ terms

$$I_m(B \sin \alpha + A \cos \alpha - B \sin \gamma - A \cos \gamma)$$
$$= [B(\sin \alpha - \sin \gamma) + A(\cos \alpha - \cos \gamma)]I_m$$
$$= I_m\left[2B\left(\cos\frac{\alpha + \gamma}{2} \sin\frac{\alpha - \gamma}{2}\right) - 2A\left(\sin\frac{\alpha + \gamma}{2} \sin\frac{\alpha - \gamma}{2}\right)\right]$$

But $\frac{1}{2}(\alpha + \gamma) = \Omega t$ and $\frac{1}{2}(\alpha - \gamma) = \omega t$ and, therefore,

Modulation product
of first side-current $\qquad I_m[2B_1 \cos \Omega t + K(B_0 - B_2) \sin \Omega t] \sin \omega t \qquad (29)$
pair for AM + PM

where B_0, B_1, and B_2 are the Bessel factors $J_0(\beta)$, $J_1(\beta)$, and $J_2(\beta)$. Hence, the amplitude of this side-current pair is controlled not only by the Bessel factor B_1 but also by factors that actually would belong only to the carrier-frequency amplitude and to the amplitudes of frequencies $F \pm 2f$ if only pure PM existed. Also this composite product shows that there are two factors in time quadrature for the carrier frequency $\Omega/6.28$. One factor has an instantaneous absolute amplitude value $2B_1I_m \sin (6.28f)t$ and the quadrature action has an instantaneous amplitude value $K(B_0 - B_2)I_m \sin (6.28f)t$. Hence, at any moment, for instance at the time when the modulating cycle passes through its first maximum value $(2\pi ft = 90$ deg), the resultant effect of the first modulation product can be computed. For the chosen instant, the respective quadrature amplitudes are found to be $2B_1I_m$ and $K(B_0 - B_2)I_m$. Then for the resultant first side-current amplitude, the value is $I_m \sqrt{(2B_1)^2 + [K(B_0 - B_2)]^2}$. The same result would have been obtained from Eqs. (27) and (28) by evaluating $\sqrt{I_{F-f}^2 + I_{F+f}^2}$. The two side currents of the first side-current pair have to be added at a 90-deg angle because currents of different frequencies are being dealt with. For a modulation index $\beta \leq 0.2$ there would be essentially only one side-current pair. Moreover, Bessel tables then show that $B_0 = J_0(\beta)$ is essentially unity, $B_1 = J_1(\beta)$ is essentially equal to 0.5β, and $B_2 = J_2(\beta)$ is essentially equal to zero. We have, therefore, in Eq. (25) only terms with Ωt and $(\Omega \pm \omega)t$ that play a practical part, and find by taking also the $(\Omega \pm 2\omega)t$ terms

$$I_t = I_m[\sin \Omega t - 0.5K \cos (\Omega + \omega)t + 0.5K \cos (\Omega - \omega)t$$
$$+ 0.5\beta \sin (\Omega + \omega)t - 0.25\beta K \cos (\Omega + 2\omega)t$$
$$+ 0.25\beta K \cos \Omega t - 0.5\beta \sin (\Omega - \omega)t$$
$$+ 0.25\beta K \cos \Omega t - 0.25\beta K \cos (\Omega - 2\omega)t]$$
$$= \underbrace{I_m(\sin \Omega t + 0.5\beta K \cos \Omega t)}_{\text{current of frequency } F}$$
$$+ \underbrace{0.5I_m[\beta \sin (\Omega + \omega)t - K \cos (\Omega + \omega)t]}_{\text{current of frequency } F + f}$$
$$+ \underbrace{0.5I_m[K \cos (\Omega - \omega)t - \beta \sin (\Omega - \omega)t]}_{\text{current of frequency } F - f}$$
$$- \underbrace{0.25\beta K I_m \cos (\Omega + 2\omega)t}_{\text{current of frequency } F + 2f}$$
$$- \underbrace{0.25\beta K I_m \cos (\Omega - 2\omega)t}_{\text{current of frequency } F - 2f} \qquad (30)$$

This shows that no matter which type of modulation is undesired, the terms with the factor $0.25\beta K$ can never play an important part, since the magnitude of the amplitude of respective spectrum current is affected not only by the factor 0.25 but also by either the factor β or K. Now if PM is the parasitic modulation, the tank circuits would surely not be so poorly designed as to cause large phase swings. Suppose that the parasitic maximum phase swing would be even as much as ±5 deg. Then $\beta = \Delta\theta = 5/57.3 = 0.0782$ radian; even if the desired AM is 100 per cent, *i.e.*, $K = 1$, the maximum amplitudes of these two spectrum currents of frequencies $F \pm 2f$ would be only $0.0195I_m$. Only 2 per cent of the normal carrier level I_m for the unmodulated condition would exist. For the terms containing the factors $0.5\beta K$, the percentage of amplitude would be only 3.99 per cent of I_m. Hence, we have for undesirable modulations, no matter which of the two is parasitic, for β values not larger than 0.2 radian, the relation

$$I_t = I_m \sin \Omega t + 0.5I_m[\beta \sin (\Omega + \omega)t - K \cos (\Omega + \omega)t]$$
$$+ 0.5I_m[K \cos (\Omega - \omega)t - \beta \sin (\Omega - \omega)t] \quad (31)$$

This result shows that the term of carrier frequency has an amplitude equal to the carrier level I_m of the unmodulated current. However each side current of respective frequencies $F \pm f$ is now represented by a rotating vector of absolute length $0.5I_m \sqrt{\beta^2 + K^2}$ since for both the first upper as well as the first lower side current,

$0.5\beta I_m$ sin $\langle \Omega \pm \omega \rangle t$ acts in quadrature with $0.5KI_m$ cos $(\Omega \pm \omega)t$, as is indicated in Fig. 20. It is assumed that PM is the desired modulation and that AM is the parasitic modulation. All sine terms are drawn vertically upward when positive, and all positive cosine terms are drawn horizontally to the right. It should be understood that the vector diagram to the left, *i.e.*, for frequency $F - f$, is controlled by an angular velocity $6.28(F - f)$ and the vector addition to the right depends on angular velocity $6.28 (F_1 + f)$. Inasmuch as the interest, in this illustration, is in the desired PM effects, it is noted that for the instant of the

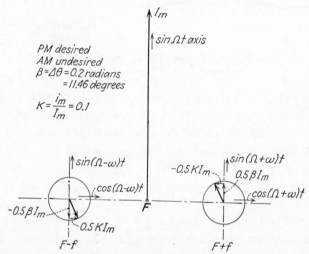

FIG. 20.—Superposition of 10 per cent amplitude modulation and phase modulation with maximum phase swings of ±11.46 deg.

modulation cycle, shown in Fig. 20, the respective quadrature effects due to parasitic AM give no longer instantaneous side-current values that are equal to $0.5\beta I_m$, but generally inclined vectors. Nevertheless, the components along the respective sine axes are still of equal lengths, as for pure PM.

From Eq. (31) it is seen that, at the time $t = 0$, no modulation effects occur since the remaining terms $0.5KI_m$ and $-0.5KI_m$ cancel each other. This is actually what should happen, as the substitution of the time $t = 0$ into the modulation frequency terms of Eq. (24) will show. The quantity β sin ωt in the M_2 term and the quantity K sin ωt in the M_1 term become zero, leaving the expression $I_t = I_m$ sin Ωt. Hence, only the unmodulated current I_m sin Ωt remains. Notice that by $t = 0$ we mean only the time associated with the sinusoidal *modulation* cycle and not the time t associated with Ωt of the carrier frequency. Figure 20 also confirms why the values of Eqs. (27) and (28) come out the same.

It should be clearly understood that all derivations in this section are based on the assumption made in connection with Eq. (24); *i.e.*, that the phase swing varies sinusoidally and that the amplitude swing is changed sinusoidally and in phase synchronism with the phase swings. We shall return to this remark during the discussions presented in Sec. 12.

12. Effects When Frequency Modulation and Amplitude Modulation Are Present.—In poorly designed signal generators for receiver testing, parasitic FM causes *unsymmetrical* selectivity curves.[1] Also back reactions from tank circuits on an h-f oscillator that is not perfectly stabilized with respect to its generated frequency F cause parasitic FM. Hence, a brief discussion of simultaneous AM and FM may not be out of place. It is true that in modern FM, it is a comparatively easy matter to remove undesired AM by the use of amplitude limiters. However, it would be rather difficult in AM work to avoid undesired FM in a similar manner,[2] except by striking directly at the cause; *i.e.*,

---

[1] "High-frequency Measurements," pp. 366–367.

[2] Frequency swing limitation has to be used. But since, for good AM, if it is to compete with good FM, we must permit a swing of ± 15 kc in order to include all audible sound frequencies, we would for a frequency swing limitation to $F \pm 15$ kc frequency levels have to include the carrier frequency amplitude as well as the first side-current pair amplitudes due to FM. As a matter of fact, the Bessel factors of the second side-current pair will also affect the first side-current amplitudes when FM is superimposed on AM. Though strange, but apparently true, at least with present-day apparatus, we can as far as a *receiver* is concerned use detectors, *i.e.*, amplitude demodulators, in AM receivers, which will respond *only to amplitude* variations but will not respond at all to *frequency* modulations in the received current. But we cannot imagine at present a frequency demodulator that is *entirely* independent of amplitude effects. To get around this difficulty we have to saturate the amplitude output of the stage preceding the discriminator so much that only a fixed voltage level is impressed on the discriminator and for all instantaneous deviation frequencies. But as far as the *transmitter* is concerned, we can in FM work completely separate AM effects from desired FM effects; in AM work only partial FM limitation is possible. There is an exception, however, to the statement that an amplitude demodulator in an AM receiver will not be affected by FM variations. Even though FM cannot be detected by a rectifier, on account of unsymmetrical resonance curves (see footnote p. 1) this causes amplitude distortions due to superimposed FM and the rectifier of an AM receiver will register such distortions. Hence, also in AM work we shall register FM effects, but *indirectly* and in the form of superimposed AM distortions.

by avoiding appreciable reactance reflections into the frequency-determining element of a tube oscillator. It should be borne in mind that frequency-determining elements are not always necessarily inductances and capacitances, *i.e.*, coils and condensers. There may be a poorly arranged piezoelectric element, the zero natural reactance of which may be partly due to external effects. Any current that is reflected back into an oscillator branch of a tube oscillator that is not perfectly stabilized may, through its superposition on the expected true oscillator current, disturb the inphase condition of the oscillator current. Through automatic phase balance this will cause a corresponding frequency shift.

Hence, the condition of most interest here is when FM is caused by reflections from a load or other secondary branch into the frequency-determining oscillator branch. In the secondary circuit or branch, whatever may be the actual case, the amplitude is $I_m(1 + K \sin \omega t) = M_1$ for desired sinusoidal AM if $i_m \sin \omega t$ is the signal current that brings about AM. Any reactive back reactions on the oscillator branch may cause a certain sinusoidal frequency variation $\Delta F \sin \omega t$ in the normally constant oscillator frequency F. Hence, the angular velocity $\Omega = 6.28F$ in the $\sin(\Omega t + \theta)$ term of Eq. (1) may have a variable term superposed on it and then we have to deal with an instantaneous angular velocity $\Omega_t = \Omega + \Delta\Omega \sin \omega t$. As far as FM is concerned, only the argument of the sine fluctuation of Eq. (1) need be considered. We find that

$$\int (\Omega + \Delta\Omega \sin \omega t + \theta)\, dt = \Omega t - \frac{\Delta\Omega}{\omega} \cos \omega t + A$$

The sine term of Eq. (24) is, therefore, $M_2 = \sin(\Omega t - \beta \cos \omega t)$ since $\Delta\Omega/\omega = \Delta F/f$ is the modulation index β for FM. The integration constant represents a *fixed* relative phase and therefore cannot affect the AM as well as the FM. Also it could not contribute to PM if such a modulation would act in addition. Hence A can be omitted in the solution. Now, the equation for simultaneous FM and AM reads $I_t = M_1 M_2 I_m$, or

$$I_t = \underbrace{I_m(1 + K \sin \omega t)}_{M_1} \underbrace{\sin(\Omega t - \beta \cos \omega t)}_{M_2} \qquad (32)$$

We can expand Eq. (32) and express it in summation terms as was done in Eq. (24); then expand the summation into individual terms as was done in Eq. (25). The result for the first side-current pair of respective frequencies $F \pm f$ will be

$$\left. \begin{aligned} I_{F-f} &= 0.5KI_m(B_0 + B_2) \cos(\Omega - \omega)t - B_1I_m \cos(\Omega - \omega)t \\ I_{F+f} &= -0.5KI_m(B_0 + B_2) \cos(\Omega + \omega)t - B_1I_m \cos(\Omega + \omega)t \end{aligned} \right\} \tag{33}$$

where $B_0 = J_0(\beta)$, $B_1 = J_1(\beta)$, and $B_2 = J_2(\beta)$. These expressions show that even though symmetrical frequency spacing exists with respect to the carrier frequency F, the amplitude of the first lower side current is

$$[0.5K(B_0 + B_2) - B_1]I_m = (c - d)I_m$$

which is smaller in magnitude than the negative amplitude $(c + d)I_m$ of the upper side current. Hence, superposition of AM on FM must produce smaller amplitudes on the lower side-band side. As a matter of fact, on account of the difference $(c - d)$ in the amplitude factor for the lower side current, we have a convenient experimental method for determining the modulation degree K for AM. Zero amplitude of the first lower side current I_{F-f} is produced by means of a suitable selection of the signal frequency f in the relation $\beta = \Delta F/f$. When, therefore, the first lower side current disappears, then $d = c$ and

$$K\% = 200 \frac{B_1}{B_0 + B_2} \tag{34}$$

A similar result has already been found for $\beta \leqq 0.2$ on page 39, where the modulation components of the first side-current pair for pure AM were combined with those for pure FM. To check this result previously found in Eq. (16), we have only to use the Bessel values of B_0, B_1, and B_2 for a small modulation index not exceeding the value of 0.2. $B_0 = 1$, $B_1 = 0.5\beta$, and B_2 is essentially equal to zero. Hence, the amplitude of the first lower side current is now $(0.5K - 0.5\beta)I_m$ and the amplitude of the first upper side current is $(0.5K + 0.5\beta)I_m$, which is the result obtained in Eq. (16) and applied in connection with Fig. 16.

It will be noted that in Eq. (16) only the sine terms were dealt with, while Eq. (33) shows cosine terms for the present treatment. Both relations say the same thing, however, though Eq. (33) holds for *any* value of β since no assumptions were made as to the magnitude of β during its derivation. The spectrum solution holds for all cases where the signal frequency f is small compared with the carrier frequency F and where $\Delta F/F$ is likewise a small quantity. All these conditions are met in modern FM engineering, since F is in the megacycle range, for instance, equal to 45 Mc, f is never higher than 16 kc, and $\Delta F \leq 75$ kc. The reason why sine terms appear in Eq. (16) is that for the case of pure FM, the derivation was based on the relation $I_m \sin (\Omega t + \beta \sin \omega t)$ with a signal current $i_m \cos \omega t$ causing the FM. For AM in Eq. (16) a signal current $i_m \cos \omega t$ was likewise used in the relation $I_m(1 + K \cos \omega t) \sin \Omega t$ from which the component currents were derived. But, for the present derivation, Eq. (32) is basic for reasons already given in connection with this equation. In deriving the equation a signal current $i_m \sin \omega t$ was assumed.

Moreover, the general solution given in Eq. (10), which holds as far as the spectrum distribution is concerned for FM as well as for PM, should not be confused with the solutions that were made for PM + AM and for FM + AM. When we search for effects produced by either two or by all three types of possible modulations acting simultaneously, we have to be consistent, not only as far as the spectrum requirement is concerned, but also as to whether we deal with sinusoidal or with cosinoidal swings. Which is the case can be determined only from the actual conditions. For instance, when a sinusoidal AM causes the flow of a sinusoidal modulated h-f current in a transmitter aerial, if a linear phase shift occurs, it must be proportional to the *sinusoidal* carrier-level modulation. The phase shift is the result of a *sinusoidal* current and consequently $\beta \sin \omega t$ is the term to be used. But when, as in this section, sinusoidal carrier-level modulations in a load branch react on the generator that produces the center frequency F, the back actions must produce *sinusoidal* frequency "wobbles" in F so that $F + \Delta F \sin \omega t$ is *at first* caused by the back reaction on the frequency-determining network. Hence, we have to deal with an instantaneous frequency since the frequency is now a varying function of time. If this is the case, the revolving vector no longer describes equal arcs in equal times, but the angle α is interrelated with the generalized angular velocity through the relation $\alpha = \int \Omega \, dt$ since $\Omega = d\alpha/dt$. Wherever possible, we should always start out by integrating the frequency, *i.e.*, the angular velocity $6.28F$ in this case. This will take care of any variation. This was done in the derivation of Eq. (32).

These remarks are added since there seems considerable confusion existing in current literature about these points.

With respect to the modulation product of the first side-current pair for FM + AM, we have only to combine all the terms of Eq. (33). Since $0.5 \cos (\Omega - \omega)t - 0.5 \cos (\Omega + \omega)t = \sin \Omega t \sin \omega t$ and $0.5 \cos (\Omega + \omega)t + 0.5 \cos (\Omega - \omega)t = \cos \Omega t \cos \omega t$, the vectorial addition

$$I_{F-f} + I_{F+f} = KI_m(B_0 + B_2) \sin \omega t \sin \Omega t - 2B_1 I_m \cos \omega t \cos \Omega t$$

This is the *first modulation product* and has a scalar value

$$\left. \begin{array}{l} \text{Amplitude of first modulation} \\ \text{product for FM + AM} \end{array} \right\} = I_m \sqrt{[K(B_0 + B_2)]^2 + 4B_1^2} \quad (35)$$

If we compare this product with AM + PM, we find

$$\left. \begin{array}{l} \text{First modula-} \\ \text{tion product} \\ \text{vector} \end{array} \right\langle \begin{array}{l} [K(B_0 + B_2)I_m \sin \omega t] \sin \Omega t \\ \quad - (2B_1 I_m \cos \omega t) \cos \Omega t \quad \text{for FM + AM} \\ [K(B_0 - B_2)I_m \sin \omega t] \sin \Omega t \\ \quad + (2B_1 I_m \sin \omega t) \cos \Omega t \quad \text{for PM + AM} \end{array} \right\} \quad (36)$$

A comparison of the absolute magnitudes yields

$$\left. \begin{array}{l} \text{Amplitude of} \\ \text{first modulation} \\ \text{product} \end{array} \right\langle \begin{array}{l} I_m \sqrt{[K(B_0 + B_2)]^2 + 4B_1^2} \quad \text{for FM + AM} \\ I_m \sqrt{[K(B_0 - B_2)]^2 + 4B_1^2} \quad \text{for PM + AM} \end{array} \right\} \quad (37)$$

We note that for PM + AM we have $B_0 - B_2$ instead of their sum and according to Eq. (36) *both* quadrature components depend on *sinusoidal* modulation functions. For FM + AM, we have the sum $B_0 + B_2$ and one quadrature component is a sine function and the other a cosine function of the signal frequency f. In Eq. (36) there is also a minus sign before the B_1 term for FM + AM, instead of the plus sign for PM + AM. This explains the fact why for superimposed PM instead of FM, there will still be the same amplitude on the lower side-current side as for the corresponding first upper side current. Hence, the *spectrum distribution*, as far as side frequencies are concerned, for one and the same β value, i.e., $\Delta\theta = \Delta F/f$, is the same for either FM or PM superimposed on AM. There is a great difference, however, as far as the respective upper and lower side-*current amplitudes* are concerned. Hence, *smaller lower side* currents *indicate that FM is parasitic;* equal side currents on each side of the carrier frequency F may still give a possibility of superimposed PM. In other words, superimposed PM will not cause unsymmetrical amplitude distortion, but superimposed FM will.

The fact that the superposition of PM on AM does produce respective side currents for frequencies $F \pm f$ of equal amplitude does not mean at all that these amplitudes are the ones that would exist if PM were not present. This is, however, more or less true when the phase swing $\Delta\theta$ is equal to 0.2 radian and smaller. But, in addition, there will be, even though not very large, equal amplitudes for frequencies $F \pm 2f$. If the amplitudes of the first and the second side currents are compared, we shall have an experimental method for determining a small superimposed PM. The method will apply to most cases where PM is parasitic, *i.e.*, for $\beta = \Delta\theta \leqq 0.2$ and for $K = 50\%$ or more. Equation (30) is basic for this experimental method since it holds for AM + PM, for phase swings equal to and smaller than 0.2 radian, and for any value of K that does not cause amplitude distortion on account of overmodulation in AM. Calling the first side-current amplitude I_1 (it does not matter whether it is the first upper or first lower amplitude since they are equal) and I_2 the amplitude of the second side current, then according to Eq. (30) we have $I_1 = 0.5I_m \sqrt{K^2 + \beta^2} \cong 0.5KI_m$ and $I_2 = 0.25\beta KI_m$, or $\beta = \Delta\theta = 2I_2/I_1$. Hence, if we measure with a search-current method the corresponding proportional deflections d_1 and d_2, we have $\Delta\theta = 2d_2/d_1$ radians or $114.6d_2/d_1$ deg for the maximum phase swing due to superimposed PM.

Moreover, if we collect all the terms for the second side-current pair for FM + AM, we find

$$
\left.
\begin{aligned}
I_{F-2f} &= 0.5KI_m(B_1 + B_3) \sin(\Omega - 2\omega)t \\
&\qquad - B_2I_m \sin(\Omega - 2\omega)t \\
I_{F+2f} &= -0.5KI_m(B_1 + B_3) \sin(\Omega + 2\omega)t \\
&\qquad - B_2I_m \sin(\Omega + 2\omega)t
\end{aligned}
\right\}
\tag{38}
$$

Also here we note that the second lower side current of frequency $F - 2f$ has an amplitude $[0.5K(B_1 + B_3) - B_2]I_m = (c' - d')I_m$, which is *smaller* than the amplitude value $-(c' + d')I_m$ of frequency $F + 2f$. Hence, there must be also a signal frequency f which makes the second lower side current disappear and for which the degree of AM can be computed from

$$
K\% = \frac{200B_2}{B_1 + B_3}
\tag{39}
$$

The modulation product of the second side-current pair is found by using the relations $\sin \Omega t \cos 2\omega t = 0.5 \sin (\Omega + 2\omega)t + 0.5 \sin (\Omega - 2\omega)t$ and $\cos \Omega t \sin 2\omega t = 0.5 \sin (\Omega + 2\omega)t - 0.5 \sin (\Omega - 2\omega)t$ in Eq. (38). The results are

$$I_{F-2f} + I_{F+2f} = -(2B_2 I_m \cos 2\omega t) \sin \Omega t \\ + [K(B_1 + B_3)I_m \sin 2\omega t] \cos \Omega t \quad (40)$$

and

$$\begin{array}{l} \text{Amplitude of second modula-} \\ \text{tion product for FM + AM} \end{array} \Bigg\} = I_m \sqrt{[K(B_1 + B_3)]^2 + 4B_2^2} \quad (41)$$

which holds for any $\beta = \Delta F/f$ value.

In the case where $\beta \leqq 0.2$, where essentially only one side-band pair is significant, the degree of FM can be computed from the actual unequal respective side-current amplitudes I_{F-f} and I_{F+f}. They are, according to computations already made, $0.5(K - \beta)I_m$ and $0.5(K + \beta)I_m$. Hence, by measuring the respective first side-current amplitudes with a search-current method, we obtain the corresponding current readings I_1 and I_2 on the lower and upper side-current side and find $\beta = \dfrac{\Delta F}{f} = I_2 - I_1$. Since the signal frequency f is known, we have also a method for finding the maximum frequency deviation ΔF from $f(I_2 - I_1)$.

Generally, it can be said that for simultaneous FM and AM the respective spectrum amplitudes on the lower side-band side are smaller than those on the upper side-band side. If FM is a parasitic modulation, its degree, *i.e.*, its frequency spectrum effect is, no doubt, small in the upper a-f range of signal currents since ΔF is small and $\Delta F/f$ must decrease with increasing signal frequency f. Hence, parasitic FM can play a practical part only in the lower signal-frequency range. Also, it should be understood that parasitic FM, unless suppressed by striking at its cause, requires networks at the reception end to accommodate all the component frequencies, but fortunately only for the lower signal frequencies. Hence, it is easier to avoid distortion due to parasitic FM than to parasitic PM. If AM is the parasitic modulation, limiters can remove the AM effect. But if the parasitic AM is caused by the FM, removal of the AM will also remove some of the modulation (see page 59).

13. Actions in Threefold Modulation (FM + PM + AM).— From the results presented in Secs. 11 and 12, with the assumption that FM and PM occurring simultaneously are proportional to amplitude changes of the carrier level I_m, we have for carrier-level variations of $I_m(1 + K \sin \omega t)$, instantaneous frequency variations about the mean carrier frequency F of $\Delta F \sin \omega t$, and phase variations $\Delta \theta \sin \omega t$, the following equation giving the instantaneous current for FM + PM + AM

$$I_t = I_m(1 + K \sin \omega t) \sin \left(\Omega t - \frac{\Delta F}{f} \cos \omega t + \Delta \theta \sin \omega t \right) \quad (42)$$

For desired AM, with FM as well as PM parasitic, only the modulation index $\beta_f = \Delta F/f$ can be effective in the lower signal-frequency range. For the upper signal-frequency range, the modulation index $\beta_p = \Delta \theta$ causes most of the additional spectrum distribution due to the parasitic modulations. This is true since both ΔF and $\Delta \theta$ cannot be large for modern circuit design in an AM transmitter. We have, according to Eqs. (25), (27), (28), and (33), for the first lower and first upper side currents, the vector currents

$$I_{F-f} = \left\{ \begin{array}{ll} 0.5K(B_0 + B_2)I_m \cos (\Omega - \omega)t & \\ \quad - B_1 I_m \cos (\Omega - \omega)t & \text{for FM + AM} \\ 0.5K(B_0 - B_2)I_m \cos (\Omega - \omega)t & \\ \quad - B_1 I_m \sin (\Omega - \omega)t & \text{for PM + AM} \end{array} \right.$$

$$I_{F+f} = \left\{ \begin{array}{ll} -0.5K(B_0 + B_2)I_m \cos (\Omega + \omega)t & \\ \quad - B_1 I_m \cos (\Omega + \omega)t & \text{for FM + AM} \\ 0.5K(B_0 - B_2)I_m \cos (\Omega + \omega)t & \\ \quad + B_1 I_m \sin (\Omega + \omega)t & \text{for PM + AM} \end{array} \right. \quad (43)$$

This shows that respective symmetrical side currents of frequencies $F - f$ and $F + f$ have, on account of the FM effect, less amplitude value on the lower side band side. Note also that, for FM + AM, the amplitude $0.5K(B_0 + B_2)I_m$ is in antiphase (one positive and one negative) with the amplitude due to FM. However, for PM + AM the PM effect is a sine term and the AM effect is controlled by a cosine function. Hence, there can be no cancellation, even though at a certain moment of the modulation cycle one term may be at its maximum value while the other is at its zero value, or vice versa. Therefore, the combined FM + PM + AM under no condition can cause complete cancellation of the first lower side current for a critical signal frequency $f = f_c$, but will cause a definite minimum.

The minimum at this critical frequency must account for the PM effect and gives a means for determining not only this effect but also the maximum phase deviation $\Delta\theta$. This will be evident from the following, where on account of small parasitic $\Delta\theta$ and ΔF swings it seems justified to assume that $\beta_p = \Delta\theta$ as well as $\beta_f = \Delta F/f$ do not exceed values larger than 0.2. Hence, in Eq. (43) we have essentially $B_0 = 1$, and $B_1 = 0.5\beta_f$ or $0.5\beta_p$, depending on whether we deal with superimposed parasitic FM or PM. The Bessel factor B_2 is negligible for such small β values. Now, for the AM effect, the term $0.5KI_m$ is correct, whether FM or PM is superimposed on AM, with the above approximation values for B_0 and B_2. For the superimposed FM effect for the first lower side current, the amplitude $-B_1I_m$, which is in antiphase with the AM term, plays a part and has an amplitude value of $0.5\beta_fI_m$. The superimposed PM effect in Eq. (43) has an amplitude value of $0.5\beta_pI_m$ but is a sine function; *i.e.*, it is in quadrature with the $0.5\beta_fI_m$ amplitude. The characteristic terms of the lower side currents have, therefore, for values of either modulation index not exceeding a maximum value of 0.2, the form

$$I_{F-f} = 0.5KI_m \cos{(\Omega - \omega)t}$$
$$- 0.5I_m[\beta_f \cos{(\Omega - \omega)t} + \beta_p \sin{(\Omega - \omega)t}]$$

The resultant scalar value becomes

$$I_{F-f} = 0.5I_m \sqrt{\beta_p^2 + (K - \beta_f)^2} \tag{44}$$

This proves the foregoing statements that for a critical signal frequency a minimum amplitude for the first lower side current will occur equal to $0.5\beta_pI_m$, *i.e.*, we have an experimental method for finding the maximum parasitic phase swing $\Delta\theta = \beta_p$ from the minimum[1] amplitude value. The minimum deflection d_1 for the critical signal frequency $f = f_c$ obtained with a search-current method is proportional to $0.5\,\Delta\theta I_m$, and the search-current method also gives a deflection d_0 for the unmodulated current of level I_m. Hence, the maximum parasitic phase swing in radians can be computed from the relation $\Delta\theta = 2d_1/d_0$. The maximum phase deviation in degrees is, therefore, computed from the relation $114.6d_1/d_0$. For any frequency other than the critical frequency,

[1] For more experimental details consult "High-frequency Measurements," pp. 377–379; theory of search-current method, pp. 379–380; and useful circuits, pp. 116–126, 164–168.

the d_1 deflections, as well as the d_2 deflections shown in Fig. 21 for the upper first side current for different signal frequencies f, are larger. It is easy, therefore, to find out experimentally whether we are obtaining deflections for the lower side current or for the upper side current.

From this figure we see that, for a known degree K of AM, we can also compute the maximum parasitic frequency deviation ΔF. Expressing the deflection readings in per cent, the deflection $d_0 = 1.0$ corresponds to 100 per cent, and all other deflections are as indicated in the figure. Since at the critical frequency $f_c =$ 1.5 kc, we find the minimum value $d_1 = 0.08$ and the dip of the

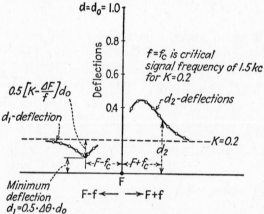

FIG. 21.—Experimental d_1 and d_2 curves for the determination of ΔF if K is known and K if $\beta = \Delta F/f$ is known.

experimental d_1 curve is 0.12 below the K level, we have $0.5 \Delta \theta =$ 0.08 and $0.5(K - \Delta F/f_c)d_0 = 0.5(0.2 - \Delta F/1.5) = 0.12$. Hence, $\Delta \theta = 0.16$ radian or ± 9.17 deg and $\Delta F = \pm 0.06$ kc or ± 60 cycles per second. To plot the deflections on a percentage scale has, furthermore, the advantage of showing with the d_1 and d_2 curves directly the effective K_e or modulation characteristics when all three types of modulations act simultaneously. Since both deflection or K_e curves run asymptotically toward the K line, which is due to AM and constant for all signal frequencies, we note that for higher signal frequencies neither parasitic FM nor PM can be very effective for the upper a-f range of signal currents in comparison with the desired AM. Whatever effect is still existent must be mostly due to parasitic PM since $\Delta F/f$ is then very small in comparison to $\Delta \theta$.

It should be clearly understood that this experimental method puts no limit on the degree K of AM, but neither $\Delta F/f$ nor $\Delta\theta$ should ever exceed values larger than about 0.2. This limitation seems amply justified if AM is the desired type of modulation. Even though the relations leading to this experimental method were obtained only from a comparison of FM + AM and PM + AM in Eq. (43) and not directly from FM + PM + AM as given in Eq. (42), it should not matter since we are interested only in amplitude effects. As a matter of fact, if we would write down the expression for pure AM as in Eq. (3), then write down the expression for pure FM as given by the

$$J_1(\beta)I_m[\sin(\Omega + \omega)t - \sin(\Omega - \omega)t]$$

term of Eq. (12), but for the value $J_1(\beta) = 0.5\beta_f$ which is permissible for β values smaller than 0.2, and then write down also the expression for PM, the same formulas would be obtained.[1]

If we expand Eq. (42) into component terms, just as was done in Eq. (25) for PM + AM, using values of β that never exceed 0.2, then the first Bessel factor $B_1 = 0.5\beta$, which value holds then for $\beta = \beta_p$ as well as for $\beta = \beta_f$. Now if we put $B_0 = 1$ and $B_2 = 0$, which is permissible for $\beta \leqq 0.2$, we have, for the lower and upper first side currents, which are essentially the only side currents that can play a practical part for such a small modulation index β, for FM + PM + AM the expressions

$$I = \left\{ \begin{array}{l} 0.5KI_m \cos(\Omega - \omega)t \\ \quad - 0.5I_m[\beta_f \cos(\Omega - \omega)t + \beta_p \sin(\Omega - \omega)t] \quad \text{for } F - f \\ 0.5KI_m \cos(\Omega + \omega)t \\ \quad + 0.5I_m[\beta_f \cos(\Omega + \omega)t + \beta_p \sin(\Omega + \omega)t] \quad \text{for } F + f \end{array} \right\} \quad (45)$$

which leads to the experimental method already found. If only the approximation $B_1 = 0.5\beta$ is used, retaining the true Bessel factor B_0 instead of the approximation $B_0 = 1$ and also retaining the small Bessel factor B_2 instead of neglecting it, we find for the first lower side current the scalar or amplitude value

$$I_{F-f} = 0.5I_m \sqrt{(B_0 + B_2)^2[\beta_p^2 + (K - \beta_f)^2] - 4B_0B_2 \frac{\beta_p^2K^2}{\beta_p^2 + \beta_f^2}} \quad (46)$$

The last term under the radical surely cannot play a great part since, on account of the factor β_f^2 in the numerator, even if $\beta_p = 0.2$, we have a multiplier of only 0.04. In addition, even if either β

---

[1] This has been done in "High-frequency Measurements," p. 380.

value is as large as 0.2 we have B_2 equal to only 0.00498. Hence, even for the upper limit where our deflection method still gives reliable results for ΔF and $\Delta\theta$, the portion $4B_0$, which is essentially equal to 4, of the last term under the radical has to be multiplied by a value $0.005 \times 0.04K^2/0.08 = 0.0025K^2$. For the most severe condition of 100 per cent AM, this factor is as small as 0.0025. We have, therefore, for the first side current the absolute amplitude

$$I_{F\pm f} = 0.5(B_0 + B_2)I_m \sqrt{\Delta\theta^2 + \left(K \pm \frac{\Delta F}{f}\right)^2} \tag{47}$$

Since, for $p = 0.5(B_0 + B_2)I_m$, we have

$$I_{F\pm f} = \sqrt{p^2\,\Delta\theta^2 + p^2\left(K \pm \frac{\Delta F}{f}\right)^2}$$

the current vectors for the respective first side currents are as in Fig. 22. From the resultant vectors it will be noted not only that

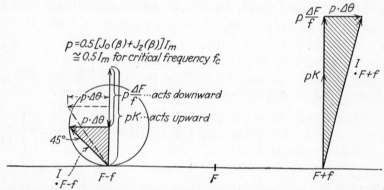

Fig. 22.—Resultant side currents for frequencies $F \pm f$ of first side current pair.

different projection (vertical) amplitudes result, but also that decidedly different directions prevail. It should be understood that the upper side-current vector spins around faster than does the lower side-current vector but that, in measuring side-current amplitudes, only the projection along the vertical coordinate is of interest. Hence, the PM effect on the lower side-current side must, for the critical frequency $f = f_c$, which produces the minimum deflection d_1, be equal to the magnitude $p\,\Delta\theta$ since the second term in Eq. (47) vanishes for this frequency. For partial cancellation of the AM by FM effect, the dotted vector triangle shows that the projection of the resultant amplitude on the vertical reference axis no longer gives $p \, \Delta\theta$ since the vertical and the horizontal portions of the dotted rectangular triangle are no longer equal.

14. Translation of Signal Currents into Corresponding Frequency and Phase Variations.—In Fig. 2, the *stimuli* that bring about FM and PM, respectively, are either frequency variations for direct FM or variations in phase for PM. Unless sound waves are used directly to bring about FM, we have to deal with either a signal or modulating current or its corresponding voltage. To use sound waves directly to produce FM has reference, for instance, to the use of a condenser microphone, which acts as a part of the circuit capacitance, the capacitance determining partly the frequency F of the carrier current. With such a system, though straightforward, we could not produce modern wide-band FM nor expect to secure good mean carrier-frequency stability. Hence, the problem is to translate a signal-current variation into corresponding frequency swings about the *mean* carrier frequency F in the case of FM, or into such *equivalent* corresponding frequency swings [Eq. (6)] about the *fixed*[1] carrier frequency F in the case of PM. The latter is primarily done by having the signal current cause corresponding relative phase variations in the carrier, while the unmodulated carrier level I_m and the carrier frequency F are kept constant.

Even though, with FM as well as with PM, the value of the center frequency F remains constant as far as the number of cycles per second is concerned, there are, according to Eqs. (7) and (6), great differences. For FM the corresponding frequency variation is directly proportional to the maximum frequency excursion ΔF during the modulation cycle [Eq. (7)]. For PM the equivalent frequency variation is likewise proportional to the maximum excursion, which is in this case, of course, a phase swing $\Delta\theta$, but it is in addition also *directly proportional* to the frequency f of the signal current [Eq. (6)].

We have also to take into consideration the time function $\cos \omega t$ affecting the instantaneous magnitudes of the FM as well as of the equivalent FM swings. Generally, if PM acts with all

---

[1] It should be clearly understood that for PM as well as for *indirect* FM, the primary oscillator can be a stabilized piezo oscillator since the carrier frequency F is *fixed* and we have frequency variations *only in equivalence*.

the features of true phase modulation, a sinusoidal current $i_m \sin \omega t$ causes in Eq. (5) the $\Delta\theta \sin \omega t$ variation. This could be brought about by means of a corresponding signal voltage impressed on respective screen grids of a balanced modulator (consult Fig. 52). The amplitude of the signal voltage is in *this* case e_m, corresponding to i_m of the signal current. The screen grids are driven in push-pull, but the control grids of the two tubes of the balanced modulator are connected together. A carrier voltage of fixed frequency F is applied between the parallel control grids and the respective cathodes, which are likewise connected together. Therefore, the carrier voltage acts in equal pull. The push-pull output on the plate side can yield only the modulation product $(KI_m \sin \omega t) \sin \Omega t$ since this is a modulator in which the unmodulated carrier is automatically suppressed. These products exist, therefore, only at instants when the signal voltage has a value. Hence, the modulation product is proportional to the signal-voltage variation.

If, as in Fig. 3*b*, this modulation product, which is an AM product, is added in time quadrature, as far as the period $1/F$ of the carrier current is concerned, with the unmodulated carrier, we shall have PM with a phase variation $\Delta\theta \sin \omega t$, which is proportional to the signal current. This phase shift takes place in the external plate circuit as shown in Figs. 52, 72 and described in detail in connection with them. Hence, the condition required in Eq. (5) can be readily satisfied; *i.e.*, a signal-current variation is readily translated into proportional phase swing modulation which is PM.

But from Eq. (6) we note that the equivalent frequency variation superimposed on the *fixed* carrier frequency F is by no means the same as the signal-current variation as far as the entire a-f range is concerned. We note that the *degree* of equivalent FM becomes *larger* for the higher signal frequencies f than for the sounds of lower pitch. For equivalent FM, we have *inherent* a-f emphasis, *i.e.*, frequency accentuation *toward* the upper signal-frequency range. This is *characteristic* with PM and does not mean distortion, since the actual PM effects are still directly proportional to signal-current variations. Hence, if in a receiver we use a phase discriminator instead of a frequency discriminator, PM would be demodulated properly and without such a-f accentuation. But when we are interested in producing equivalent FM variations *with no accentuation* of this type and as with FM

[Eq. (7)], then we can do this only if we cause at the output of the balanced modulator a modulation product which is not only of the general form $(KI_m \sin \omega t) \sin \Omega t$ but which has an amplitude

$$\frac{KI_m}{f} \sin \omega t$$

instead of the amplitude $KI_m \sin \omega t$. When such a modulation product, namely, $(KI_m/f) \sin \omega t \sin \Omega t$, is added in time quadrature, i.e., as $(KI_m/f) \sin \omega t \cos \Omega t$, with the unmodulated carrier $I_m \sin \Omega t$, we cause in Eq. (5) not maximum $\Delta \theta$ excursions but maximum $\Delta \theta / f$ excursions. The equivalent change in instantaneous frequency in Eq. (6) is no longer $f \Delta \theta \cos \omega t$ but is $\Delta \theta \cos \omega t$. Hence, the equivalent FM is *exactly* the same as though direct FM had been the cause. A *frequency* discriminator will, so to speak, not "feel" whether the cause of its FM into AM conversion was due to direct FM or indirect FM. This is exactly what is done in the well-known Armstrong transmitter.

The only "link" still missing is how the $1/f$ effect is injected into the balanced amplitude modulator. This task is simple also.

Since Eq. (6) was obtained by *differentiation* of the argument α of the main sinus function $\sin \alpha$ of Eq. (5) in order to account for the instantaneous frequency F_t, and since in the representations of Fig. 7 *equivalent* PM is an *integration* of FM, we must integrate the signal current before applying the corresponding voltage to the balanced modulator. Integrating, for instance, $i_m \cos (6.28f)t$ yields $[i_m \sin (6.28f)t + A]/(6.28f)$; i.e., a similar function of time whose amplitude is also inversely proportional to the signal frequency f. The integration constant A is here of no practical concern. *Electrically*, such an integration takes place in *any* condenser since its terminal voltage is proportional to $\int (i_m \cos \omega t) \, dt$, the constant of proportionality being the reciprocal of the capacitance, i.e., equal to $1/C$. All that is necessary, therefore, is to apply the actual signal voltage to a series combination of a high resistance and a condenser. Then have the voltage of the condenser affect the balanced modulator. This is usually done through an amplifier tube on whose fixed grid-cathode bias is superimposed the integrated voltage that is now proportional to e_m/f, since $1/C$ as well as $1/6.28$ are constants. This is described in detail on pages 223 to 225. It is, therefore, seen that we can produce true FM effects even though PM is primarily instrumental if the complex signal current due to any signal or intelligence is made to flow through the resistance-condenser combination.

The signal current translation into a similar variation of the carrier frequency F in direct FM presents no engineering difficulty either. As a matter of fact, very large frequency swings can be secured directly since in practice a variable reactance is reflected into the oscillator branch that determines the carrier frequency F. This is done by a superimposed current which is fed back into that branch and which can, therefore, cause frequency variations that are directly proportional to the signal current. (For details, consult pages 155 to 182.) From this it is again evident why for *direct* FM the primary oscillator cannot be a piezo oscillator whose frequency is inherently stabilized.

15. Translation of Frequency Modulation and Phase Modulation into Amplitude Modulation.—Since both FM and PM are time axis modulations that are in quadrature with modulations in amplitude, customary types of demodulators cannot be used for separating the signal component, *i.e.*, the intelligence, from the modulated carrier current.

In the first detector and the i-f networks of an FM receiver, everything is the same as for customary types of superheterodyne circuits used in AM receivers. However the band-pass networks have to accommodate a frequency spectrum corresponding to the maximum deviation ratio $\Delta F/f_{max} = 5$, where f_{max} is the highest desired signal frequency and is generally taken as 15 kc. With respect to the second detector, this must do the same thing, but in the *other direction* from that which brought about the frequency modulation in the transmitter. As far as PM is concerned, even though a variable phase swing causes PM, we have learned that it causes also equivalent frequency swings with an amplitude value $f \Delta \theta$. Therefore, we can consider a PM current as one for which the equivalent frequency swing is proportional to the signal frequency as well as to the signal amplitude. This can be taken care of by means of a frequency-correcting network, which connects to the output of a discriminator.

Equation (10) shows that an FM current has the form

$$I_t = I_m \sin \left(\Omega t + \beta \sin \omega t \right) = I_m \sin \delta \tag{48}$$

in which $\beta = \Delta F/f$ for FM and $\beta = \Delta \theta$ for PM. This expression represents the results of FM or PM and it is the action that has to be reversed in the second detector of a receiver.   All that interests us in this expression is the main sine function which is the argument δ since it, and not the amplitude I_m, which for pure FM as well as pure PM must remain constant, controls the modulation energy. Any amplitude variation must be in quadrature with the FM and will require a different means of detection.   In case of FM the argument δ is the outcome of an integration since for FM, according to Fig. 2, we start with an instantaneous frequency $F_t = F + \Delta F \cos \omega t$ which multiplied by 6.28 yields the corresponding instantaneous angular velocity Ω_t.   In order to obtain the instantaneous phase angle of the modulated current, we integrated Ω_t and found $\int (\Omega + \Delta\Omega \cos \omega t)\, dt = \Omega t + (\Delta\Omega/\omega) \sin \omega t$, if the integration constant is ignored.   This constant represents a fixed relative phase, which can contribute nothing to the modulation.   The outcome is the δ value in Eq. (48).

This means, in other words, that our demodulator in the FM receiver must *differentiate* in order to reverse the integration action in the transmitter.   Performing this differentiation, we have $d\delta/dt = \Omega + \omega\beta \cos \omega t$ which yields exactly the original function $\Omega + \Delta\Omega \cos \omega t$ that caused FM in the transmitter.   Hence, the demodulation of direct FM with a time rate detector should not cause distortion as long as the demodulator has a linear range for the entire peak-to-peak frequency swing of, say, 150 kc if $\Delta F = \pm 75$ kc.   We still have PM and indirect FM to consider, the latter being used in the Armstrong transmitter.

With respect to Fig. 3b, we learned that PM can also be produced by adding the modulation product $(KI_m \sin \omega t) \sin \Omega t$, as obtained at the output side of a balanced amplitude modulator, to the unmodulated current vector $I_m \sin \Omega t$ and in time quadrature with it.   Hence, the modulation product is added as $(KI_m \sin \omega t) \cos \Omega t$, which is now a cosine function of the carrier current variation.   The geometrical addition shown in Fig. 3b indicates that the resultant vector OP_1 is longer than I_m and has a magnitude $\sqrt{OP^2 + PP_1^2} = I_m \sqrt{1 + K^2 \sin^2 \omega t}$.   It makes, at any instant, an angle $\theta_t = \tan^{-1} (PP_1/OP) = \tan^{-1} (K \sin \omega t)$ with the vector OP which represents the $I_m \sin \Omega t$ variation of the unmodulated carrier of frequency F.

If we can express the resultant vector OP_1 at any instant in the form of Eq. (48), we know from the proof given above that a linear differentiator, or, as it is called, a frequency discriminator, will demodulate the modulation intelligence. Since this PM is caused primarily by AM, we have to express K in terms of equivalent phase effects. Writing down the expression for the instantaneous value of the resultant vector OP_1, we find

$$I_t = I_m \sqrt{1 + K^2 \sin^2 \omega t} \sin (\Omega t + \theta_t)$$
$$= I_m \sqrt{1 + K^2 \sin^2 \omega t} \sin (\Omega t + \Phi \sin \omega t) \quad (49)$$

where for all values of primary AM, $i.e.$, $K \leqq 1$, a corresponding maximum phase swing Φ obtains. From the expression $\theta_t = \tan^{-1} (PP_1/OP) = \tan^{-1} (K \sin \omega t)$, we note that for Φ in degrees we have $\tan \Phi = K$. Now, let us examine the most severe primary amplitude modulation condition for which condition $K = 1$. Figure 3b, as well as the corresponding equations, shows that then $PP_1 = OP$ and $\Phi = 45$ deg. This is the maximum phase swing that can be produced with a balanced modulator ahead of this PM device. This assumes that the $I_m \sin \Omega t$ vector, which is suppressed in the balanced amplitude modulator, is added in quadrature and is not a vector that is shorter or longer than I_m but is equal to it. Since in Eq. (48), which we have to satisfy for no distortion, the maximum phase swing $\beta = \Delta\theta$ is in radians, we have to obtain Φ also in radians. For the 100 per cent primary AM assumed above, this gives $\Phi = 45/57.3 = 0.758$ radian. Hence, we cannot equate Φ radians to the AM factor K, which causes Φ and is $K = 1$. Therefore, for phase swings as large as 45 deg, the resultant vector OP_1 will not travel with its extremity on a circle. Therefore, considerable harmonic distortion will take place.

Now consider the case where only 20 per cent AM is effective in the balanced modulator that produces the modulation product $KI_m \sin \omega t \sin \Omega t$ before it is shifted 90 deg with respect to the carrier angular velocity Ω. We then have $K = 0.2$ and find $\Phi = \tan^{-1} (0.2) = 11.3$ deg or $11.3/57.3 = 0.1974$ radian, which is essentially equal to $0.2 = K$. Looking at trigonometric tables, we find that $K = 0.2$ is about the upper limit producing phase swing linearity at any instant of the modulation cycle of the $0.2 I_m \sin \omega t$ variation. This is true since for the most severe condition of the modulation cycle the value $K = i_m/I_m = 0.2$ causes a tangent essentially equal to the angle in radians. Hence, we have

$$I_t = I_m \sqrt{1 + K^2 \sin^2 \omega t} \; \sin (\Omega t + K \sin \omega t) \quad \text{for } K \leqq 0.2 \text{ and } K = \Delta\theta$$
$$(50)$$

and exactly the same expression as in Eq. (48) is obtained. Equations (49) and (50) show that AM also takes place, but is negligible for $K \leqq 0.2$. Otherwise it has to be avoided by clipping off the amplitude variations by means of an amplitude limiter. This will, however, take some of the modulation energy away and will cause a certain amount of distortion as can be seen from page 59. Hence, pure PM as expressed in Eq. (50) can be readily demodulated with a frequency discriminator. But it has to be realized that a frequency-correcting network has to follow in order to make up for the a-f emphasis toward the higher a-f range on account of the f term in Eq. (6).

Now the next step is to find out how indirect FM can be demodulated. At first sight it looks as if, since indirect FM has all the features of direct FM, Eq. (48) holds and indicates that a linear frequency discriminator will demodulate this type of modulation without harmonic distortion. It will be remembered, however, that indirect FM is initiated by an amplitude modulation product in quadrature with the unmodulated carrier as in Fig. 3b. The only difference that exists is that Armstrong uses a $1/f$ network based on integration (consult page 77), of the signal current between the signal-frequency source and the balanced amplitude modulator. Hence, a signal voltage of amplitude e_m/f is impressed in push-pull on the screen grids of the two modulator tubes. This means that the modulation product taken off at the output side of the balanced modulator is now proportional to

$$\underbrace{\left(\frac{KI_m}{f} \sin \omega t \right)}_{\text{variable amplitude}} \sin \Omega t = p \sin \Omega t$$

When this product is shifted by 90 time degrees and combined with the unmodulated carrier, there results an instantaneous current value

$$I_t = I_m \sin \Omega t + p \cos \Omega t = I_m \sqrt{1 + \frac{K^2}{f^2} \sin^2 \omega t} \; \sin (\Omega t + \theta_t) \quad (51)$$

where

$$\theta_t = \tan^{-1} \left(\frac{K}{f} \sin \omega t \right) \quad (51a)$$

Matters are much more favorable in this case than for PM without $1/f$ correction. We see, for instance, that the undesired AM has now only a KI_m/f extreme component amplitude swing instead of KI_m; *i.e.*, it becomes smaller as the signal frequency f is raised. As far as the resultant amplitude variation that is actually effective is concerned, we find even for 100 per cent primary AM an extreme resultant amplitude of only $I_m \sqrt{1 + m}$ where $m = f^{-2}$. Hence, even for the lowest audible frequency of $f = 16$ cycles per second, we have essentially unity for the square-root value. This assumes that the proportionality constant that causes the $1/f$ effect is unity. The other favorable factor is the fact that the maximum phase amplitude ψ in $\theta_t = \psi \sin \omega t$ now depends on K/f instead of on K. We have for such a substitution the expression

$$\left. \begin{aligned} I_t &= I_m \sqrt{1 + \frac{K^2}{f^2} \sin^2 \omega t} \, \sin \, (\Omega t + \psi \sin \omega t) \\ \tan \psi &= \frac{K}{f} \end{aligned} \right\} \qquad (52)$$

Hence, *the largest maximum phase excursion takes place at the lowest signal frequency f;* this is important. In the Armstrong system a maximum phase swing of ± 30 deg is not exceeded. But, according to the foregoing numerical speculations, if also here $\psi \leqq 11.3$ deg then we can use $\Delta \theta$ instead of ψ which corresponds to a maximum of 0.2 radian. Consequently, for angles even as low as ± 30-deg maximum phase excursions, a certain amount of distortion will take place, as was already discussed on page 6. To find out the order of this distortion, we need only consider the argument of the main sine function $\sin \, (\Omega t + \psi \sin \omega t)$. Since generally the constant of proportionality for the $1/f$ correction, as well as the gain of the modulation network, will not result in unity values, we have to replace K by $k = qK$, where q takes care of the resultant constant of proportionality. Then we have $\tan \psi = k/f$ and for the sine function the argument $\gamma = \Omega t + \tan^{-1} (k/f \sin \omega t)$ which for $k/f = \rho$ leads to the demodulation solution which must be the time rate of change of γ, or

$$\frac{d\gamma}{dt} = \Omega + \frac{\rho f \cos \omega t}{1 + \rho^2 \sin^2 \omega t} = \Omega + \frac{k \cos \omega t}{1 + \rho^2 \sin^2 \omega t} = \Omega + k\mu \quad (53)$$

where ρ denotes the maximum phase swing. We note that only amplitude distortion prevails. Hence, the term $\mu = \cos \omega t/(1 + \rho^2 \sin^2 \omega t)$ represents the magnitude of the distortion.

It is, therefore, seen that for direct FM and for indirect FM, which does not produce maximum phase swings much larger than about 11.3 deg, a linear time-rate demodulator can, as is shown in Fig. 23, translate without distortion frequency variations into corresponding amplitude variations. A linear time-rate demodu-

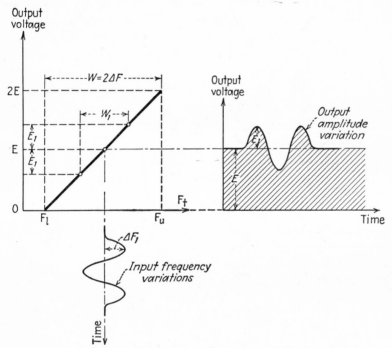

Fig. 23.—Conversion of frequency variations into amplitude variations.

lator is a device that gives output voltages that are directly proportional to frequency variations. The frequency variations are about the center frequency F and the $2 \Delta F$ demodulator accommodates a complete peak-to-peak frequency swing. Since the output of any modulation device is always some function of the amplitude, one or even two amplitude limiter stages should be used ahead of the FM-AM translator. This ensures that relatively large undesired amplitude variations do not remain in the output of the last limiter where they can affect the frequency amplitude converter.

The converter, or frequency discriminator, shown in Fig. 23, is assumed to have an ideal characteristic in order to bring out clearly the modulation conversion. The characteristic is such that for the upper cutoff frequency F_u of the slope filter a voltage $2E$ is obtained at the output of this filter. For the center or carrier frequency F we have only a voltage of E volts; at the lower cutoff frequency F_l zero output voltage prevails. The characteristic also covers a maximum range or frequency width of $W = 2\Delta F = 150$ kc in order to meet current practice. Hence, if the input voltage has frequency swings over the limits of ± 75 kc, the total width W for which the slope converter is designed will be made use of and maximum permissible frequency excursions will be converted into 100 per cent AM at the output of the modulation converter. If, however, not so intense an FM is arriving at the input side of the modulation converter then, as is indicated in this figure, we shall cover a total frequency space or width of only W_1 for corresponding frequency fluctuations of $\pm \Delta F_1$. The degree of amplitude modulation experienced at the output side of the FM-AM translator is then no longer 100 per cent but is $K = 200 \Delta F_1/W_1$ per cent.

The ideal characteristic has the disadvantage that it taxes the receiver even at times when no FM exists, since for absence of FM the output voltage is not zero but $= E$ volts. This characteristic has the disadvantage that it is not symmetrical, at the center frequency F, with respect to a differential action due to output voltages on each side of this frequency. To eliminate these disadvantages, commercial frequency discriminators are designed such that at the center frequency F there is no output voltage at all. For a certain positive ΔF_1 swing we obtain, say, a certain positive output voltage proportional to the magnitude ΔF_1 of this swing; for the same negative swing $-\Delta F_1$, we obtain an equal negative output voltage from the discriminator. Such an action is brought about by push-pull modulation translation. Since such discriminators use rectifiers, they will inherently also bring about subsequent amplitude demodulation so that signal frequency output occurs. In such discriminators a certain positive frequency deviation ΔF_1 from the center frequency F causes an increase of the output voltage of one tube section; at the same time, a decrease occurs at the output of the other tube section (two rectifers under one envelope). As far as the input side of the two sections is concerned, they behave exactly alike. This explains the differential action at the output side and shows that we have not only frequency discrimination but also an apparatus from which, for equal simultaneous positive voltages of frequencies $F + \Delta F_1$ and $F - \Delta F_1$, there can be no output voltage. This feature will eliminate certain types of static interference. To accomplish such differential action, the output branches of the rectifier units are connected in indirect series. The respective output voltages therefore add and cause a double amplitude effect; in absence of FM, no output effects exist.

The elimination of certain types of static is based on the fact that when certain abrupt interference (consult Fig. 31) arrives at the i-f stages of the FM receiver, it produces, in virtue of the band-pass action of such a network, a series of spectrum amplitudes of the same polarity acting simultaneously and symmetrically with respect to the mid-frequency of the band-pass network. Hence, such disturbances can only enter the discriminator, but cannot produce any output voltage that will act on the a-f stages of the FM receiver. It should be understood, however, that if a relatively significant FM at the same mid-frequency also occurs, the instantaneous relative phase of the interfering spectrum energy distribution with respect to the FM carrier may have any value whatsoever. This is explained on page 104 and shows that if the phase of the interference is, for instance, 90 deg leading the FM current of mid-frequency F and if the interference intensity I is larger than the desired FM intensity D, then the instantaneous phase of the resultant of I and D is also varied, owing to the I action. This equivalent PM caused by the interference will affect the output voltage of the discriminator and will, therefore, also register some of the interference at the a-f output of the FM receiver. This is not true, however, when I is much smaller than D, as the explanation in connection with Fig. 29 shows.

16. Determination of Maximum Frequency and Maximum Phase Deviation and of the Mean Carrier Frequency.—Experimental methods of determining maximum frequency and maximum phase deviations are required in order to assure, for instance, that the maximum permissible frequency swing of ±75 kc is not exceeded. Otherwise a wider frequency spectrum than permissible might be produced, which might even exceed the width of the guard band between adjacent frequency channels and cause interchannel interference. The Crosby method of determining maximum frequency deviations consists in determining the conditions for which the Bessel curve of zeroth order,[1] the $J_0(\beta)$ curve, intersects the β axis; *i.e.*, where the Bessel factor governing the amplitude of the carrier frequency F becomes zero. This occurs,

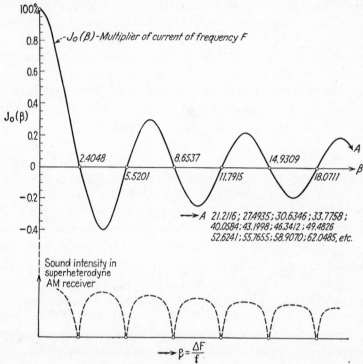

Fig. 24.—Experimental determination of the maximum frequency deviation ΔF.

a cording to Fig. 24, for the first point of intersection for a β value of 2.4048, for the second intersection for $\beta = 5.5201$, etc. Since $\beta = \Delta F/f$ and the signal frequency f is known, we can compute the maximum frequency excursion ΔF, which causes zero amplitude effect for the carrier frequency F when the ΔF swing is sufficient to produce such values as are given in this figure. The method consists, therefore, in determining the disappearance of the current amplitude of carrier frequency F when a suitable FM exists either by varying the signal frequency f, if the order of this frequency is of no concern, or by varying the value of ΔF.

[1] Any Bessel curve, such as the $J_1(\beta)$ or the $J_2(\beta)$ curve, could be used with the respective β-axis intersections. But on account of other zero spectrum amplitude effects (consult p. 41), it is best to use the $J_0(\beta)$ curve.

Any of the search-current methods[1] can be used although an ordinary superheterodyne receiver of the type customary for amplitude modulation will do. The first step is to tune the superheterodyne receiver to the carrier frequency F of an *unmodulated* FM transmitter. The i-f selectivity should be as narrow as possible. The oscillator frequency of the superheterodyne is so chosen that a low beat sound, say a 100-cycle note, is heard in a headset. Suppose a 4-kc signal ($f = 4,000$ cycles per second) is gradually applied to the modulator of the FM transmitter by raising the signal voltage $e_m \cos \omega t$ from zero level on upward. As the voltage is raised, the degree of FM is also increased and, therefore, also the value ΔF in β, because $f = 4$ kc is fixed. Hence, β will also increase with the signal voltage applied to the modulator and will cause more and more side currents. As the frequency spectrum spreads, the modulation energy moves more into the side bands and, according to Fig. 24, the amplitude $I_m J_0(\beta)$ of carrier frequency F decreases until for a β value of 2.4048 the carrier frequency amplitude must vanish altogether. Hence, by *increasing* the applied signal frequency voltage from zero volts upward, we gradually *decrease* also the intensity of the beat note of 100 cycles per second heard in the headset of the AM receiver until essentially zero sound effect is noted for the $\beta = 2.4048$ condition. Hence, at this point we have

$$\Delta F = 2.4048 \times 4 = 9.6192 \quad \text{kc}$$

which is altogether too small a frequency excursion for modern wide-band FM work. A further increase of the signal voltage applied to the modulator again raises gradually the intensity of the 100 cycles per second note toward a certain maximum sound sensation. Then the intensity decreases again gradually until for $\beta = 5.5201$ essentially silence again occurs. This gives the maximum frequency swing $\Delta F = 5.5201 \times 4 = 22.08$ kc. If the signal frequency had been 15 kc for this condition, then the maximum frequency swing would have been $5.5201 \times 15 = 82.8$ kc.

Hence, if a suitable voltmeter is connected across the input terminals of the modulator as such measurements are being made, the readings on it can be expressed in terms of corresponding frequency swings. Since for the determination of large ΔF swings,

---

[1] Consult footnote, p. 71.

especially for lower signal frequencies, many side currents are produced in the FM transmitter, it is necessary that the i-f band of the receiver set used in these determinations be set at its narrowest selectivity in order to avoid beat effects with other side currents. It is also best to work with a headset receiver, or with a visual indicator that is affected by a 100 cycles per second resonance network which could be a mechanical resonance metal strip with

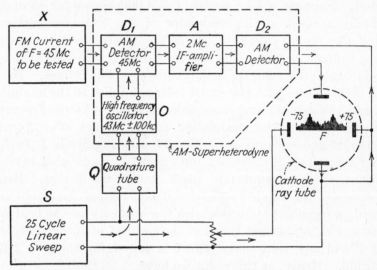

Fig. 25.—Visualization of spectrum distribution of the modulation energy.

a length so that it vibrates only when 100 cycles per second currents excite it by means of the magnetic field produced in a coil carrying the 100 cycles per second output current. A low-pass filter ahead of the indicator will avoid side-current beat effects if the filter has a cutoff frequency f_c of such a value that the signal frequency f is larger than $2f_c$.

Since for low signal frequencies, such as 60 cycles per second, and for a maximum frequency deviations of ± 75 kc an essentially continuous frequency spectrum prevails and the significant total band width is equal to $2 \Delta F$, a heterodyne frequency meter can be used for finding the band width w. By dividing the band width w by 2 we obtain the value of ΔF.

The entire useful frequency spectrum can also be made visible[1] on the screen of a cathode-ray tube if an arrangement such as is

[1] This procedure is similar to the one described by R. J. Pieracci, *Proc. IRE*, **28,** 374, 1940.

shown in Fig. 25 is employed.   In this figure X denotes the FM source to be tested with respect to the frequency spread and maximum frequency excursions; O, D_1, A, and D_2 are sections of a superheterodyne unit.   In this illustration the frequency of the test current is taken as 45 Mc while the i-f amplifier A works with a center frequency of 2 Mc.   Hence, the oscillator frequency of O is set to a center frequency of 43 Mc.   It will be noted that the oscillator O, which causes the beat effect to initiate a carrier of center frequency of 2 Mc by superposition of the test current coming from X and the oscillator current in the first detector D_1, is also frequency modulated with maximum frequency deviations of ± 100 kc, which are *larger* than the frequency deviations that will ever occur in the test current.   The FM in the oscillator O is caused by a quadrature tube modulator Q, which is also known as a reactance tube (for details see Secs. 29, 30).   This quadrature tube Q is driven by a *linear* sweep voltage coming from the output of a saw-tooth oscillator S.   The same sweep voltage also acts directly on one deflection condenser of the cathode-ray tube. The linear sweep scans, therefore, the center frequency of 43 Mc of the local oscillator O, 100 kc below and 100 kc above the center frequency of 43,000 kc.   Hence, it must also register at the amplifier A any other signals that it meets during such frequency swings, as long as the signals do not fall outside the peak-to-peak swing of 200 kc.   Owing to the beat action between the 43-Mc oscillator current and the test current of center frequency of 45 Mc, we have decreased the center frequency of 45 Mc to a new center frequency of 2 Mc as far as the center frequency of both sources X and O are concerned.   However, the center frequency of 43 Mc experiences *linear* off swings toward 42.9 and 43.1 Mc and, therefore, currents of such an instantaneous local oscillator frequency can cause *beat effects with any of the side currents* of source X due to any ΔF swing of the test current, provided the magnitude of this swing does not exceed ± 100 kc.   The result is that in the mixer D_1 we have at its output just as many side components as are in the original test current, *i.e.*, in the FM current to be examined.   The only difference is that these side components are with reference to a center frequency of 2 Mc instead of 45 Mc.   The succeeding amplifier A will enlarge the effects of these components, and the detector D_2 will separate the positive swings of the spectrum components.   The output of D_2 applies, therefore, to the other deflection condenser of the cathode-ray tube spectrum pulses, which resemble sharp resonance curves for each side current. Hence, when a large ΔF swing exists in the FM of the test current, the spectrum width noted on the screen of the cathode-ray tube must be equal to $2 \Delta F$ for a low-signal frequency f of about 50 cycles per second. Suppose we had actually a ΔF modulation of ± 75 kc, or at least very close to it, operative in the test FM current. Then all that is necessary is to change the signal frequency f gradually to higher values toward a value in the neighborhood of 15 kc, since this would give a β value of about 5, and then to note at what signal frequency f the center current amplitude vanishes. This must occur for a β value of 5.5201. Since, according to Table III, we have only about eight significant side currents on each side of the center frequency for β values in this neighborhood, *i.e.*, close to 5, it will be an easy matter to recognize the center amplitude and to observe it vanish as the signal frequency f is varied around 15,000 cycles per second. Suppose the experiment shows that for $f = 13.2$ kc the center amplitude disappears, then $\Delta F = 5.5201 \times 13.2 = 72.9$ kc. Hence, assuming that the ΔF condition is the same for the 50 cycles per second signal current modulation, then the width marked by the cathode-ray pattern gives the 72.9-kc calibration. The band width caused by any other degree of FM in the current to be tested, with respect to ΔF swings, can be estimated from this calibration width.

On page 40 another method is shown for experimentally determining ΔF, as well as $\Delta \theta$ swings.

The mean carrier frequency F can be readily determined when the test current is not subjected to FM. This is done by beating the test current with a current coming from a source of stabilized and known frequency. If the test current is modulated in frequency, the unbalance in a frequency discriminator can be used for the determination of the mean frequency F. The discriminator output is fed into a low-pass filter with a cutoff at a very low frequency of about 25 to 30 cycles per second. The unbalance is measured with a microammeter. For the correct frequency value F there can be no deflection in this meter. (For details consult sections on discriminators.)

17. Effect of Band-restriction Filters on Currents Modulated in Frequency.—The required band width as indicated by the significant Bessel amplitudes can be narrowed only if it does not cut off significant side currents. Suppose we are dealing with the frequency spectrum distribution shown in Fig. 8. This figure shows that for $\beta = 2$ the significant terms have amplitudes proportional to the Bessel factors $J_n(\beta) = B_n$, which are $B_0 = 0.2239$, $B_1 = 0.5767$, $B_2 = 0.3528$, and $B_3 = 0.1289$, giving for all practical purposes the solution

$$I_t = 0.2239I_m \sin \Omega t + 0.5767I_m \sin (\Omega + \omega)t$$
$$- 0.5767I_m \sin (\Omega - \omega)t + 0.3528I_m \sin (\Omega + 2\omega)t$$
$$+ 0.3528I_m \sin (\Omega - 2\omega)t + 0.1289I_m \sin (\Omega + 3\omega)t$$
$$- 0.1289I_m \sin (\Omega - 3\omega)t \quad (54)$$

for the FM current at any instant. We note that here we have three significant side currents on each side of the center frequency

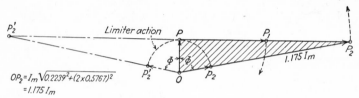

$$OP_2 = I_m \sqrt{0.2239^2 + (2 \times 0.5767)^2}$$
$$= 1.175\,I_m$$

$$PP_1 = 0.5767\,I_m = P_1P_2\,; \quad OP = 0.2839\,I_m$$

Fig. 26.—Vector diagram for one side-current pair for distribution of $\beta = 2$ of Fig. 8.

F. Suppose we use a band-pass filter that passes only the first side-current pair besides the current $0.2239I_m \sin \Omega t$ of carrier frequency. We have then the vector addition shown in Fig. 26 where vector OP represents the vector of the carrier frequency F with respect to position as well as amplitude value. The addition of the two side currents, which can also be passed by the filter, results in the quadrature vector PP_2. The resultant instantaneous current vector is then OP_2 which is *longer* than the amplitude or carrier level I_m of the unmodulated current. A lengthening of the current vector can be produced only by a simultaneous AM, which did not exist in the spectrum solution (54) since it includes *all* the significant terms. Since both side currents move about P, we swing the phase of the resultant current emerging from the band-pass filter over $\pm\Phi$ degrees during the modulation cycle while the length of the resultant varies between the limits $0.2238I_m$ and $1.175I_m$. Hence, we have an AM of $100(1.175 - 0.2238)/(1.175 + 0.2238) = 68$ per cent with *twice* the frequency of modulation. The resultant vector moves from OP_2

with a maximum value of $1.175I_m$ over a minimum value of $0.2239I_m$ to position OP_2' of maximum value of $1.175I_m$ and back over the minimum amplitude value to position OP_2 of maximum value during the modulation cycle.   When, therefore, the band-pass filter feeds into an amplitude limiter that saturates at amplitudes of $0.2239I_m$, the AM produced by the band-pass filter is removed and the resultant vector flutters between the Op_2 and Op_2' limits.   Hence, all the *even* harmonic side currents are, so to speak, again injected by means of the limiter action.   Since we have also *odd* harmonic side currents, they must account for the distortion that remains.   From Eq. (54), as well as from the frequency spectrum of Fig. 8, we note that in this particular case the distortion of the only remaining odd harmonic is due to the amplitude $0.1289I_m$, which when geometrically taken into account shows that neglecting such a side-current pair causes a small distortion only.

18. Interference and Its Partial Elimination in FM Systems.— Generally, interference can be due to other FM stations on the same or adjacent channels.   It can also be caused by AM stations as well by arriving carriers that are not modulated at all.   Besides these, we have to deal with noise interference and random[1] disturbances, which occur in any high-gain amplifier.

Quite often distortions in FM receivers are not due to interference at all but to poor circuit design in the receiver.   Conditions in FM are in many respects vastly different from AM conditions.   With FM the harmonic distortion does not depend principally on tube characteristics, as with AM, but more or less on the transmission characteristics of the transfer networks, such as the coupled tuned circuits in the i-f stages, the coupling to the discriminator, and the like.   Fortunately, it is easier to design a linear transfer network than it is to design a linear tube such as would be needed for distortionless AM systems.   In linear networks for FM systems we cannot use designs that would be called free from nonlinear distortion when used in AM systems, since for AM a transfer characteristic that is symmetrical with respect to the carrier frequency F in amplitude as well as in phase is good engineering practice.   In FM systems such a design would be satisfactory only for the lower signal-frequency range.   Only in this range is the modulation index $\beta = \Delta F/f$ fairly large if we

---

[1] For details, consult "Phenomena in High-frequency Systems," pp. 255–256 and "High-frequency Measurements," pp. 31–32, 325.

assume maximum frequency deviations of about ± 75 kc, say, for signal frequencies below 100 cycles per second. Since we have to deal with the entire signal-frequency range, say up to 16 kc, and for different values of ΔF, *i.e.*, maximum frequency excursions that are not necessarily so high as ± 75 kc because the frequency excursions may be the result of sounds of less than maximum loudness, we have to deal quite often with modulation indexes that cannot be called relatively large. Hence, *all band-pass networks* must have transmission characteristics whose *amplitude* and whose *phase are linear functions* for all frequencies included in the band width. If only a symmetrical transfer characteristic were used, as for AM systems, nonlinearity of the phase characteristic would cause also nonlinear signal distortions. The effects of curvature in the amplitude characteristic could be avoided in many cases by the use of an amplitude limiter.

Generally, if two unmodulated carriers arrive in an FM receiver simultaneously and the difference of the respective carrier frequencies is relatively small compared with the magnitude of each carrier frequency, then the superposition of both unmodulated waves in the mixer stage of the FM receiver causes not only beat effects that produce AM, but also effects that result in PM and, therefore, also equivalent FM. It is the equivalent FM that will be translated by the discriminator into AM and then will be heard as interference in the speaker of the receiver. The AM effect can be cut out by the amplitude limiters that precede the discriminator. According to Eq. (6), we have the term $(F_1 - F_2)\, \Delta\theta \cos [6.28(F_1 - F_2)t]$ for the equivalent FM, where F_1 and F_2 denote the respective carrier frequencies of the unmodulated currents that combine in the mixer stage. As it is assumed that the difference of these two frequencies is in the a-f range, we see that a *larger frequency difference causes more equivalent FM* and, therefore, more interference, since the maximum equivalent frequency excursion is proportional not only to the maximum phase swing $\Delta\theta$ but also to $F_1 - F_2$. As we shall learn in Sec. 19 and as was already seen from the discussion on page 6, if the amplitude of one of the respective interfering unmodulated arriving waves is twice the value of the other amplitude, then the quadrature addition causes a maximum phase deviation of $\Delta\theta = \pm 26.6$ deg or ± 0.4642 radian. Hence, a difference frequency of 50 cycles per second would produce an equivalent maximum frequency swing of $50 \times 0.4642 = 23.21$ cycles per second; *i.e.*, a degree of FM that would be completely outweighed by $\Delta F = \pm 75$ kc or the correspondingly smaller values existing for weaker FM signals. But, if we receive two interfering unmodulated waves with a carrier frequency difference of, say, 16 kc, which is considered the upper limit of the a-f range, we find an equivalent maximum frequency excursion as high as $16 \times 0.4642 = \pm 7.43$ kc, which would give rise to appreciable interference. Fortunately, the sensation to the human ear is not great in the very upper a-f range.

If the amplitudes of two arriving interfering waves have equal values then the quadrature addition in the mixer stage causes a 45-deg maximum phase deviation. This is equivalent to 0.785 radian and the equivalent frequency excursion would be as much as $16 \times 0.785 = \pm 12.55$ kc. But, if the two interfering waves have one and the same carrier frequency, then no audible frequency due to beat effect can exist and the equivalent FM is zero. This is a great feature since it shows that waves of almost the same carrier frequency or equal in frequency cannot cause appreciable interference in an FM receiver; in AM receivers the well-known beat whistle interference makes reception almost impossible.

These statements naturally apply also to two modulated carrier waves, as far as their mutual interfering beat effects are concerned. Hence, if two arriving FM signals are on the same channel, there can be no appreciable beat effect. As a matter of fact, if the two center frequencies of two FM stations are varied to approach one and the same carrier frequency value, there will be no beat note heard. This is not true with AM since any amplitude beat effects affect the demodulator and can be heard from 16 cycles per second on upward.

With FM it may be said that wide-band transmission is superior to narrow-band transmission. Wide-band transmission refers to modern practice where maximum frequency swings up to ± 75 kc are used in present-day good engineering practice. Such large frequency swings can override interfering phase flutters and their equivalent disturbing frequency swings. Hence, we obtain a better signal-to-noise power ratio. According to Armstrong this ratio varies, for noise voltages at the output of the amplitude limiter less than the desired voltage, directly with the square of the band width.

It should be understood that the type of noise also plays a part since, as is shown on page 85, some noise can be almost completely avoided at the output of a discriminator with a differential output. We have to distinguish also between impulse and fluctuation noise. Crosby has, for instance, introduced the term "improvement threshold" above which the FM signal-to-noise ratio is greater than the AM signal-to-noise ratio by a certain factor. This factor is proportional to the maximum deviation ratio $\Delta F/f_{max}$, where

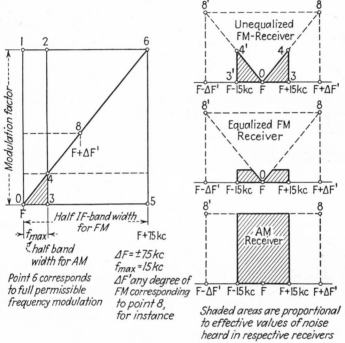

FIG. 27.—Noise diagram for FM and AM receivers.

f_{max} stands for the highest signal frequency f of interest, and is generally taken as 15 kc, and ΔF denotes the largest frequency excursion of ± 75 kc, which is taken as full modulation swing. Hence, the factor is directly proportional to the band width since this width is, for large β values, essentially equal to $2\,\Delta F$. The constant of proportionality is somewhat greater for impulse noise than for fluctuation noise. For wide-band FM, a higher carrier level is needed in order to reach the improvement threshold. The carrier level must also be higher for impulse noise than for fluctuation noise. When standard audio accentuation (consult pages 221 to 223) is employed, we have for ± 75-kc excursions, when the peak noise is less than 50 per cent of the peak h-f carrier, a signal-to-noise ratio of 53 db or more for fluctuation noise and 48 db or more for signal-to-impulse noise ratio. Since in the FM receiver a-f deaccentuation *should be used* (consult pages 221 to 223) in order to offset the a-f accentuation in the transmitter, the signal-to-noise ratio is still more improved by a properly designed FM receiver. We gain for fluctuation noise another 13 db and for impulse noise 12 db, against corresponding gains of 5.6 and 7.5 db in an AM receiver with frequency deaccentuation.

Figure 27 illustrates the receiver noise spectra for both FM and for AM and is the outcome of an analysis given originally by M. G. Crosby.[1] The horizontal length 0-3 denotes half the band width occupied by the audio frequencies and f_{max} stands for the highest signal frequency and is generally taken as 15 kc. The length 0-5 denotes half the band width of the i-f channel, which for present-day practice would be 0.5×225 kc for 150-kc peak-to-peak frequency excursions.[2] The modulation factor for either FM or AM is plotted as ordinate and, since we may compare any degree of modulation, the height 0-1 may be arbitrarily chosen. The modulation factor for FM depends on the characteristic of the slope filter or differentiator. Since this characteristic, according to Fig. 23, translates FM into AM, the ideal modulation factor for FM, when expressed in terms of output AM is $K = 2 \times \Delta F/w_1$. It is the peak-to-peak frequency swing, which causes the particular degree of FM, divided by the channel width of the i-f stages. For the average slope characteristic we do not have the ideal conditions depicted in Fig. 23, and the foregoing relation for K has to be multiplied by a factor that is smaller than unity in order to allow for the modulation conversion efficiency. As far as the modulation factor for AM is concerned in this comparison, it has to take the customary detector demodulation or rectifier efficiency into account. If the efficiency is not very high, more a-f amplification will make up for the low demodulator efficiency.

---

[1] CROSBY, M. G., Frequency Modulation Noise Characteristics, *Proc. IRE*, **25**, 472, 1937.

[2] In Fig. 27 the half-band width has been assumed equal to $\Delta F = 75$ kc since this satisfies the linear half portion of the discriminator characteristic. The transfer networks in all i-f circuits are, however, to be designed to accommodate all significant possible side currents. Good engineering practice calls then for a full band width of $1.5 \times 2\Delta F$, *i.e.*, 50 per cent more than the peak-to-peak frequency swing.

The noise analysis is based on the expressions

$$D_t = D \sin \left(\Omega t + \frac{\Delta F}{f} \cos \omega t \right) \Bigg\}$$
$$I_t = I \sin [\Omega_1 t + \Phi(t)]$$

(55)

where D_t is the instantaneous value of the *desired* FM current and I_t is the instantaneous value of the undesired or *interfering* current, which in this case is assumed as being due to noise. I stands for the resultant instantaneous peak voltage of the interfering noise and $\Omega_1/6.28$ for the frequency of the noise resultant or component, whichever may be the case. These two expressions have to be added geometrically and yield, for $\beta = \Delta F/f$, an expression for the resultant instantaneous current of the form

$$D_t + I_t =$$
$$\sqrt{D^2 + I^2 + 2DI \cos [(\Omega - \Omega_1)t - \Phi(t) + \beta \cos \omega t]} \cdot \sin \varphi \quad (56)$$

where

$$\varphi = \Big\{ \Omega t + \beta \cos \omega t$$
$$+ \tan^{-1} \frac{\sin [(\Omega - \Omega_1)t - \Phi(t) + \beta \cos \omega t]}{(D/I) + \cos [(\Omega - \Omega_1)t - \Phi(t) + \beta \cos \omega t]} \Big\} \quad (57)$$

For the demodulation, *i.e.*, the modulation translation from FM into AM, it is *only* the argument φ that interests us. The AM effect in the amplitude is avoided in most cases in the limiter stages preceding the differentiator or discriminator. In addition, it is a quadrature modulation with respect to FM.

According to the theory of FM into AM translation given on page 82, the *discriminator has to differentiate* and register effects with respect to the instantaneous carrier frequency F_t. Here we have only to differentiate Eq. (57) with respect to the time and divide it by 2π to find $F_t = \frac{1}{2\pi} \frac{d\varphi}{dt}$. This yields for $(\Omega - \Omega_1)/(2\pi) = F_2$ and $2\pi F_2 = \Omega_2$

$$F_t = F - \Delta F \sin \omega t - \frac{A}{(B/C) + 1} \quad (58)$$

for

$$A = F_2 - \frac{1}{2\pi} \frac{d\Phi(t)}{dt} - \Delta F \sin \omega t$$

$$B = \frac{D}{I} + \cos \{ \Omega_2 t - \Phi(t) + \beta \cos \omega t \} = \frac{D}{I} + a$$

$$C = \frac{I}{D} + a$$

(58a)

Here, F_t is the instantaneous frequency when both desired FM and interfering resultant noise are superimposed. In this expression I refers to the instantaneous peak voltage of a noise that is a function of the time, where the resultant noise undergoes PM and, therefore, causes equivalent FM. But, as for customary PM and its FM equivalent, this corresponds in this case to a noise spectrum, *i.e.*, to many components in the spectrum. By using a single noise component of constant amplitude i but of variable frequency, we have in Eqs. (58) and (58a) the substitution $I = i$ and $\Phi(t) = 0$, since i is no longer dependent on t. Hence, in this case Eq. (58) simplifies to

$$F_t = F - \Delta F \sin \omega t - \frac{F_2 - \Delta F \sin \omega t}{\frac{(D/i) + b}{(i/D) + b} + 1}$$

(59)

for

$$b = \cos (\Omega_2 t + \beta \cos \omega t)$$

(59a)

Equation (59) is not difficult to apply since, for instance, F_t stands for the instantaneous frequency *due to noise only* if the frequency excursion ΔF due to the desired FM is put equal to zero. Doing this, we arrive at the expression for the instantaneous frequency due to noise

$$F_{noise} = F - \frac{F_2}{1 + \frac{(D/I) + \cos \Omega_2 t}{(i/D) + \cos \Omega_2 t}} = F + \Delta F'(t)$$

(60)

which is a simple expression to apply since only the second term can contribute to undesirable or interfering FM. The second term is a time function, which is not at all difficult to evaluate, since F_2 is the difference frequency between the center frequency of the current that carries the useful modulation energy in form of FM and the frequency of the resultant noise current. D and i are the peak amplitudes of the desired current and the noise component, respectively.

Since only the second term of Eq. (60) causes noise modulation, only this term is to be compared with the term $-\Delta F \sin \omega t$ which is instrumental in producing in Eq. (55) the term $\beta \cos \omega t$ where $\beta = \Delta F / f$. Therefore, when a large ratio of desired interference component amplitude is assumed, D/i is large in comparison with unity and the variable portion $\Delta F'(t)$ of Eq. (60) simplifies to

$$\Delta F''(t) \cong \frac{F_2}{1 + \dfrac{(D/i)}{(i/D) + \cos \Omega_2 t}} = \frac{F_2(i + D \cos \Omega_2 t)}{(D^2/i) + D \cos \Omega_2 t + i}$$

$$\cong \frac{F_2(i + D \cos \Omega_2 t)}{(D^2/i) + D \cos \Omega_2 t} = \frac{F_2 i(i + D \cos \Omega_2 t)}{D(D + i \cos \Omega_2 t)} \cong \frac{i}{D} F_2 \cos \Omega_2 t$$

Hence, the maximum frequency deviation due to noise interference is

$$\Delta F'' = \frac{i}{D} F_2 = \frac{i}{D} (F - F_1) \tag{61}$$

On page 84 we found, for the ideal slope characteristic of Fig. 23, that the degree of amplitude modulation after the translation of FM into AM is equal to the ratio of peak-to-peak frequency swing to i-f channel width w and we have, therefore, the expression

$$K\% = \frac{200i(F - F_1)}{wD} \tag{62}$$

From this expression it is to be noted that the percentage equivalent AM, after FM into AM conversion in an FM receiver, is *smaller* the *wider* the *channel width* and decreases with the peak value D of the desired FM current, but it is directly proportional to the peak value i of the interference component. Hence, the loudness of the interfering noise is inversely proportional to the signal-to-noise ratio D/i.

At this point it should be clearly understood that the assumption was made that D/i is large compared with unity and this is the limitation assumed in the diagram of Fig. 27 for the noise spectra. The plot of Eq. (62) follows, therefore, the equation $K = k(F - F_1)$ where the linear ascent of the line is k and is given by the factor $200/w$. Making this plot we have the ascending line 0-4 in Fig. 27 representing the FM audible noise output.

Here the area of triangle 0-4-3 represents, therefore, the FM receiver output; the area of triangle 0-6-5 is the output of the FM-AM translator of the FM receiver. Rectangular area 0-1-2-3 represents the output of an AM receiver, since in such a receiver f_{max} is the cutoff frequency beyond which even with a high-fidelity a-f system we would not notice audible distortion. Even though Eq. (62) is based on the ideal slope characteristic, it should not matter. For all other suitable discriminator characteristics, we have only to multiply the ratio of peak-to-peak frequency deviation to i-f band width by a factor that is smaller than unity in order to account for the modulation translation efficiency. If the factor were 0.5, for example, it would then only be necessary to step up the a-f amplification in order to obtain the same loudness as for the ideal case shown in Fig. 27.

Moreover, Fig. 27 shows that if there were no inherent a-f cutoff (mostly owing to the fact that the average ear cannot perceive sound sensations for frequencies much higher than about 16 kc), the largest degree of noise modulation would be realized at 6. At this point $2(F - F_1)$ has a value equal to the band width w and Eq. (62) will read $K\% = 100i/D$; at an upper cutoff frequency corresponding to point 4 it is $200f_{max}i/(wD)$ only. The ratios of these degrees of AM due to noise at the slope detector output is, therefore, equal to the i-f channel width w divided by twice the highest *audible* frequency f_{max}. In other words, 3-4 is the highest noise condition instead of 5-6, owing to the limited frequency response range of the human ear.

For AM reception the modulation factor is equal to the noise-to-carrier ratio for *all* noise frequencies. Hence, the noise that causes undesirable AM will affect the output of the detector just like the desirable AM and we have the rectangular area 0-1-2-3 as a measure for the noise spectra for AM. Consequently, from Fig. 27 we note that the ratio of FM noise voltage E_f in an FM receiver to the AM noise voltage E_a in an AM receiver is

$$\frac{E_f}{E_a} = \left\{ \begin{array}{l} \dfrac{f_{max}}{w} \quad \text{for impulse noise} \\[2em] \dfrac{2f_{max}}{\sqrt{3}\,w} \quad \text{for fluctuation noise} \end{array} \right\} \tag{63}$$

The ratio for impulse noise is found by dividing the area of triangle

0-4-3 by the rectangular area 0-1-2-3. If the ordinates of the triangle are squared, we obtain an area A_1; if the ordinates of the rectangle 0-1-2-3 are squared, we obtain an area A_2. The fluctuation noise ratio is found from A_1/A_2. The areas of the squared ordinates have to be used since we have to deal with rms values.

19. Phase Modulation, Equivalent Frequency Modulation, and Amplitude Modulation of Two Received Carrier Currents.— It is now of interest to investigate in detail what will happen when two carrier waves of different frequencies F_1 and F_2 arrive simultaneously in an FM receiver. The simplest case occurs when the corresponding antenna currents are not modulated at all and induce instantaneous voltages $E_1 \cos \Omega_1 t$ and $E_2 \cos \Omega_2 t$ in the pickup coil of the FM receiver. As is shown in another publication,[1] the resultant instantaneous incoming voltage, which is effective on the control grid of the first tube of the FM receiver, is

$$E_t = E_I \cos 0.5(\Omega_1 + \Omega_2)t + E_{II} \cos \Omega_1 t \qquad (64)$$

where

$$\left.\begin{aligned} E_I &= 2E_2 \cos 0.5(\Omega_1 - \Omega_2)t \\ E_{II} &= E_1 - E_2 \end{aligned}\right\} \qquad (64a)$$

Hence, there is generally a resultant voltage consisting of two distinct components. One component voltage has a mean frequency $\frac{1}{2}(F_1 + F_2)$ and a fluctuating amplitude, the fluctuation of which is in step with the difference frequency $\frac{1}{2}(F_1 - F_2)$. Hence, this component voltage is modulated in amplitude with an AM of 100 per cent since the cosine term in Eq. (64a) varies between the limits of zero and unity. The positive peak level is $2E_2$ and the negative peak level vanishes for $K = 100\%$. The other voltage component has a frequency F_1 and an amplitude $E_1 - E_2$. Hence, it is not modulated and is of smaller amplitude than either of the original amplitudes E_1 or E_2 that produced it. It is also shown in the cited publication that the resultant instantaneous voltage affecting the grid of the first tube of the FM set in this application can be brought into the form

$$E_t = [\cos (mt + \theta_t)] \sqrt{(E_1 + E_2)^2 \cos^2 (0.5d)t + (E_1 - E_2)^2 \sin^2 (0.5d)t}$$
$$= [\cos(mt + \theta_t)] \sqrt{E_1^2 + E_2^2 + 2E_1 E_2 \cos (\Omega_1 - \Omega_2)t} \qquad (65)$$

---

[1] "High-frequency Measurements," p. 22.

where

$$m = \tfrac{1}{2}(\Omega_1 + \Omega_2); \qquad d = \Omega_1 - \Omega_2; \\ \left.\theta_t = \tan^{-1}\left\{\frac{E_1 - E_2}{E_1 + E_2}\tan\,[0.5(\Omega_1 - \Omega_2)t]\right\}\right\} \qquad (65a)$$

Hence, in addition to AM between the limits $E_1 - E_2$ and $E_1 + E_2$, we have also *phase modulation* since Eq. (65) has the form

$$E_t = E_{m_t}\cos\,\{[0.5(\Omega_1 + \Omega_2)]t + \theta_t\} \qquad (66)$$

No assumptions were made in the derivation of Eq. (66), which holds for any values of F_1 and F_2 as well as for any values of E_1 and E_2 that may occur in practice. The argument $\alpha = 0.5(\Omega_1 + \Omega_2)t + \theta_t$ gives, therefore, a means for computing the equivalent FM from the relation

$$F_t = \frac{1}{2\pi}\frac{d\alpha}{dt} = 0.5(F_1 + F_2) + \frac{1}{2\pi}\frac{d\theta_t}{dt} \qquad (67)$$

The differentiation of $d\theta_t/dt$ is conveniently done after the values of the amplitudes E_1 and E_2 and F_1 and F_2 have been inserted in the formula for θ_t given in Eq. (65a). The angle θ_t can also be obtained from the first relation for E_t given in Eq. (65). It is necessary only to plot the value $(E_1 + E_2)\cos\varphi$ along the X axis and the value $(E_1 - E_2)\sin\varphi$ along the Y axis of a rectangular coordinate system for $\varphi = 0.5(\Omega_1 - \Omega_2)t$ where the corresponding difference frequency is *half* the value of $F_1 - F_2$, although in the second relation of Eq. (65) it will be noted that the actual difference frequency $F_1 - F_2$ plays a part. Suppose these quadrature components are plotted and we find, for instance, that at the instant of time which makes $0.5(\Omega_1 - \Omega_2)t = 45$ deg, we have $\sin\varphi = \cos\varphi = 0.7071$ and $\theta_t = \tan^{-1}[(E_1 - E_2)/(E_1 + E_2)]$. Hence, for equal amplitudes of the incoming currents in the aerial, there would be no phase deviation at this instant; for $E_2 = 0.5E_1$ we would have $\theta_t = \tfrac{1}{3}$ and an instantaneous phase swing $\theta_t = 18.4$ deg. Hence, when two unmodulated currents of different carrier frequencies and with any amplitude relationship affect the grid of the first tube of an FM receiver, we have the case of a *twofold modulated current*, namely, AM + PM, which can also be interpreted as AM with simultaneous equivalent FM as far as the actions in the discriminator are concerned.

The most important thing is not the AM, since an amplitude limiter can prevent such modulation from reaching the discriminator, but the instantaneous equivalent deviation frequency $\frac{1}{2\pi}\frac{d\theta_t}{dt}$. It is this term which affects the output current of the discriminator. We note from the expression for θ_t in Eq. (65a), that there will be equivalent frequency swings as long as there is a time function in any of the terms that make up the value of the relative phase θ_t. Hence, it is the factor $\Omega_1 - \Omega_2$ in the θ_t relation of Eq. (65a) that partly determines the degree of PM and, therefore, also the degree of equivalent FM as experienced by the discriminator. Hence, when the arriving unmodulated waves have exactly the same carrier frequency ($F_1 = F_2$), then $\Omega_1 - \Omega_2 = 0$ and there can be no PM and, therefore, no effects in the discriminator of an FM receiver. Moreover, when the difference between the respective carrier frequencies is relatively small, the degree of PM is also small and, consequently, the equivalent FM likewise must be small. It appears, therefore, from this discussion that a great difference exists when FM reception is compared with AM reception. An AM receiver would, for small frequency differences that are in the a-f range, produce decided beat-frequency interference since, according to the last square-root expression of Eq. (65), the AM produced in the resultant voltage causes audible amplitude variations of beat frequency $F_1 - F_2$. Besides, when frequency equality exists and one voltage is the desired voltage and the other is an interference voltage, the amplitude ratio E_1/E_2 will show to what extent the interfering wave blanks out the desired wave. Hence, when each arriving wave is a modulated wave, the AM receiver will experience considerable interference in comparison with such effects in an FM receiver.

Since, according to the first expression of Eq. (65), the resultant amplitude has a cosine part with an amplitude value of $E_1 + E_2$ and a sine part with a value of $E_1 - E_2$, it is seen that, at any instant when $0.5(\Omega_1 - \Omega_2)t = 0$ deg, the sine term vanishes and the amplitude of the resultant is $E_1 + E_2$; at an instant when $0.5(\Omega_1 - \Omega_2)t = 90$ deg, the resultant voltage must be $E_1 - E_2$ since the cosine term vanishes. Hence, the AM occurs between the limits $E_1 - E_2$ and $E_1 + E_2$ and for equal arriving amplitudes we have 100 per cent modulation.

When we tune to a desired station, we emphasize the corresponding desired current $D \sin \Omega_1 t$ that circulates in the input network of an FM receiver; an interfering station must cause a much smaller amplitude I in the interfering current $I \sin \Omega_2 t$. The superposition of these two currents gives then a solution similar to that used in connection with Eq. (65), since for the substitution $\Omega = \Omega_1 - \Omega_2$

$$
\begin{aligned}
I_t &= D \sin \Omega_1 t + I \sin \Omega_2 t = D \sin \Omega_1 t + I \sin \Omega_1 t \cos \Omega t \\
&\qquad\qquad\qquad\qquad\qquad\qquad + I \cos \Omega_1 t \sin \Omega t \\
&= \underbrace{(D + I \cos \Omega t)}_{a} \sin \Omega_1 t + \underbrace{(I \sin \Omega t)}_{b} \cos \Omega_1 t \\
&= a + jb = \sqrt{a^2 + b^2} \sin \left(\Omega_1 t + \tan^{-1} \frac{b}{a} \right)
\end{aligned}
$$

or

$$
\begin{aligned}
I_t &= \sqrt{D^2 + I^2 + 2DI \cos (\Omega_1 - \Omega_2)t} \sin \left\{ \Omega_1 t + \tan^{-1} \left[\frac{I \sin (\Omega_1 - \Omega_2)t}{D + I \cos (\Omega_1 - \Omega_2)t} \right] \right\} \\
&= I_{m_t} \sin \alpha_t
\end{aligned} \tag{68}
$$

holding for any amplitude ratio D/I and any frequency ratio F_1/F_2. In our receiver, for unequal frequencies F_1 and F_2 and for selective tuned circuits, I is much smaller than D. This is usually true also for present-day allocation of stations on the same channel ($F_1 = F_2$) where the stations are almost certain to be so located that only the desired wave provides a strong signal field intensity. Therefore, the expression for both the instantaneous value of the amplitude I_{m_t} and the instantaneous angle α_t can be simplified. Hence, for I, small in comparison to D, we obtain the approximations

$$
\left. \begin{aligned}
I_{m_t} &= D \left[1 + \frac{I}{D} \cos (\Omega_1 - \Omega_2)t \right] \\
\alpha_t &= \Omega_1 t + \frac{I}{D} \sin (\Omega_1 - \Omega_2)t
\end{aligned} \right\} \tag{69}
$$

and

$$
I_t \cong D \left[1 + \frac{I}{D} \cos (\Omega_1 - \Omega_2)t \right] \sin \left[\Omega_1 t + \frac{I}{D} \sin (\Omega_1 - \Omega_2)t \right] \tag{70}
$$

Comparing this result with the customary AM + PM case for which we have

$$
I_t = I_m(1 + K \cos \omega t) \sin (\Omega t + \Delta\theta \sin \omega t) \tag{71}
$$

we note that we have now an AM of degree $K = I/D$, as was found above, and a superimposed PM with a maximum phase swing I/D which is controlled by a sine function of the beat frequency $F_1 - F_2$ instead of by the signal requency f. Since the time rate of change $d\alpha_t/dt$ of the α_t approximation given in Eq. (69) and employed in Eq. (70), when multiplied by 1/6.28, gives the instantaneous value of the equivalent carrier frequency, we find

$$F_t = F_1 + \frac{I}{D} (F_1 - F_2) \cos (\Omega_1 - \Omega_2)t \qquad (72)$$

Since F_1 is the fixed carrier frequency of the incoming desired current $D \sin (6.28F_1)t$, the factor $I(F_1 - F_2)/D$ is the equivalent

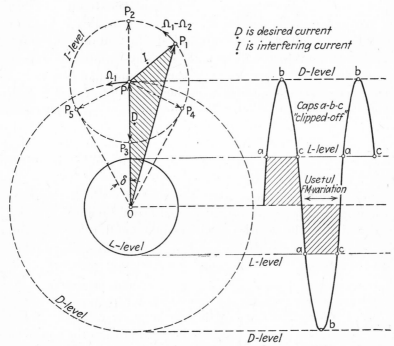

FIG. 28.—Diagram for two received unmodulated carriers of different frequencies $\Omega_1/6.28$ and $\Omega_2/6.28$.

maximum frequency deviation due to the PM produced by the interference. Hence, the amplitude of the corresponding frequency excursions is also proportional to the difference frequency $F_1 - F_2$, but, in addition, depends on the amplitude ratio I/D. This shows that the frequency discriminator cannot be affected at all by the equal carrier frequencies of the two incoming unmodulated waves and that the effect cannot be large when only a small frequency difference exists.

Figure 28 depicts the PM and AM effects produced by two such arriving waves. Assume that a desired antenna current $D \sin \Omega_1 t$ affects an FM receiver. Inasmuch as it is an unmodulated current, it can be represented by a vector OP of absolute length equal to the carrier level D spinning around counterclockwise with a constant angular velocity $\Omega_1 = 6.28F$. Suppose that at the instant when D is in the OP position an interfering current $I \sin \Omega_2 t$ also arrives, that its instantaneous position with respect to OP is PP_1, and that its absolute length is equal to the level I of the unmodulated interfering current. The vector OP_1 is the instantaneous resultant and is longer than the vector representing the desired level D. Inasmuch as PP_1 is likewise a rotating vector, it will spin around its instantaneous center P with an angular velocity $\Omega_2 = 6.28F_2$. The instantaneous center P is at the correct place only at the instant that produces the shaded vector triangle. Since P is the extremity of vector D, this instantaneous center for the I vector must move every second over an arc of $2\pi F_1$ radians where F_1 is the frequency of the desired current in cycles per second. Hence, it will, so to speak "drag" the locus of P_1, which is also a circle, with it, and it is only the *relative motion with respect to both vectors* that is of interest here. We can, therefore, assume that the page on which this vector representation appears, spins just as fast around point O in a clockwise direction as the vector OP moves in a counterclockwise direction. Therefore vector OP is fixed, *i.e.*, stationary. The relative motion then occurs with an angular velocity $\Omega = 6.28(F_1 - F_2)t$ with respect to the vector $OP = D$, which is stationary. This was also found in the second expression of Eq. (65) as well as in Eq. (68). Now as far as this relative angular velocity Ω is concerned, we note that it must always be smaller than the component angular velocities Ω_1 and Ω_2, which are the cause of it. After a certain time the vector I will be in position PP_2 and the instantaneous inphase condition produces a resultant vector OP_2 whose scalar value is due to algebraic addition $D + I$ of the absolute levels of the respective antenna currents. Here the resultant vector OP_2 has a still greater length than it had in the OP_1 position. After the vector I has advanced another 180 deg, it will be in position PP_3 and through algebraic subtraction from vector D

(because of the instantaneous antiphase condition) will produce a resultant vector OP_3 which has a level of only $D - I$. Hence, during the complete beat-frequency cycle, we have an AM between the level limits $D - I$ and $D + I$, and a degree of amplitude modulation $K = 100I/D$ per cent. The unmodulated current of smaller level behaves, therefore, like a modulating current $I \sin (\Omega_1 - \Omega_2)t$, which causes AM. From the figure it will be noted that the resultant vectors OP_4 and OP_5 show extreme out-of-phase conditions, with exactly the same negative and positive phase δ with respect to the desired vector $OP = D$. This is the PM effect with the corresponding maximum phase swings $\pm\Delta\theta$. According to Eq. (70), we have $\Delta\theta = I/D$ for a small ratio of I/D. Since the relative vector spin of I occurs along a circle with the uniform angular velocity $\Omega_1 - \Omega_2$ of the beat frequency, the equivalent maximum frequency deviation produced must be equal to $(F_1 - F_2) \Delta\theta$ where $\Delta\theta$ is in radians. Since both AM and PM, as well as the equivalent FM, are caused by the incoming currents $D \sin \Omega_1 t$ and $I \sin \Omega_2 t$, they give a means for determining in a simple way the maximum phase swing $\Delta\theta$. Both currents have to be added in quadrature since they are of different frequencies, namely, F_1 and F_2. Hence, the resultant level must be $D + jI$ with a maximum phase swing $\Delta\theta = \tan^{-1} (I/D)$. For example, for $I = 0.2D$ we have $\Delta\theta = \pm 11.3$ deg maximum phase swing during the modulating cycle of frequency $F_1 - F_2$. The magnitude of this phase swing is independent of the frequency difference $F_1 - F_2$. This angle corresponds to $11.3/57.3 = 0.197$ radian, giving an equivalent frequency swing of $0.197(F_1 - F_2)$. If the frequency difference were 100 kc, we would have an equivalent maximum frequency excursion of 19.7 kc and for a 1-kc frequency difference we would have an equivalent frequency swing of only 197 cycles per second. For $F_1 = F_2$ there is no PM at all and, therefore, also *no* equivalent frequency swing due to interference that can affect the discriminator output.

Now in AM receivers the ratio of the a-f interference to the useful audio signal is generally equal to the ratio of the h-f interference voltage to the useful h-f voltage applied to the detector. These respective voltages are the ones applied from the output of the last i-f stage to the amplitude demodulator.

But in an FM receiver the stronger of the two modulated currents has a tendency to remove the weaker one (on account of the I/D effect in Eq. 70). Hence, when examining *two FM carriers*, we can, as in Fig. 28, again add vectorially the desired signal vector D to the interference vector I and find the resultant R as in Fig. 29. The respective FM's cannot affect the length of these vectors, since they still will be equal to the respective carrier levels D and I if the two received currents are $D \sin (\Omega_1 t + \beta \sin \omega t)$ and $I \sin (\Omega_2 t + \beta' \sin \omega' t)$, where β' and ω' express the fact that the intensity of FM and the frequency $\omega'/6.28$ of the modulating signal do not have to be the same for the interfering current and the desired FM signal current.

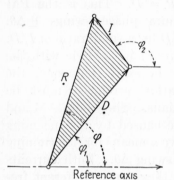

FIG. 29.—Resultant effect of two frequency-modulated currents of different center frequency.

At the instant shown, vector D has advanced an angle φ_1 with respect to the reference axis; I has advanced an angle φ_2; and the instantaneous resultant vector R now represents a larger level and has a relative phase advance φ. Since D is now frequency modulated, it no longer spins counterclockwise with a constant angular velocity Ω_1, but in addition experiences an oscillatory angular velocity swing about Ω_1 since the corresponding instantaneous carrier frequency is now $F_1 + \Delta F \cos \omega t$. For the interference vector, a similar superimposed oscillatory swing occurs since the vector I has an instantaneous carrier frequency $F_2 + \Delta F' \cos \omega' t$. Also, in the vector representation of this figure, the *maximum angle* between the resultant R and the desired vector D can never exceed an angle of $\tan^{-1} (I/D)$. For an interference level I equal to half the value of the desired carrier level D, this angle is $\tan^{-1} 0.5 = 26.6$ deg, *irrespective of the instantaneous beat frequency* of $F_1 + \Delta F \cos \omega t - F_2 - \Delta F' \cos \omega' t$. The frequency modulation of the desired current vector is therefore $\dfrac{1}{2\pi} \dfrac{d\varphi_1}{dt}$, the frequency modulation of the interference vector is $\dfrac{1}{2\pi} \dfrac{d\varphi_2}{dt}$, and the FM of the resultant vector R, which will affect the discriminator output, is $\dfrac{1}{2\pi} \dfrac{d\varphi}{dt}$. Hence, even though the angular variation of the interference vector I were several thousand degrees, it could hardly cause much change in φ since this angle cannot exceed a value of 45 deg even for $I = D$.

Suppose the desired current $D \sin \Omega_1 t$ has a deviation ratio $\Delta F / f = 15$ due to a maximum frequency swing of 75 kc and a signal frequency $f = 5$ kc. We have, then, equivalent phase advances and retardations of $15 \times 57.3 = \pm 859.5$ deg and, therefore, several complete revolutions during one modulation cycle for either the desired vector D or the resultant vector R. Therefore, the interference I cannot affect the resultant FM very much as long as D is greater than I during all portions of the modulation frequency cycle.

In order to obtain an idea of how much more effectively FM avoids interference than does AM, reference is made here to Eqs. (70) and (72). Equation (70) shows that in an AM receiver the interference I causes a degree of modulation equal to $K = I/D$, where D is the amplitude of the desired current. The modulation conversion from FM into AM in a discriminator, even for the most ideal translation, is equal to the peak-to-peak frequency excursion divided by the channel width w. Since the discriminator is designed for the very maximum peak-to-peak frequency swing, *i.e.*, 2×75 kc, the channel width is 150 kc or $2\,\Delta F$ where ΔF is the largest permissible frequency excursion. Now, from Eq. (72) we note that the equivalent frequency swing is $I(F_1 - F_2)/D$. Hence, the peak-to-peak frequency swing is equal to twice this value and the FM to AM translation gives an equivalent AM of a degree

$$ K = \frac{(F_1 - F_2)I}{D\,\Delta F} $$

which when multiplied by 100 gives K in per cent. We have, therefore, the comparison:

$$ K = \begin{cases} \dfrac{I}{D} & \text{Interference modulation in an AM receiver} \\[2em] \dfrac{I}{D}\dfrac{F_1 - F_2}{\Delta F} & \begin{array}{l}\text{Interference modulation in an FM receiver for} \\ \Delta F \text{ as the largest permissible frequency devi-} \\ \text{ation } (\pm 75 \text{ kc})\end{array} \end{cases} \tag{73} $$

These formulas show that for AM the ratio of interference level I to desired carrier level D determines essentially the intensity of the a-f interference heard in an AM receiver. In other words, the desired carrier level has to be high enough with respect to the interference level to "drown out" the interfering sound. However, for an FM receiver we have, in addition to this ratio, which should also be small (since the formulas are based on such assumptions), a factor $(F_1 - F_2)/\Delta F$ which shows that for equal carrier frequencies $(F_1 = F_2)$ for the interfering and desired signals no interference is possible at all; for a small difference of $F_1 - F_2$ not much interference can exist; for the highest audible beat frequency $(F_1 - F_2 = 15$ kc) that can be handled and heard in an FM receiver, the factor $(F_1 - F_2)/\Delta F$ still causes a reduction of interference. For $\Delta F = \pm 75$ kc this factor is equal to 0.2 and the resulting interference in an FM receiver would be only 20 per cent of that obtained with an AM receiver. Fortunately, matters are even more favorable, since in *properly designed* FM receivers the a-f emphasis in the upper a-f range employed in FM transmitters is compensated by a corresponding frequency deemphasis in the receiver, also in the upper a-f range. Hence, an audio frequency as high as 15 kc due to interference modulation will also be deemphasized. Moreover, for a 2-kc tone due to $F_1 - F_2$, we have $(F_1 - F_2)/\Delta F = \frac{2}{75} = 0.0267$ or only 2.67 per cent FM interference as compared with the corresponding interference in an AM receiver. We note also in Eq. (73) that wideband FM, *i.e.*, large ΔF values, avoids more interference.

20. Superposition of Currents in Transfer Networks.—Suppose we have to deal with the superposition of two currents $A \sin \Omega_1 t$ and $B \sin \Omega_2 t$ in any FM transfer network. The vectorial addition of $A + B$ at any instant will lead to a resultant instantaneous vector R, which has a relative phase θ with respect to the reference axis shown in Fig. 30. We have, therefore, no longer phases of zero and φ as for the respective component vectors.

Four possible cases can be distinguished. For case 1, both component vectors revolve with the same constant speed $\Omega = \Omega_1 = \Omega_2$. We have then the relationship depicted in Fig. 30 with a phase angle θ which is equal to an inverse tangent function of the phase difference φ between the component currents of respective amplitudes A and B, and the amplitudes A and B themselves. For such conditions there can be neither amplitude modulation nor phase modulation as well as no equivalent frequency modulation. But it is of interest to note that even though the instantaneous relative phase $\theta_t = \theta$ is fixed, it can be the result of ratios

$B \sin \varphi /(A + B \cos \varphi)$ which may have any value from minus infinity to plus infinity. Hence, the tangent function is not so convenient a variation for practical applications as are the sine and cosine functions, which vary only between the limits -1 and $+1$. This statement will be evident if we realize that in FM systems we are not interested in a fixed phase but in a variable phase θ_t. This phase is then either an equivalent phase variation for direct FM or is a true phase variation in case of PM. Each of these two possible conditions will produce corresponding

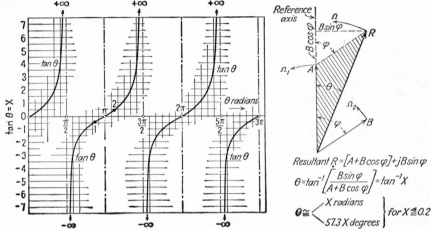

Fig. 30.—Behavior of resultant relative phase deviation when two electromagnetic waves with different center frequency and modulation arrive.

responses in the output branch of a frequency discriminator. But, fortunately, we note that also here portions of the tangent function, for instance, between 1 and 2 of Fig. 30, refer to "linear" variations. This linear relationship between the value of the relative phase of the resultant current and the value of X prevails for values of $X \leq 0.2$.

Since for the other cases that will be described later the value of X is by no means constant, we should realize that the intersections of the successive tangent curves with the θ axis are the most suitable operating points for satisfying a linear relation. This is true because they are mid-points along the straight portions of the tangent curves. They are also points of "inflection" that can be found from any expression for the value of X by setting the second derivative $d^2\theta$ of the relative phase with respect to the variable in the expression for X equal to zero.

Hence, for case 1, this would generally mean that $d^2\theta/dX^2 = 0$. This will lead to points $\theta = 0$, π, 2π, 3π, etc. However, in the expression for X there are three quantities that can affect the result if variation of any of these quantities should take place. One is the amplitude A of one component current, the second is the amplitude B of the other component current, and the third is the phase difference φ between the component currents. Hence, if amplitude A should undergo variations, we find the most suitable operating points from $d^2\theta/dA^2 = 0$; for amplitude modulation of the carrier $B \sin \Omega_1 t$ we find the operating point from $d^2\theta/dB^2 = 0$. The third possible variation is when the phase difference φ varies; then we have the relation $d^2\theta/d\varphi^2 = 0$ for finding the operating point.

Inasmuch as the angle θ of the relative phase of the resultant current depends on A, B, and φ, any desired as well as parasitic variations in any of these factors must produce modulations in the resultant current. We can, therefore, generally say that for the superposition of two currents there is a tendency for producing a variation in the value of the relative phase θ. But this is PM and, consequently, also equivalent FM. Even though the component currents are primarily fixed in amplitude and in relative phase, at least as far as the corresponding voltages that cause them are concerned, a transfer network, in virtue of its impedance, may cause such modulations. This will happen if the network does not have a linear phase shift for all frequencies of the band width that play a part. For nonlinear phase responses the relative phase φ cannot remain constant. In addition there must be impedance actions of the transfer network such that equal current amplitudes result for all frequencies of the band width when one and the same voltage amplitude, but of any frequency in the band width, is applied. This will satisfy the condition that neither A nor B be altered owing to the action of the transfer network.

Case 2 refers to the general application that concerns us in FM systems. It is when both component currents are modulated in amplitude. This could be due to a condition such that the amplitude response of the transfer network is not flat over the entire band width. For instance, an i-f network has an impedance characteristic with respect to the frequency, which increases near the lower and upper cutoff frequencies; or the characteristic, when due to overcoupled tuned circuits, is such as to cause a lower response near the mid-frequency of the pass band. Hence, generally for this case we no longer have constant amplitudes A and B, but $A + a(t)$ and $B + b(t)$ where $a(t)$ and $b(t)$ indicate any time functions that may occur due to such defective transfer characteristics. A simple variation would be $a \cos \omega t$ and $b \cos \omega t$ causing currents $(A + a \cos \omega t) \sin \Omega_1 t$ and $(B + b \cos \omega t) \sin \Omega_1 t$, respectively. It is always correct to use $a(t)$ and $b(t)$ where (t) stands for any time function that satisfies the amplitude frequency characteristic of the transfer network. Doing this we find, instead of the $\theta = \tan^{-1} X$ formula of Fig. 30, the expression

$$\theta_t = \theta + \Delta\theta_t = \tan^{-1} \left\{ \frac{[B + b(t)] \sin \varphi}{A + a(t) + [B + b(t)] \cos \varphi} \right\}$$
$$= \tan^{-1} [X(t)] \quad (74)$$

showing that generally there is no linear phase deviation in the relative phase θ_t with respect to the time function (t). Even this is not always true for values of the ratio under the $\tan^{-1}$ bracket $\leqq 0.2$. Nevertheless, this relation must have a portion on the corresponding $\tan \theta_t$ curve for which $\theta_t = k_0 + k(t)$ holds; *i.e.*, a portion for which the variation in the variable portion of θ_t is directly proportional to the time function (t), the constant of proportionality being k, since k_0 accounts only for the fixed portion θ of the relative phase. The most suitable operating point is again the mid-point of the linear portion of the corresponding curve of $X(t)$ plotted against θ_t. The operating point is then found as above from $d^2\theta_t/d(t)^2 = 0$. Doing this, we find a solution of the form

$$\frac{d^2\theta_t}{d(t)^2} = \frac{mp}{q} = 0 \quad (75)$$

where either factor m or factor p must be zero in order to render $mp/q = 0$ as necessary for the determination of the most suitable operating point. Hence, in the second differentiation it is only necessary to evaluate the numerator mp. Doing this we find that m no longer contains the time function (t) and, therefore, cannot cause PM. Hence, the factor

$$p = Bb \sin^2 \varphi + (A + B \cos \varphi)(a + b \cos \varphi)$$
$$+ [(a + b \cos \varphi)^2 + b^2 \sin^2 \varphi](t) = 0 \quad (76)$$

is to be used in the evaluation for the operating point. This expression will be greatly simplified if we realize that for the operating point there can be no phase modulation since the phase variations take place about this point. No PM will occur when all terms affected by the modulation function (t) disappear. Hence, for the operating point we obtain

$$Bb \sin^2 \varphi + (A + B \cos \varphi)(a + b \cos \varphi) = 0,$$

or

$$\cos \varphi = -\frac{Aa + Bb}{Ab + Ba} = -n \qquad (76a)$$

We are not interested in the steady or fixed component θ of θ_t about which phase swings take place, but only in the instantaneous phase swings or phase deviations themselves. Hence, $d\theta_t/d(t)$ is the expression to use for finding these swings, and we have

$$\frac{d\theta_t}{d(t)} = \frac{[b(A + B \cos \varphi) - B(a + b \cos \varphi)] \sin \varphi}{[(A + B \cos \varphi) + (a + b \cos \varphi)(t)]^2 + [B \sin \varphi + (b \sin \varphi)(t)]^2}$$

For the operating point all terms with the variable (t) function must vanish, and therefore

$$\frac{d\theta_t}{d(t)}\Bigg|_{\substack{\text{operating} \\ \text{point}}} = \frac{[b(A + B \cos \varphi) - B(a + b \cos \varphi)] \sin \varphi}{(A + B \cos \varphi)^2 + B^2 \sin^2 \varphi} \qquad (77)$$

Since Eq. (77) holds for the operating point, it must be satisfied by Eq. (76a). We find for the numerator of Eq. (77)

$$[b(A - nB) - B(a - nb)] \sin \varphi = (bA - Ba) \sin \varphi \qquad (77a)$$

and for the denominator, by squaring, the relation

$$A^2 + B^2(\cos^2 \varphi + \sin^2 \varphi) + 2AB \cos \varphi = A^2 + B^2 + 2AB \cos \varphi \qquad (77b)$$

The instantaneous phase excursion then becomes

$$\Delta\theta_t = \tan^{-1}\left[\frac{(bA - Ba) \sin \varphi}{A^2 + B^2 + 2AB \cos \varphi}(t)\right] = \tan^{-1}[\rho(t)] \qquad (78)$$

Hence, for values of $\rho(t) \leqq 0.2$ we may expect linearity; *i.e.*, the phase swings will be proportional to the time function (t) that causes the PM. For such values, we will have the formula

$$\Delta\theta_t \cong \frac{(bA - Ba) \sin \varphi}{A^2 + B^2 + 2AB \cos \varphi}(t) \qquad (79)$$

This is a very general formula since almost any time function can be substituted for (t). For a sinusoidal AM effect of $i_m \sin \omega t$ we have $(t) = i_m \sin \omega t$ and linear response takes place as long as $i_m \rho$ does not exceed values of 0.2.

Case 3 refers to a condition for which the vector A has no modulation and has the form $A \sin \Omega t$, while the vector B is partly modulated in amplitude and is of the form

$$(B + bi_m \sin \omega t) \sin (\Omega t + \varphi);$$

i.e., it is applied with a phase of φ with respect to the completely unmodulated carrier $A \sin \Omega t$.

Case 4 refers to a condition where a completely modulated modulation product $(KI_m \sin \omega t) \sin (\Omega t + \varphi)$ is added geometrically to an unmodulated carrier $I_m \sin \Omega t$. Such a scheme was briefly mentioned on page 6 in connection with Fig. 3. If φ is 90 deg, we have the case of Fig. 3.

From this discussion it is seen that poorly designed transfer networks will cause PM owing to amplitude distortion and will, consequently, also produce equivalent FM effects. For instance, for the case where the time function (t) in Eq. (79) is equal to $i_m \sin \omega t$, the equivalent frequency swing will be

$$\frac{1}{2\pi} \frac{d(\Delta\theta_t)}{dt} = f\rho \cos \omega t$$

In a similar manner, expressions can be derived in which a nonlinear phase shift with respect to the pass frequencies causes "directly" a change in the value of φ. The discussion in connection with the explanations given in Fig. 28 shows also that when two or more interference pulses enter the band-pass transfer networks simultaneously, there will be mutual modulation effects, even though each pulse by itself would cause no effects at the output of a balanced frequency discriminator. The mutual effects cause PM and equivalent FM. The strongest PM effect will occur when both disturbances have the same mean frequency[1] and one interference is, in equivalence, 90 deg out of phase with respect to the other interference. As a matter of fact this may happen whenever recurrent disturbances overlap. It also happens when a useful modulated carrier acts at the mean frequency of a simultaneous pulse interference and if the interference produces

---

[1] For details, consult Sec. 21, p. 117.

a larger equivalent amplitude than does the signal modulated carrier. The discriminator will then register chiefly the noise at its output.

21. Different Kinds of Interference Impulses.—In connection with Fig. 27 we have already discussed how much less sensitive FM receivers are to the interfering effects of fluctuation or random noise than are AM receivers. By fluctuation noise is usually understood such noise as is experienced in receivers with very high amplification. It is often also called interchannel noise. This noise causes a continuous distribution of random h-f currents, which do not have a fixed relative phase relationship. This is the reason why, for such distributions, the rms method was used in connection with the amplitudes of the noise areas in Fig. 27, which led to the second comparison formula of Eq. (63). Since for an AM receiver the band width is equal to twice the maximum signal frequency f_{max}, which is normally taken as 15 kc, and, according to Fig. 27, the height 0-1 is constant for the total band width $2f_{max}$, the sum of the squared amplitudes for this band width is likewise constant. Hence, fluctuation noise must be proportional to the factor $\sqrt{f_{max}}$ for an AM receiver while for an FM receiver, according to Fig. 27, we have a slope 0-4 instead of the horizontal 1-2. This leads to the comparison for a constant k

$$\text{Fluctuation or random noise} \left\{ \begin{array}{l} k\sqrt{\int_0^{f_{max}} \left[\dfrac{F_1 - F_2}{\Delta F} \right]^2 d[F_1 - F_2]} = \dfrac{kf_{max}}{\sqrt{3}\,\Delta F}\sqrt{f_{max}} \quad \text{for FM} \\[2em] k\sqrt{f_{max}} \quad \text{for AM} \end{array} \right\} \quad (80)$$

Strong noise impulses of very short duration will usually cause an energy distribution over the entire band width of the i-f networks. The duration spread in Fig. 31a is inversely proportional to the band width. Hence, in wide-band FM we have approximately the distribution indicated in Fig. 31a when a single sharp impulse acts on a band-pass transfer network having a lower cutoff frequency F_2 and an upper cutoff frequency F_1. Therefore, the resultant current depends upon both cutoff frequencies used in the i-f networks. As an approximation, as far as the explanation is concerned, the envelope or amplitude curve is filled up with a h-f current of center frequency $F = 0.5(F_1 + F_2)$ of the pass

band.   Even though the energy is mostly under the center portion
or peak envelope contour of Fig. 31a, as far as the spread as applied
to the discriminator is concerned, it is more or less uniform, as is
shown in Fig. 31c.   Only the shaded portion $2f_{max}$ wide will be
heard as interference noise.   Hence, a balanced discriminator
will produce in each half of its circuit, at the same instant, opposite
output voltages with zero voltage as the net result.   That is what

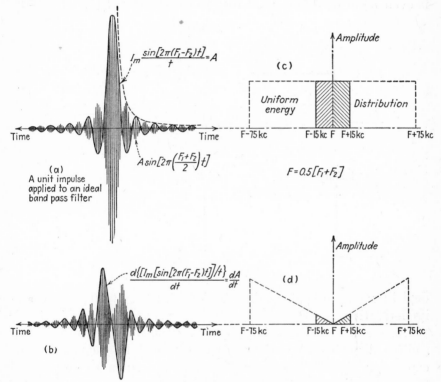

FIG. 31.—Unit impulse (a) causes uniform energy distribution while the derivative (b) of
unit impulse causes energy distribution (d).

occurs when certain impulses enter the i-f stages and subsequently,
after passing the limiter, affect a balanced discriminator.   But,
when a useful FM signal, which has the same mean frequency
also exists, PM due to mutual effect can result, especially when
quadrature addition as shown in Fig. 3 takes place.   The stronger
of the two currents will then be the one that mostly affects the
output of the discriminator.   The higher the initial peak (center
peak) shown in Fig. 31a, the more phase shift, and, therefore, also
equivalent frequency shift, will be produced in the desired FM

wave. But the limited band width of $2\,\Delta F$ often checks such tremendous frequency excursions as far as the output effect is concerned. Figure 31*b* shows the derivative of the unit pulse shown in Fig. 31*a*. Such differentiations take place when inductive coupling is used, since the driving voltage $M\,di/dt$ transfers the pulse energy into the circuit that is coupled to the circuit carrying the current i. Figure 31*d* shows the energy distribution, which is even more favorable than for the pulse of Fig. 31*a*. Figure 32

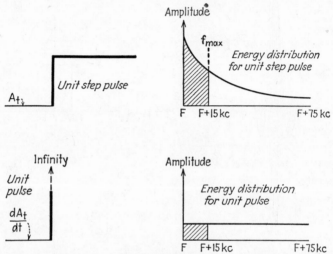

FIG. 32.—Impulses and their noise distributions.

depicts energy-frequency distributions for a unit step pulse and its derivative.

As far as the action in a band-pass network is concerned, a sudden disturbance, as just illustrated, can be defined by the expression $A(t) \sin [2\pi Ft + \theta(t)]$, where F stands for the center frequency of the pass band.

22. Frequency Multiplication in FM Systems.—We have to distinguish three typical frequencies in FM systems: the instantaneous carrier frequency F_t, the maximum deviation frequency ΔF, and the signal frequency f, which is also known as the frequency of the current that modulates. The signal frequency in high-fidelity work should remain the same as at the input of the modulator of the transmitter and, therefore, requires no multiplication or change. Only multiplication of the instantaneous carrier frequency F_t and of the maximum deviation frequency ΔF is needed. In present-day FM transmitters the primary FM source is not wide-band FM as in the final transmitted electromagnetic wave and multiplication of the primary frequency deviations is necessary.

Inasmuch as the deviation frequency $\Delta F \cos \omega t$, at any instant of time, is equal to the difference between the instantaneous carrier frequency F_t and the center frequency F, a multiplication of the instantaneous carrier frequency F_i means that the deviation frequency ΔF is multiplied also and by the same factor as is F_t. In indirect FM, as in the Armstrong transmitter, the value of F_t is the outcome of an equivalent frequency swing $\Delta \theta \cos \omega t$ about a fixed carrier frequency F. The phase modulation n the Armstrong system causes $(\Delta \theta / f) \sin \omega t$ phase swings and in turn equivalent $f(\Delta \theta / f) \cos \omega t$ frequency deviations. This behaves exactly like the actual instantaneous carrier frequency $F + \Delta F \cos \omega t$ in case of direct FM, since for indirect FM for all signal frequencies f, we have $\Delta \theta = \Delta F$, if the constant of proportionality is taken as unity.

The requirement for the frequency multiplier is, therefore, that the input as well as the output network handle all spectrum currents[1] due to currents of frequencies F_t. The output pass band must be equal to the width of the input pass band times the order of frequency multiplication. In indirect FM successive frequency multiplication is used with an intermediate network, which causes a difference-frequency or center-frequency conversion, because a much larger frequency deviation multiplication is needed than the corresponding carrier frequency multiplication. In direct FM comparatively large frequency swings can be produced directly in the primary FM oscillator and a much smaller deviation frequency multiplication is needed. In direct FM, therefore, the center-frequency multiplication is of the same order as the deviation frequency multiplication. For instance, in the RCA transmitter, as well as in the FM transmitter of the General Electric Company, two frequency triplers are used. This means that, on account of a ninefold frequency multiplication, the final output network has to be designed for a band width somewhat wider than required by the maximum peak-to-peak frequency swing. Since this maximum peak-to-peak output swing is never more than $2 \times 75 = 150$ kc, at the input side of the last tripler it is $^{15}\!\%_3 =$ 50 kc. It has this same value at the output of the first tripler and

---

[1] It should be recalled that it is the number of significant side currents and not the instantaneous carrier currents of frequencies F_t that determines the band width.

is equal to $^{50}\!\!/_3$ = 16.67 kc at the input side of the first tripler. Hence, the largest permissible maximum frequency excursion in the primary FM will not exceed ±8.335 kc. Since the maximum deviation ratio $^{75}\!\!/_{15}$ = 5 = β causes the widest pass-band spread, we find from Table III that the total band width is $16f$ = 16 × 15 = 240 kc for the final output network of the FM transmitter. This is also the band-width requirement for an FM receiver, which applies, of course, also to the i-f stages. It is, however, customary to design these networks for a band width of only 225 kc. At the input side of the last tripler, as well as at the output side of the first tripler, we have a permissible maximum frequency deviation of $^{75}\!\!/_3$ = 25 kc. The corresponding maximum deviation ratio is $^{25}\!\!/_{15}$ = 1.667 = β, requiring a band-width design for only eight significant side currents. Hence, a width of $8f$ = 120 kc is needed. For the input side of the first tripler we have a maximum deviation ratio that is only one-ninth as large as in the antenna current or only $^5\!\!/_9$ = 0.556 = β. This requires, according to Table III, a band-width design of about $4f$ or 60 kc. The present-day Western Electric FM transmitter uses only eightfold frequency multiplication by means of three frequency doublers in cascade. Details of these arrangements are described in Secs. 23 and 47.

In the Armstrong system shown in the block diagram of Fig. 33, a stabilized 200-kc primary frequency F_1 is used for controlling the ultimate center or mean frequency F of the radiated electromagnetic FM wave. Since, in this system, theoretically we should not go over a maximum phase swing of more than 0.2 radian if harmonic distortion is to be avoided,[1] the value of $\Delta\theta/f$ should never exceed 0.2 radian. Hence, it is the lowest desired signal frequency that determines the equivalent deviation frequency multiplication necessary. Since for indirect FM the value of $\Delta\theta$ expressed in radians is equal to ΔF in cycles per second, because the ratios $\Delta\theta/f$ and $\Delta F/f$ must be the same in this case, we can readily determine what is the lowest signal frequency f for which

---

[1] Figure 3 shows that for maximum phase angles of such a magnitude that the modulation product, *i.e.*, the quadrature amplitude b, does not form a portion of the circle of radius a, we have also superimposed AM. In Fig. 3b, OP = a; PP$_1$ = b. It is true that we can remove this parasitic amplitude modulation, but we should bear in mind that for PM + AM we have also so-called "theoretical" cross-spectrum effect; *i.e.*, even though an amplitude limiter can readily remove the AM effect, it is still part of the modulation energy, and the receiver that responds only to FM will miss certain components, which were removed, and will produce distortion.

full permissible FM can take place. The full permissible frequency swing ΔF is ± 75 kc. Since, in the block diagram of Fig. 33, we have an over-all frequency deviation multiplication of $16 \times 4 \times 48 = 3{,}072$, the primary maximum frequency deviation cannot exceed values higher than $75 \times 10^3/3{,}072 = 24.4$ cycles

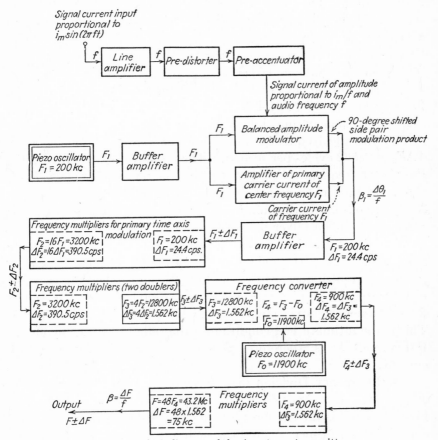

Fig. 33.—Block diagram of the Armstrong transmitter.

per second for any condition. Hence, for no harmonic distortion $\Delta F/f = 24.4/f$ should never be larger than 0.2; for the upper limit 0.2, we obtain a signal frequency $f = 24.4/0.2 = 122$ cycles per second. Hence, if harmonic a-f distortion is to be avoided, signal frequencies below 122 cycles per second cannot cause full frequency modulation for such an order of deviation frequency multiplication. Allowing somewhat less than 10 per cent harmonic distortion, we can use for the ratio $\Delta F_1/f$ a value of 0.5 radian and find that below a signal frequency $f = 24.4/0.5 = 48.8$ cycles per second we cannot expect full FM.

In the block diagram of Fig. 33, we note at first that we have a primary FM current of center frequency $F_1 = 200$ kc, as generated and stabilized by the first piezo oscillator. According to the foregoing computations, the largest ΔF_1 deviation is 24.4 cycles per second. This primary FM works through a buffer amplifier and a cascade of frequency multipliers, giving at its output 16 fold frequency multiplication. Hence, at the output of the 16 fold multiplier, we have a larger center frequency $F_2 = 16 \times F_1 = 16 \times 200 = 3,200$ kc and also a larger frequency deviation $\Delta F_2 = 16\Delta F_1 = 16 \times 24.4 = 390.5$ cycles per second. Another fourfold frequency multiplication causes, at the output of the second cascade frequency multiplier, the center frequency $F_3 = 4 \Delta F_2 = 1,562$ cycles per second. Then, a mixer stage beats down the center frequency $F_3 = 12,800$ kc to a center frequency $F_4 = 900$ kc without changing the frequency deviation. Hence, $\Delta F_4 = \Delta F_3 = 1.562$ kc both before and after this carrier frequency translation. The mixer has also the feature that another center-frequency stabilization is secured by means of a piezo oscillator of stabilized reference frequency of 11,900 kc. Another cascade of frequency multipliers causes a 48 fold multiplication, with a final center frequency $F = 48F_4 = 48 \times 900 = 43.2$ Mc and a final frequency deviation $\Delta F = 48 \Delta F_3 = 48 \times 1.562 = 75$ kc. This is the ultimate FM condition in the radiated electromagnetic FM wave. It is, therefore, also operative in the received FM current.

23. Frequency Division in FM Systems.—When *direct* FM is employed, the center frequency of the oscillator cannot be stabilized since it is the carrier frequency that is being varied for such a modulation. Since, even with such systems, at least eightfold frequency multiplication is used, a drift in the center frequency will drift the entire significant frequency spectrum with all the important side currents. This is apt to cause adjacent channel interference.

It is necessary, therefore, to stabilize the center frequency *after* the current is modulated in frequency. The subsequent stabilization depends on the requirement that, even though the carrier frequency undergoes variations, for no drift occurring, the *total number of carrier frequency cycles per second must remain constant* and be equal to the number of cycles per second of the assigned carrier frequency F of the transmitter station. The mean or center frequency F of the radiated electromagnetic wave is altogether too high for direct stabilization. Besides that, during the modulation for low-signal frequencies f, very large values of the modulation index β are effective. For a 50-cycle-per-second signal frequency and full FM, we would have $\beta = 75 \times 10^3/50 = 1{,}500$ and essentially 1,500 side currents on each side of the center frequency F and spaced only 50 cycles apart. It would, therefore, be almost impossible to synchronize the current of center frequency with a stable frequency source. It will also become clear that it is essentially impossible, if we realize that for such large values of β as occur at times the modulation energy is spread over almost the entire frequency spectrum corresponding to the β value, with most of the energy toward the edges of the spectrum distribution. As a matter of fact, the amplitude of the center frequency F would be rather *insignificant*. It is the frequency of this amplitude that we have to keep in step with a fixed control frequency.

For this reason we have to reduce the number of side currents, and indeed so much that essentially only the first side-current pair exists even for the largest β values, *i.e.*, for full modulation with low-signal frequencies. This can be readily accomplished by division of the deviation frequency ΔF since this causes the same division in the corresponding modulation index β. By using a sufficient degree of deviation division, we shall not only reduce the number of possible side currents but also *emphasize the amplitude* of the current whose frequency is to be stabilized. This is due to the fact that, for small values of β, the $J_0(\beta)$ term, which determines the amplitude of the center frequency, approaches the value of unity. Hence, we have not only reduced the number of important side currents, but also obtained a carrier-frequency amplitude that is relatively large and, therefore, can more readily be kept in correct center-frequency step. This is especially a requirement when mechanical center-frequency stabilization is employed.

Figure 34 shows an application of such a center-frequency stabilization. It is used in the FM transmitter of the Western Electric Company and is shown for the case of a channel assignment of a carrier frequency $F = 46.5$ Mc/sec. Figure 34b is a more elaborate block diagram than Fig. 34a, since the automatic mechanical frequency adjuster is also indicated. The primary oscillator has a center frequency $F_1 = 5.8125$ Mc. When three stages of frequency doublers are used, we have $2 \times 2 \times 2$ or

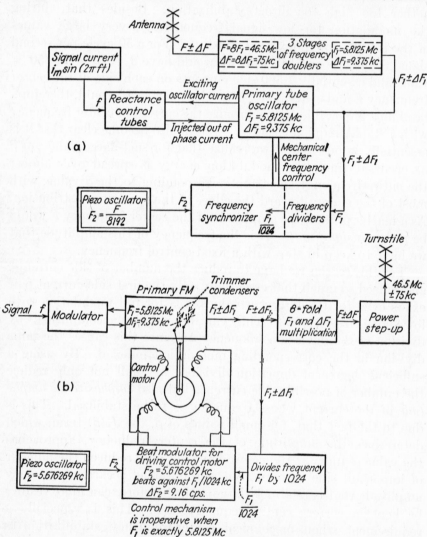

Fig. 34.—Western Electric Company's FM transmitter.

eightfold frequency multiplication. Hence, $F = 8F_1 = 46.5$ Mc for the center frequency of the radiated electromagnetic FM wave. For full FM we have a maximum permissible frequency deviation ΔF of ± 75 kc in the radiated wave. The primary FM must, therefore, have a corresponding maximum permissible frequency

deviation $\Delta F_1 = {}^{75}\!/_8 = 9.375$ kc. This frequency deviation can
be readily produced with a balanced reactance tube modulator
that acts in multiple with the frequency-determining branch
of the primary tube oscillator of center frequency F_1. As will be
shown on page 242, an effective signal-frequency voltage of about
0.6 volt can produce such maximum permissible frequency swings
in the master oscillator frequency F_1. From this point on, our
frequency division sets in. As described in detail with respect to
Fig. 75, ten frequency halvers are used, each halver being based
on regenerative modulation for which a subharmonic frequency of
half of the frequency at the input side is obtained at the output
side. Hence, we have a total frequency division of $2^{10} = 1,024$.
The reduced center frequency F_2 is then $F_1/1,024$ or 5.676269 kc,
and the reduced primary frequency swing of ΔF_1 is 9.375/1,024
or $\Delta F_2 = 9.16$ cycles per second. This would be the largest
frequency excursion for full permissible primary FM. When,
therefore, a piezo oscillator of stabilized frequency $F_2 = 5.676269$
kc beats with the center frequency $F_1/1,024$ and F_1 should drift
the least, a motor mechanism adds or subtracts a suitable capacitance in the frequency-determining branch of the primary oscillator. This in turn brings the center frequency F_1 again to the
exact value of 5.8125 kc.

The piezo oscillator of stabilized subharmonic center frequency
F_2 supplies currents of this frequency to a mixer-modulator, which
also carries currents due to the output of the frequency divider
circuits. Hence, when the primary center frequency F_1 is correct,
no beat effects can occur in the mixer modulator. The only
action that can be effective is due to the small equivalent maximum
frequency swing $\Delta F_2 = 9.16$ cycles per second for the largest
permissible frequency deviation, and smaller ΔF_2 swings for smaller
degrees of FM. For equivalent β_2 values equal to and smaller
than 0.2, we have only one side-current pair of appreciable magnitude and an equivalent center-frequency amplitude, which is
essentially unity, $i.e.$, at its very maximum value. We find that
this will occur for all signal frequencies f above the value of f_2
in the expression $\beta_2 = \Delta F_2/f_2 \leqq 0.2$. This value is $f_2 = 9.16/0.2 =$
45.8 cycles per second. Hence, there will never be more than
one side-current pair of appreciable magnitude for all important
signal frequencies, because the important signal frequencies lie
above this value of f_2. The action of the most severe frequency

swing of 9.16 cycles per second in F_2 on the synchronous motor mechanism can be only, in effect, a small phase liberation of a few degrees, which is several times less than a complete cycle. For instance, for the most severe lower frequency limit of 45.8 cycles per second, the equivalent phase liberation is only 0.2 $\times$ 57.3; *i.e.*, it is equal to ± 11.47 deg. The effect on the motor mechanism can be only a small "forward and backward vibration or a buzz" of the rotor of a pitch of 45.8 cycles per second. On account of the inertia effect of the rotor, the rotor could hardly follow to-and-fro phase swings of ± 11.47 deg with a speed of 45.8 cycles per second. Hence, for correct primary frequency F_1, the mechanism cannot change the trimmer condenser settings of the primary oscillator. But when F_1 drifts toward larger center-frequency values, the rotor starts to turn slowly in a definite direction and can be made to increase the trimmer capacitances so as to bring back the correct center frequency F_1. If the primary center frequency F_1 should drift toward a somewhat smaller value, it will cause the rotor to move slowly in the other direction thus decreasing the trimmer capacitance. This increases the center frequency until again the correct center-frequency value of 5.8125 Mc results, at which time the mechanism becomes again inoperative on the trimmer condensers.

Inasmuch as the mechanism of Fig. 34*b*, which reestablishes the correct center frequency F_1 of the primary FM, is based on synchronous motor action and on beat-current effects, it is evident that no relaxation oscillators could be successfully used for frequency division. We require an FM current, even though of reduced center frequency and frequency deviation, which is still the product of the primary FM. For this reason regenerative modulation is employed for causing frequency division. This is continued on page 154.

24. Heterodyning in FM Systems.—We have to deal with three distinctive types of heterodyning used in FM as far as their respective purposes are concerned. One purpose of heterodyning is to produce i-f currents in a mixer detector, as is well known in the superheterodyne technique. An intermediate center frequency of 4.3 Mc is generally used and the frequency of the local oscillator can be chosen 4.3 Mc above or below the assigned center frequency F. Since such a frequency value for the i-f stages is high as compared with i-f values used in customary AM systems, we have a greater frequency separation between the desired signal and the image response. This is a decided advantage. The second purpose of heterodyning in FM systems is to obtain center-frequency stabilization without resorting to frequency division. A third purpose is to have a means for increasing the primary frequency deviation relatively more than the corresponding increase in the center frequency. This could not be done by means of frequency multiplication alone.

Heterodyning gives, therefore, a means of changing the center frequency over very wide limits to a lower center frequency with only one stage, *i.e.*, the mixer or converter stage. Suppose we have an FM current of primary center frequency F_1 with a frequency swing of $\Delta F_1 \cos \omega t$. If this current beats with an unmodulated local current of frequency F_2 which is, as customary, higher than F_1, we obtain an instantaneous beat or difference frequency of $(F_2 - F_1 - \Delta F_1 \cos \omega t)$. Hence, the new reference or center frequency is $F_2 - F_1$, which may differ considerably from the value of F_1 that is to be reduced. But the deviation frequency in the original or primary FM is still preserved as $\Delta F_1 \cos \omega t$.

This leads to two other important uses. One use applies to the case utilized in the Armstrong transmitter and shown in Fig. 33. Here we have to multiply the primary ΔF_1 swing of only 24.4 cycles per second by a factor as much as $16 \times 4 \times 48 = 3,072$, in order to obtain wide-band frequency swings of ± 75 kc in the radiated wave for the largest permissible FM. Now, if the frequency conversion between the FM current of the instantaneous frequency $12,800 + 1.562 \cos \omega t$ and the unmodulated local piezo current of frequency of $11,900$ kc had not been used for lowering the center frequency to a value of $12,800 - 11,900 = 900$ kc, but without disturbing in the least the maximum frequency swing of ± 1.562 kc, the primary center frequency of $F_1 = 200$ kc would also have been multiplied by the factor $3,072$. This would have yielded a final center frequency of $200 \times 3,072 = 614.4$ Mc instead of the assigned and required value of 43.2 Mc. Hence, we have a convenient means, by combining mixer AM, as occurring in the frequency converter, and successive frequency multiplication, for producing wide-band FM by multiplying the frequency swing at a greater rate than the center frequency.

The reduction of the order of the center frequency, without changing the corresponding primary frequency deviation $\Delta F_1 \cos \omega t$

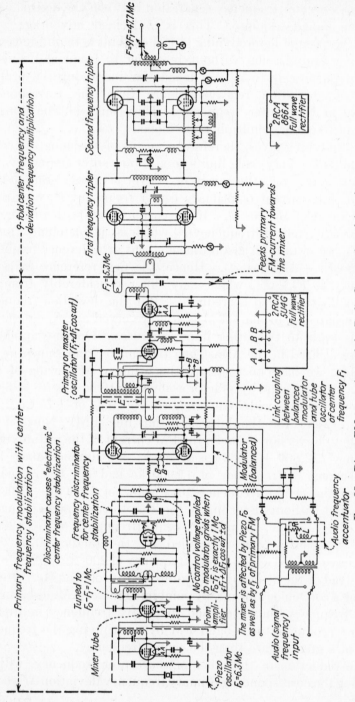

Fig. 35.—Direct FM transmitter of the Radio Corporation of America.

in the center frequency F_1 as well as slow drifts d in the original center frequency F_1, gives a means for changing the ratio $\Delta F_1/F_1$, *i.e.*, the percentage of FM. This ratio should not be confused with the ratio $\Delta F_1/f$, which would be the primary modulation index. If d stands for a frequency drift in the primary center frequency, which may be either positive or negative, frequency conversion in a mixer stage gives a means for *emphasizing* the percentage drift after frequency conversion is made. For a local oscillator frequency of F_0, we have after frequency conversion takes place, an instantaneous carrier frequency, which is now only $F_0 - (F_1 + d) - \Delta F_1 \cos \omega t$. The reduced center or mean frequency is then $F_0 - (F_1 + d)$ and the percentage of center-frequency drift is $100d/(F_0 - F_1)$ instead of $100d/F_1$.

An application of this feature is employed for the stabilization of the mean frequency F of the radiated FM wave. This is done in the FM transmitter of the General Electric Company (Fig. 73) as well as in the transmitter of the RCA, shown in Fig. 35. Suppose that in this figure the primary carrier frequency is $F_1 = 5.3$ Mc and that a center-frequency drift d, which may be positive or negative, exists during a certain interval of time. Suppose that owing to this drift the center frequency F_1 becomes as much as one-fifth of 1 per cent higher than its normal value. Then $d = 10.6$ kc is the corresponding center-frequency drift. As explained in detail on page 241 and shown in Fig. 35, a small primary FM current of frequency $F_1 + \Delta F_1 \cos \omega t + d$ is applied to a mixer tube, which at the same time experiences also a current coming from a piezo oscillator of stabilized frequency F_0, which in this illustration is taken as 6.3 Mc. The output branch of the mixer is tuned to the difference frequency $F_0 - F_1 = 1$ Mc and is coupled to a frequency discriminator. The discriminator is so balanced that for a difference frequency of 1 Mc/sec, which corresponds to the correct reduced center frequency, no output voltage results. The output branch of the discriminator affects the steady bias of two quadrature tubes that bring about primary FM in the associated oscillator. However, if the primary center frequency F_1 is no longer correct but is 0.2 per cent higher, for example, then the difference frequency will show a reduced center frequency of $F_0 - (F_1 + d) = 6.3 - (5.3 + 0.0106) = 0.9894$ Mc. The percentage change due to the center frequency drift d is now $100 \times 0.0106/1 = 1.06$ per cent, instead of 0.2 per cent as it was in the radiated FM wave.   Hence, we have a higher resolving power for the frequency drift in the intermediate 1-Mc center frequency.

Since now a frequency of only 0.9894 Mc is effective in the external plate branch of the mixer stage, the corresponding voltage applied to the discriminator will upset the balance of the discriminator and will cause a corresponding output voltage of definite polarity.   Call it positive.   This output voltage will change the fixed bias effective in the reactance tubes and, accordingly, will change also the mutual transconductance of these tubes.   This in turn will change the fixed portion of the reactance injected into the frequency-determining branch of the primary oscillator.   Now, if the frequency drift had been negative, *i.e.*, if it had caused a decrease of 10.6 kc in the correct primary center frequency F_1, then the discriminator would have been unbalanced in the other direction and would have caused a *negative* output voltage, which has still the same value as before.   Hence, just as much bias correction in the other direction would act on the reactance tubes and a frequency correction in the opposite sense will be applied to the primary oscillator.   The center-frequency control is so effective that the center frequency F can be readily kept within 0.0025 per cent of the assigned or correct frequency. The frequency stabilization action is also so effective that it would check down the desired FM, since the FM produces a superimposed useful frequency swing $\Delta F \cos \omega t$.   The actual difference frequency F_1 is

$$F_1 = \underbrace{F_0 - F - d}_{\substack{\text{reduced} \\ \text{center frequency}}} - \underbrace{\Delta F \cos \omega t}_{\substack{\text{swing due to} \\ \text{FM}}} \tag{81}$$

For this reason a "preventor" is employed so that any $\Delta F \cos \omega t$ fluctuations cannot reach the reactance tube modulator.   This preventor is, in the General Electric FM transmitter (Fig. 73), the $C_3 R_3$ filter.   The design of this filter is based on the fact that frequency drifts d occur slowly, while the desired useful frequency modulations $\Delta F \cos \omega t$ due to modulation usually play a part only, say, from 40 cycles per second on upward and, hence, these frequency variations occur relatively rapidly.   When, therefore, a series combination of a resistance R_3 and a condenser C_3 is connected across the output of the frequency discriminator (across the cathodes), only slow drift voltages will be effective on the respective grids of the reactance tube modulators. The R_3C_3 network is, therefore, so designed that it acts more or less as a short circuit to currents of the useful a-f range; it behaves as a high impedance toward the slow-frequency drift variations.

25. Wave Propagation in the Present-day FM Band.—This section on wave propagation has reference to the commercial channels of 44.5, 44.7, 44.9, 45.1, . . . , 48.3, 48.5, and 48.7 Mc; the commercial channels of 48.9, 49.1, 49.3, 49.5, 49.7, and 49.9 Mc; the commercial channels of 43.1, 43.3, 43.5, 43.7, 43.9, 44.1, and 44.3 Mc; as well as the educational channels of 42.1, 42.3, 42.5, 42.7, and 42.9 Mc.

Since for this ultrahigh-frequency range[1] we have more or less optical propagation conditions as compared with the standard broadcast range used in present-day AM systems, we have to realize that the "line-of-sight" wave propagation plays an important part. Hence, the terrain between the transmitter and receiver aerials should have no continuous obstructions that are large compared with the operating wave length. To go around obstructions, it becomes necessary to have at least one aerial high over ground, if it is not possible to have both the transmitter aerial and the receiver aerial high over ground. As will be shown in this section, the electric field intensity ε decreases inversely with the *square* of the distance to the transmitter aerial for the above FM channel allocations, while the ground wave for customary AM systems in the standard broadcast frequency band decreases only inversely with this distance. The inverse square law relation has nothing to do with the type of modulation and depends only on the order of the frequencies to which the FM channels are assigned.

We must also realize that we have only one effective service area for such FM assignments since for these frequencies the action of the ionized layer normally does not play a part in the useful wave propagation. Any field produced by the action of this layer is altogether too unreliable and erratic for normal practical usage. Normally, the ionized layer never returns any rays of such carrier frequencies entering it. However, for waves in the ultrahigh-frequency range, we experience a certain amount of atmospheric refraction so that the path has a slight curvature when near the ground. This is usually taken care of in the propa-

---

[1] "Phenomena in High-frequency Systems," p. 362.

gation formulas by assuming a linear propagation but an earth surface which has a radius that is 33 per cent larger than the actual earth radius. The curvature effect is somewhat more pronounced during the night when the air is denser near the surface of the ground.

Inasmuch as even half-wave aerials for the above frequency ranges are relatively small antennas, we can use antenna arrays that are suitable for horizontally polarized waves or arrays that are suitable for vertically polarized waves.[1] For vertical polarization a half-wave-length rod aerial is placed vertical to ground and at least several wave lengths above it. The height above the ground is taken in this case to the mid-point of the dipole with respect to the ground, and the radiation pattern is theoretically circular around the dipole. For horizontal polarization a horizontal dipole well above ground is used. Maximum transmission then occurs broadside with the well-known figure-eight radiation pattern as far as horizontal planes are concerned. Even though an antenna may send out horizontally polarized waves, this does not necessarily mean that the electric field vector is still only horizontally polarized at the reception end. We receive not only components that are due to direct radiation and indirect radiation reflected from ground, but also radiation that may be due to reflection from other obstacles that are large compared with the operating wave length.

Generally, experiments show that the signal-to-noise ratio is more favorable for vertically polarized waves received near the ground. This refers, for instance, to "car-to car" FM communications with vertical aerials. The reason for this is that near the ground a vertically polarized wave gives a more effective received field intensity than does an arriving horizontally polarized wave. But, in ordinary FM work it is customary to have the transmitter antenna at least several wave lengths above ground, and then a better signal-to-noise ratio is obtained for horizontally polarized transmission and reception. This is the reason why it is more customary in the United States to employ horizontal polarization and to arrange, for instance, the several dipoles of turnstile structures in horizontal layers or bays. This arrangement also has the

[1] "Phenomena in High-frequency Systems," pp. 499–517; TREVOR, B., and P. S. CARTER, *Proc. I.R.E.*, **21**, 387, 1933; PETERSON, H. O., *RCA Rev.*, **4**, 162, 1939; BEVERAGE, H. H., *RCA Rev.*, January, 1937.

advantage that theoretically a circular radiation pattern results; besides, it leads to a rugged antenna structure.

Figure 36a shows that for a transmitter antenna T and a receiver antenna R we have to deal with a direct wave propagation along a path d_1 and an indirect wave propagation along a path $d_2 + d_3$. Hence, the component transmitted along the indirect path must be delayed in phase by an angle $\delta = 360 d_4/\lambda$ deg, where

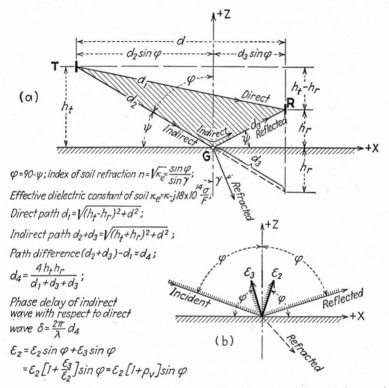

FIG. 36.—Direct and indirect propagation in 40- to 50-Mc range of carrier frequencies.

d_4 denotes the path difference and λ is the operating wave length expressed in the same dimension as d_4. Figure 36b shows what occurs when, for instance, vertically polarized waves are concerned and the indirect wave propagation is being considered. Since the angle of incidence ψ must be equal to the angle of reflection, we have the geometry indicated in the diagrams (a and b). Inasmuch as the electric vector ε_2 representing the field intensity of the incident wave must be perpendicular to the direction of propagation, ε_2 is drawn perpendicular to the incident ray. The reflected ray causes the corresponding field vector $\mathcal{E}_3$, and $\mathcal{E}_z = \mathcal{E}_2 + \mathcal{E}_3$ represents the vectorial sum of these vectors. From the geometry in Fig. 36b, it may be seen that near the reflection point G the resultant vertically polarized field intensity is

$$\mathcal{E}_z = \mathcal{E}_2(1 + \rho_v) \sin \varphi \qquad (82)$$

where ρ_v denotes the coefficient of reflection for vertically polarized waves. If the ground were a perfect reflector, *i.e.*, if no portion of the incident wave energy could be absorbed along a path of refraction, $\mathcal{E}_3$ would be equal to $-\mathcal{E}_2$, and ρ_v would have a value equal to unity. We must, therefore, take into consideration the condition of the ground. Electrically, the properties of ground can be expressed by a dielectric constant κ and an ohmic resistance. For ground, the latter[1] is conveniently expressed in terms of resistivity per centimeter cube. The reciprocal of the resistivity is the specific conductivity σ which is expressed in mhos per centimeter cube.

At this point it may not be out of place to emphasize that two absolute systems of units are in use: the em-cgs system and the es-cgs system. In current literature some curves for σ express the electromagnetic unit for σ as $k10^{14}$, instead of as $k10^{-14}$, which is correct. The factor k has for soil values like 5, 6, 7. This is a serious confusion when such curves are to be applied, since the error is 10^{28}. To clear up this situation, it should be understood that in the em-cgs system the unit of the resistance is a velocity dimension and 1 em-cm/sec $= 10^{-9}$ ohm. Hence, the corresponding conductivity is the reciprocal of this value. In the es-cgs system, we have, however, 1 es-sec/cm $= 9 \times 10^{11}$/ohms. We are dealing here with a dimension that is the reciprocal of a velocity since the ratio of emu/esu is equal to the square of the velocity of wave propagation in free space (equal to 9×10^{20} cm²/sec²). Therefore

$$\sigma, \text{ mhos/cm cube} = \left\langle \begin{array}{ll} 9 \times 10^{11}\sigma & \text{esu} \\ 10^{-9}\sigma & \text{emu} \end{array} \right\rangle \qquad (83)$$

A specific conductivity of 8×10^{-5} mho yields then $9 \times 10^{11} \times 8 \times 10^{-5} = 72 \times 10^6$ esu or $10^{-9} \times 8 \times 10^{-5} = 8 \times 10^{-14}$ emu.

At this point it should also be understood that the path along which an electromagnetic disturbance progresses depends on the index n of refraction of the medium where $n = \sqrt{\kappa - jp}$ and $p = 1.79731 \times 10^{15} \ \sigma/F$. The quantity σ is in em-cgs units and F in megacycles. If δ is the latitude and γ the longitude of a space point a distance r from a radiator the received field intensity at the space point is

$$\mathcal{E}_{(\delta,\gamma,r)} = \mathcal{E}_{(\delta,\gamma,)}\epsilon^{j2\pi\left(n\frac{r}{\lambda}-Ft\right)}$$

[1] For other details, consult "High-frequency Measurements," pp. 290–297.

where $\lambda^m = 300/F^{Mc}$ and r also is in meters. If $\mathcal{E}_1$ is the intensity at unit distance r_1 we have for the equatorial plane of a linear radiator

$$\mathcal{E} = \frac{\mathcal{E}_1 \cos \delta}{r} \epsilon^{j2\pi\left(\frac{r}{\lambda}-Ft\right)}$$

$$= \frac{\mathcal{E}_1 \cos \delta}{r} \underbrace{\epsilon^{j(Br-2\pi Ft)}}_{\substack{\text{distri-}\\\text{bution}}} \underbrace{\epsilon^{-A(r-r_1)}}_{\substack{\text{absorp-}\\\text{tion due}\\\text{to electric}\\\text{constants}\\\kappa \text{ and } \sigma\\\text{of medi-}\\\text{um when}\\\text{wave pro-}\\\text{gresses}\\\text{from dis-}\\\text{tance } r_1 \text{ to}\\\text{distance}\\r \text{ from}\\\text{radiator.}}}$$

In the above expression

$$\frac{2\pi}{\lambda} n = B + jA$$

$$A = \frac{2\pi}{\lambda} \sqrt{\frac{\kappa}{\cos \Phi}} \sin \frac{\Phi}{2}$$

$$B = \frac{2\pi}{\lambda} \sqrt{\frac{\kappa}{\cos \Phi}} \cos \frac{\Phi}{2}$$

$$\Phi = \tan^{-1} (p/\kappa)$$

Hence when σ and κ vary within the medium we have to deal with a curved path.

The intensity $\mathcal{E}_3$ due to the reflected ray will add vectorially to the intensity $\mathcal{E}_2$ of the incident ray. The resultant intensity $\mathcal{E}_z$ along the vertical Z axis will be the field intensity that would be measured near reflection point G with a vertical pole aerial which is conveniently 0.42 wave length long.[1] The stronger the intensity $\mathcal{E}_3$ of the reflected ray, the stronger the field, and this intensity of the reflected ray depends on the electromagnetic index of refraction n of the ground. According to optics, the refracted ray will *always* bend toward the normal (Z axis in Fig. 36) when the ray passes from a less dense medium into a denser one. The index of refraction n is then equal to the ratio of the speed in the less dense medium to the speed in the denser medium. Hence, in our case, it is equal to the ratio of the speed of the electromagnetic wave in air to the speed of the wave in the particular ground under consideration. The speed of the wave in air is essentially $c = 3 \times 10^{10}$ cm/sec, since both the dielectric constant κ and the magnetic permeability μ have the conventional unity values in air. For the average ground we have

---

[1] In many cases the value of $\mathcal{E}_z$ vanishes at G.

likewise $\mu = 1$, but an effective dielectric constant κ_e which is complex since we have both a ground resistance and a ground specific capacity or dielectric constant κ. The group velocity of propagation in ground is, therefore, slower than in air. The decrease in the propagation speed is, however, different on account of variation in the value of the effective dielectric constant κ_e, since this constant expresses to what extent we have a transparent dielectric. Hence, for ground, we have a speed of propagation that is equal to $c \sqrt{\kappa_e}$ and an index of refraction n which is $n = \sqrt{\kappa_e}$. Because the actual dielectric constant κ is really a specific capacity, it produces quadrature effects, compared with the effects produced by the ground resistance as well as by its reciprocal, the conductivity. These quadrature effects depend on the frequency of the reflected wave, which in this particular example is the instantaneous carrier frequency F_t. Since, even for the largest permissible frequency swings, F_t never deviates more than 75 kc from the assigned carrier-frequency value F, this deviation being only about one-fifth of 1 per cent, we may use F instead of F_t. We find then for the complex value of the effective dielectric constant

$$\kappa_e = \left\{ \begin{array}{ll} \kappa - j18 \times 10^{14}\dfrac{\sigma}{F} & \text{for } \sigma \text{ in em-cgs} \\[2ex] \kappa - j2 \times 10^{-6}\dfrac{\sigma}{F} & \text{for } \sigma \text{ in es-cgs} \end{array} \right\} \tag{84}$$

where κ expresses how many times larger the dielectric constant of the ground is than the dielectric constant of the air. The specific conductivity σ is expressed in the indicated cgs units and the carrier frequency F is in megacycles per second. Hence, for a 44.5-Mc wave and ground constants of $\kappa = 15$ and $\sigma = 5 \times 10^{-14}$ em-cgs units, we have $\kappa_e = 15 - j2.02$, *i.e.*, an absolute value $\sqrt{15^2 + 2.02^2} = 15.14$. Since these numerical values of κ and σ apply to actual conditions, it is seen that for such high frequencies as are used for frequency allocations in the FM band, we may expect very efficient reflections. In this particular example, the effective dielectric constant κ_e is hardly affected by the ground conductivity and is almost equal to the actual dielectric constant κ, which is a real value. Table IV gives typical useful values for the electrical constants of ground. If the es-cgs unit for σ is desired,

TABLE IV

Type of ground	Electrical characteristics of ground	
	Specific conductivity σ, em-cgs units	Dielectric constant κ (numerical)
Ocean water.........................	4×10^{-11}	80
River water.........................	45×10^{-15}	80
Dry soil.............................	10^{-16}	3 to 5
Fertile farm soil......................	$(5 \text{ to } 15)10^{-14}$	10 to 30
Sandy soil close to ocean.............	10^{-15}	8 to 10
Moist ground........................	30×10^{-14}	30
Inland soil..........................	10^{-13}	15

the em-cgs unit, *i.e.*, the σ values of this table, are to be multiplied by 9×10^{20} according to Eq. (83).

The resultant vertical field intensity $\mathcal{E}_z$, as expressed in Eq. (82) and shown in Fig. 36, is only the value that would be effective in a vertical rod antenna located slightly above the reflection point G. The actual reception occurs for vertically polarized waves. Consider a vertical rod antenna at the reception location R which is located at a distance h_r above the tangential reflection surface, while the transmitting antenna T is located at a height h_t above ground.[1] At R we receive then the vertical component (in case the rod of the receiver antenna is vertical) of the resultant due to the field intensity arriving along the direct path d_1 and the field intensity of the reflected wave arriving along the path d_3. Hence, generally, the intensity $\mathcal{E}_1$, which arrives on the direct path d_1 as is shown in Fig. 37 if no interfering obstacle changes the polarization, must be perpendicular to path d_1 and larger than the vector intensity $\rho_v \mathcal{E}_1 \epsilon^{-j\delta}$, which arrives along path d_3 and is perpendicular to this path. The resultant is, therefore, generally not perpendicular to the ground at R and only the component of the resultant along the direction of the antenna dipole can be effective in

[1] It should be understood that in optical-wave transmission and reception we no longer deal with effective heights in field-intensity formulas nor with actual heights, but with heights like h_t and h_r in Fig. 36, which are measured with respect to the mid-point of the antenna structure and the tangential reference ground plane. The height of the mid-point of the antenna structure of a vertical dipole would be to the center of the dipole, as indicated in Fig. 36. For a horizontal dipole it would be to any point on the axis of the dipole. For a five-bay turnstile antenna the mid-point of the antenna structure would be in the plane of the third bay.

producing a current in the antenna. If the rod antenna were turned parallel to the direction of the resultant, then the full available field intensity would be operative on the received current value. The same thing is true when the resultant field near the reflection point G is being measured with a rod antenna. Here, generally, the resultant (Fig. 36) of ε_2 and ε_3 has a slight forward tilt and for maximum receiver effects the rod antenna has to be tilted also and until it is aligned parallel to the resultant vector of $\varepsilon_2 + \varepsilon_3$. With respect to Fig. 37 and the reception location R,

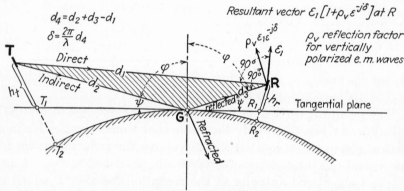

Fig. 37.—Transmission for curved earth. (Tangential plane $T_1 - G - R_1$ used as fictitious ground plane.)

we have to bear in mind that the direct and indirect field intensities have a phase difference that is due to *two entirely different causes*. One cause is the path difference $d_4 = (d_2 + d_3) - d_1$ producing, according to Fig. 36, a phase delay $\delta = 360 d_4/\lambda$ deg. This phase difference is taken care of by the factor $\epsilon^{-j\delta}$ in the expression for the indirect component field vector (Fig. 37). The other cause is the phase angle of the reflection coefficient ρ_v and is, therefore, contained in the expression for ρ_v. We have for the resultant field ε_r at R and the vertical reflection coefficient ρ_v, the formulas

$$\left.\begin{array}{l} \varepsilon_r = \varepsilon_1(1 + \rho_v\epsilon^{-j\delta}) \\[2mm] \rho_v = \dfrac{p\kappa_e - q}{p\kappa_e + q} \end{array}\right\} \tag{85}$$

where
$$\left.\begin{array}{l} q = \sqrt{\kappa_e - 1 + p^2} \\[1mm] p = \sin\psi \\[1mm] \delta = 360\,\dfrac{d_4}{\lambda}\ \text{deg.} \end{array}\right\} \tag{86}$$

For horizontally polarized waves we have the corresponding

formulas

$$\left.\begin{array}{l} \mathcal{E}_r = \mathcal{E}_1(1 + \rho_h\epsilon^{-j\delta}) \\[2mm] \rho_h = \dfrac{p - q}{p + q} \end{array}\right\} \qquad (87)$$

if ρ_h denotes the reflection coefficient for horizontal polarization. We note that the ground properties play a great part in determining the effective electromagnetic field at R.

The effective dielectric constant κ_e of Eq. (84) gives a means of finding from known numerical values for κ and σ to what extent the ground is transparent to electromagnetic waves in the frequency range of the FM waves. If, for instance, the j term with the specific conductivity σ and the carrier frequency F is negligible in comparison with the κ term, then the index of electromagnetic refraction n is equal to $\sqrt{\kappa}$ and the ground may be considered a perfectly transparent dielectric. This was approximately the case for the numerical example given in connection with Eq. (84). Since this equation has the form $\kappa_e = a - jb$, it gives directly the phase Φ of the reflection coefficient and we have $\Phi = \tan^{-1}(-b/a)$. For j terms very small in comparison with the real a term, which make κ_e essentially equal to κ, i.e., make the ground essentially transparent, no wave energy can be absorbed in the ground. The incident electromagnetic wave then is reflected toward the receiver with no decrease in amplitude and with a phase of the reflection coefficient that is either zero or 180 deg.

Suppose that we take a numerical case for which the imaginary term is 10 per cent or less of the actual κ value in Eq. (84). Let us consider the case from Table IV for fertile farm soil having a dielectric constant $\kappa = 25$ and $\sigma = 5 \times 10^{-14}$ em-cgs units for a carrier frequency of $F = 49.9$ Mc. We have, then, κ_e essentially equal to 25. In Eq. (86) we find that q is very nearly equal to 5, since p^2 under no condition can reach a value more than unity, as unity is also the upper limit for p. From Eqs. (85) and (87) we find the respective reflection coefficients

$$\rho \cong \begin{cases} \dfrac{\sin\psi - 5}{\sin\psi + 5} & \text{for horizontally polarized waves} \\[4mm] \dfrac{5\sin\psi - 5}{5\sin\psi + 5} & \text{for vertically polarized waves} \end{cases}$$

Now suppose that the angle of incidence ψ with respect to the tangential plane in Fig. 37 is 15 deg. Then $\sin \psi = 0.2588$ and we find for the horizontal polarization $\rho_h = -4.7412/5.2588 = -0.901$ and for the vertical polarization $\rho_v = -3.706/6.294 = -0.589$. Hence, for vertically polarized waves, the reflected wave is considerably reduced in amplitude. Using all terms under the square root in determining the value of q, we find from Eq. (86) that $q = \sqrt{24.067} = 4.92$, instead of the approximation 5, and that $\rho_h = -4.6612/5.1788 = -0.901$, which is exactly the value found with the approximation. The exact evaluation $\rho_v = -3.626/6.214 = -0.584$ shows also that for the vertical polarization the approximation yielding the value of -0.589 seems close enough. We note that in each case we have a reflected wave which on account of the *minus* sign is 180 deg out of phase due to the reflection coefficient, besides the additional phase shift due to the difference distance d_4.

Generally, it may be said that for horizontal polarization we may expect at G essentially 100 per cent reflection with a phase change of 180 deg in the frequency band used for FM work. This is also true for vertically polarized waves when the angle of incidence ψ does not exceed 0.5 deg for reflections over land or river water. However, such assumptions cannot be made for reflections over ocean water since then the conductivity is altogether too high. This explains why horizontally polarized waves for aerials located well above ground give better signal-to-noise ratios, than vertically polarized waves.

Since for small grazing angles both polarizations are subject to ideal reflections with a phase shift of 180 deg, we can now derive the radiation formula. In empty space the electric field intensity ε in volts per meter for a dipole of effective height (effective length) h_e meters, at a distance d meters from the dipole, and for a current I amp, is given by the relation $\varepsilon = 185 h_e I \cos v/(\lambda d)$. The operating wave length λ is likewise in meters and v is the angle that the propagation direction makes with the equatorial plane of the dipole. If we use a half-wave-length rod as the transmitter aerial, we have an effective length of $h_e = 0.3185\lambda$ since for an actual length h of the dipole we have $h_e = 2h/\pi$ and $h = 0.5\lambda$. At the mid-point of the dipole where current value I is active, we have a radiation resistance of about 74 ohms with a radiated power of $P = 74I^2$ watts. Hence, in the foregoing formula

$I = \sqrt{P}/8.6$ and we find

$$\varepsilon = 185 \times 0.3185\lambda \, \sqrt{P}/(8.6\lambda d) = 6.85 \, \sqrt{P}/d \quad \text{volts/meter}$$

This is the field intensity in the equatorial plane of a half-wave dipole or rod antenna at a distance d meters for a radiated power of P watts. By equatorial plane is meant the plane through the mid-point of the rod and perpendicular to the rod.

This formula applies to both the direct and the indirect path of the system shown in Fig. 36a. For the indirect path transmission, phase and reflection effects must also be considered. The phase delay due to the path difference d_4 is $\delta = 2\pi d_4/\lambda$, where in the formulas for $d_2 + d_3$ and d_1 the value of d^2 is large compared with the values of $(h_t + h_r)^2$ and $(h_t - h_r)^2$. Therefore, we may use the approximations $d_2 + d_3 \cong d + 0.5(h_t + h_r)^2/d$ and $d_1 \cong d + 0.5(h_t - h_r)^2/d$. Hence, $d_4 = d_2 + d_3 - d_1 \cong 2h_t h_r/d$ with a corresponding phase delay $\delta = 4\pi h_t h_r/\lambda d$. This is the phase delay at R for the indirect wave with respect to the direct wave with propagation over plane ground and generally for small grazing angles and holding for either type of polarization. According to the numerical outcome of Eqs. (85) and (87), for horizontally polarized waves we have the reflection coefficient ρ_h essentially equal to -1 and the resultant field intensity at R is

$$\varepsilon_r = \varepsilon_1(1 - \epsilon^{-j\delta}) = (1 - \cos\delta + j\sin\delta)\varepsilon_1 = m\varepsilon_1$$

But the phase delay $\delta = 720 h_t h_r/(\lambda d) = 720p$ deg. can, on account of the very small value of p due to the large value of d in comparison with the relatively small value of the product of $h_t h_r$, correspond only to values of δ not exceeding about 11 deg. For such angles $\cos\delta$ is essentially equal to unity and $\sin\delta$ is equal to $4\pi h_t h_r/(\lambda d) = \delta$. Hence,

$$\varepsilon_r = \varepsilon_1(1 + j\delta) = \varepsilon_1\delta \, \sqrt{1 + \delta^2}$$

since the phase angle is $\tan^{-1}\delta$ and, on account of its smallness, is equal to δ radians. Hence, for horizontal polarization, on account of $\sqrt{1 + \delta^2}$ being practically equal to unity, we have $\varepsilon_r = \varepsilon_1\delta$. But according to the above derivations, we have for a half-wave sender antenna $\varepsilon_1 = 6.85 \, \sqrt{P}/d$ and, therefore,

$$\varepsilon_r = \frac{6.85\delta \, \sqrt{P}}{d} = 86.1 \, \frac{h_t h_r \, \sqrt{P}}{\lambda d^2} \tag{88}$$

The electric field intensity $\mathcal{E}_r$ at the receiver R is in volts per meter, and the respective heights h_t and h_r, as well as the operating wave length λ and distance d, are in meters. Since Eq. (88) was derived for horizontally polarized waves, it is assumed that the transmitter dipole or half-wave rod is placed horizontally. Theoretically, a similar horizontal dipole facing broadside to the transmitter half-wave rod should give maximum reception effects and give a field intensity in accordance with Eq. (88). Since in FM transmitters turnstiles are usually employed, the field intensity received is $G\mathcal{E}_r$ where G denotes the gain produced by the transmitter antenna over the field radiated by a single horizontal half-wave dipole.

Since d meters are equivalent to $d/1{,}609$ miles, h meters equal to $3.281h$ ft, $\mathcal{E}$ volts$/m = 10^6 \mathcal{E}\mu$ volts$/m$, and λ meters equivalent to $(300 \text{ m/sec})/(F \text{ Mc/sec})$, we have the comparison formulas

$$\mathcal{E}_r^{\mu v/m} = \begin{cases} 0.0103 \ \dfrac{h_t h_r F \ \sqrt{P}}{d^2} & \text{for FM frequency allocations} \\[3mm] \dfrac{4{,}257 \ \sqrt{P}}{d} & \text{for customary standard broadcast allocations} \end{cases} \qquad (89)$$

In each case half-wave radiators are used, the radiated power P is in watts, the respective heights h_t and h_r in feet, the distance d in miles, and the carrier frequency F in megacycles. It should be understood that these formulas have nothing to do with the *type* of modulation or type of signal current, except that the upper formula applies to the carrier-frequency range used for the FM frequency allocations mentioned at the beginning of this section. A television signal, or any AM signal using frequencies F of this range (around 50 Mc), gives field intensities at R in accordance with the upper formula; for the standard broadcast frequencies, the lower formula holds. What is of importance is the fact that for the FM range of carrier frequencies the field intensity decreases with the *square* of the distance, instead of only inversely with the distance. Generally, we can write the lower formula as $k \ \sqrt{P}/d$, if the ground absorption is not taken into account. The factor k depends partly on the effective height h_e of the antenna system. If this expression is compared with $k_1 F \ \sqrt{P}/d^2$ which represents the upper formula of Eq. (89), we see that here k_1 depends on the *actual* elevations h_t and h_r above the tangential plane through the point G of reflection (Fig. 38). The field intensity is also proportional to the carrier frequency F, which indicates an advantage for the higher carrier-frequency allocations in the FM range. For the standard broadcast frequency assignments, the carrier frequency, even though not seen in the lower expression of Eq. (89), is indirectly effective on the value of ε_r. For daytime reception we have to deal mostly with the ground wave for which the

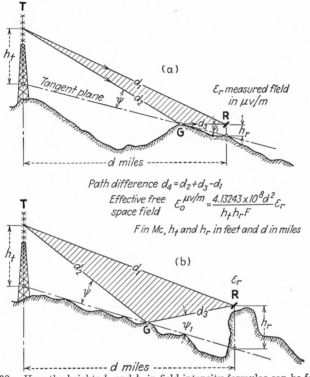

FIG. 38.—How the heights h_t and h_r in field-intensity formulas can be found.

Sommerfeldian numerical distance plays a part. This numerical distance is effective in determining the attenuation or absorption factor by which ε_r is to be multiplied. This factor has smaller values for the higher carrier frequencies in the standard broadcast range. Hence, the very *opposite* happens in this range as far as the variation of propagation with the carrier frequency F is concerned.

The upper formula of Eq. (89) holds very well for horizontally polarized waves, even applying also to vertically polarized waves for small grazing angles if the point of reflection does not happen to be located on a fairly good conducting surface such as, for instance, ocean water. For such a surface at the point of reflection, the ground is no longer dielectrically transparent, *i.e.*, free of losses, and the reflected wave is returned not only with most any phase angle instead of with a phase reversal, but also with a greatly diminished amplitude. For all such cases we can write down expressions that can be used for computations by means of Eqs. (85), (86), and (87). We then have, since $p^2 = \sin^2 \psi$ cannot be very large in comparison with customary values of κ_e in Eq. (86), for line-of-sight distances that are large compared with the respective elevations h_t and h_r (as is usually the case when we are several miles from the transmitter station), the approximation $q = \sqrt{\kappa_e - 1}$ and the formulas

$$\mathcal{E}_r = \begin{cases} \mathcal{E}_1 \left(1 + \dfrac{\kappa_e \sin \psi - \sqrt{\kappa_e - 1}}{\kappa_e \sin \psi + \sqrt{\kappa_e - 1}} \epsilon^{-j\delta} \right) & \text{for } \textit{vertically} \text{ polarized waves} \\ \\ \mathcal{E}_1 \left(1 + \dfrac{\sin \psi - \sqrt{\kappa_e - 1}}{\sin \psi + \sqrt{\kappa_e - 1}} \epsilon^{-j\delta} \right) & \text{for } \textit{horizontally} \text{ polarized waves} \end{cases} \qquad (90)$$

for $\delta = 4\pi h_t h_r / (\lambda d)$ where h_t, h_r, λ, and d must be expressed in the same dimensions. Hence, we may again expect higher resultant field intensities for horizontal polarization. According to Fig. 36 $\sin \psi = (h_t + h_r)/(d_2 + d_3)$ which for d large in comparison to h_t and h_r yields the approximation $\sin \psi = (h_t + h_r)/d \cong \psi$. We have, then, for the respective reflection coefficients

$$\rho \cong \begin{cases} \dfrac{\psi - \sqrt{\kappa_e - 1}}{\psi + \sqrt{\kappa_e - 1}} \cong \dfrac{2(h_t + h_r)}{d \sqrt{\kappa_e - 1}} - 1 = \rho_h & \text{horizontal} \\ \\ \dfrac{\psi \kappa_e - \sqrt{\kappa_e - 1}}{\psi \kappa_e + \sqrt{\kappa_e - 1}} \cong \dfrac{2\kappa_e(h_t + h_r)}{d \sqrt{\kappa_e - 1}} - 1 = \rho_v & \text{vertical} \end{cases} \qquad (91)$$

Therefore, for horizontal polarization

$$\mathcal{E}_r \cong \mathcal{E}_1 \left\{ 1 + \left[\frac{2(h_t + h_r)}{d \sqrt{\kappa_e - 1}} - 1 \right] \epsilon^{-j\delta} \right\} \qquad (92)$$

and for vertical polarization

$$\mathcal{E}_r \cong \mathcal{E}_1 \left\{ 1 + \left[\frac{2\kappa_e(h_t + h_r)}{d \sqrt{\kappa_e - 1}} \right] \epsilon^{-j\delta} \right\} \qquad (93)$$

These formulas can be readily evaluated in numerical cases.

As to the formulas given, note that we have to use the heights h_t and h_r, which are expressed in feet in Eq. (89). Generally, we are confronted with wave propagation paths as indicated in Fig. 37. As far as the line-of-sight distance d_1 of the direct path and the two propagation portions d_2 and d_3 of the indirect transmission path are concerned, we have exactly the same triangulation as in Fig. 36, where plane earth was assumed. The only difference is that the tangential plane represented by the line T_1GR_1 in Fig. 37 is substituted for the plane ground with only point G in the actual ground. Even though the normal primary service radius is not great for such high carrier frequencies as are used for FM, we still should not neglect the curvature of the earth. We should also realize that we have a certain amount of electromagnetic refraction in the earth's atmosphere close to ground for such short waves. This refraction is usually taken into account by still taking the propagation paths straight, but assuming an equivalent radius of the earth which is about 33 per cent larger than the actual radius.

With this in mind we see that we have actually only three distances that we know in Fig. 37: the height TT_2, the height RR_2, and the curved distance T_2GR_2. At first we know nothing about the exact location of the earth point G in the hypothetical reference plane indicated by T_1GR_1. The distance TT_1 is then the distance from the hypothetical reference ground plane at the transmitter to the mid-point of the actual transmitter antenna structure. For a simple horizontal half-wave antenna it would be the distance from the ground plane to the rod antenna. For a vertical dipole it would be the distance from the ground plane to the mid-point of the rod antenna. For a five-bay turnstile it would be the distance from the ground plane to the plane of the third bay. It does not matter whether it is the third bay from the top or from the bottom of the turnstile, since with an odd number of bays it will be always the same plane, as in this case it is always the third bay plane. For an even number of bays, say six, the point T is $3\frac{1}{2}$ bay planes up from the bottom of the turnstile or $3\frac{1}{2}$ bay planes down from the top.

In Eq. (89) and the other corresponding Eqs. (92) and (93), we require the heights h_t and h_r of Fig. 37. Hence, we have to find first the point G. This is readily done since the angle of incidence ψ must be equal to the angle of reflection ψ and points

T and R are known. When, as is usually the case, the path difference d_4 is smaller than one-sixth of the operating wave length, we have, for the respective dimensions used in Eq. (89), for the path delay due to d_4 a value $\delta = h_t h_r F/d \leq 433 \times 10^3$. From the distances GT_2 and GR_2 in miles, we find the heights $T_1 T_2$ and $R_1 R_2$ in feet from the relations $T_1 T_2 = 0.5 GT_2^2$ and $R_1 R_2 = 0.5 GR_2^2$. These formulas account for the curvature of the earth's surface and for the small downward atmospheric refraction, which causes a slightly longer propagation path than indicated by the line-of-sight distance. Hence, the required heights h_t and h_r can be computed from the formulas

$$\left. \begin{array}{l} h_t = TT_2 - 0.5 GT_2^2 \\ h_r = RR_2 - 0.5 GR_2^2 \end{array} \right\} \tag{94}$$

where h_t, h_r, TT_2, and RR_2 are in feet and GT_2 and GR_2 are in miles.

Equations (89), (90), (92), and (93) assume ideal unobstructed wave propagation conditions; *i.e.*, only the one reflection at the ground point G occurs. For this reason the FCC requires that the values of the free-space field intensity ε_0 of Fig. 38 be found from computations based on actual measurements of the effective field intensity at a distance of several miles from the transmitter in different directions and within the line-of-sight distance. The procedure, as well as the formula in this figure, holds *only* for waves having *horizontal* polarization where ψ is a small angle (almost grazing angle of incidence). This procedure would not be reliable for the case of vertically polarized waves.

It should be realized that for hilly ground contours in certain directions of the transmitter T toward a reception point R, there may be several ground points where electromagnetic reflections toward R are possible. It is, however, the path triangle for which the path difference d_4 has a minimum value that counts, since this minimum path will cause the largest effective field intensity ε_r at the reception location R. The stipulation of a minimum value for d_4 for given locations T and R will also result in the smallest product value of $h_t h_r$. In Fig. 38 two cases are indicated using a five-bay turnstile transmitter aerial in order to produce, at least theoretically, a horizontal circular radiation pattern in the equatorial plane through the third bay or crossed dipoles. Figure 38a then depicts the most common arrangement where the reception point R, with a resultant field intensity ε_r, is so located that h_r

is essentially equal to the true elevation of the receiving horizontal dipole above ground.   The dipole is perpendicular to the TR direction.   In Fig. 38b it will be noted that the most suitable transmission path triangle requires at the receiver location R a height h_r which is *many times larger* than the actual elevation of the receiving dipole above ground.   The ground elevations above normal sea level are drawn with an exaggerated elevation scale in these figures, which means that the line-of-sight distance d_1 is drawn way out of proportion and altogether too small with respect to the elevation scale.   For this reason the angles ψ and ψ_1 cannot always be shown as equal for such exaggerated elevation scales.   The paths d_2 and d_3 should, therefore, be drawn in such a manner that the respective heights h_t and h_r come out proportional to their horizontal distances from the point G where the ground reflection takes place.   In this arrangement h_t and h_r are measured vertically rather than perpendicularly to ground, as in Fig. 37.

Figure 39 is presented here with the kind permission of the engineering department of the FCC and is helpful in computing field intensity contours.   For these curves, the power P is in kilowatts, G expresses the transmitter antenna field gain, and ε denotes the desired field intensity in microvolts per meter.   For example, the field intensity ε has a value of 50 for the 50 μv/m contour.   The quantity h stands for the transmitter antenna height h_t in feet, and $\tau = 50hG \sqrt{P}/\varepsilon$.   With respect to field gain, reference is made to page 149.   In connection with Fig. 39 we compute first the value of τ from the inscribed formula.   Then, from Fig. 39 we find the distance d in miles for the calculated value of τ, from the point of intersection of a vertical with the appropriate power curve.

Suppose we have a 30-ft receiving antenna and a transmitting antenna height of 750 ft and want to determine the distance in miles to the 50 μv/m contour for an FM station in the 42- to 50-Mc band.   Suppose that the antenna power is 500 watts, and the antenna array is such that we have a field gain of 2.   We must, on account of the square-root law of the upper relation of Eq. (89), multiply the true antenna power of 500 watts by 2^2 in order to obtain the effective power that causes ε.   We obtain $4 \times 500 = 2{,}000$, which means that the effective value of $P = 2$kw.   The distance to the 50 μv/m contour is found by estimating in Fig. 39 the 750-ft curve.   It is halfway between the 500-ft and the 1,000-ft curves. We then find the intersection of the horizontal line through the 750-ft ordinate with the 2-kw 45-deg line belonging to the 50 μv/m contour. We proceed then vertically downward

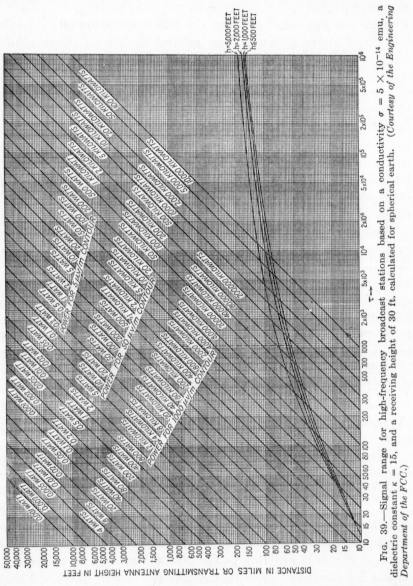

Fig. 39.—Signal range for high-frequency broadcast stations based on a conductivity $\sigma = 5 \times 10^{-14}$ emu, a dielectric constant $\kappa = 15$, and a receiving height of 30 ft. calculated for spherical earth. (*Courtesy of the Engineering Department of the FCC.*)

in order to find the intersection with the 750-ft curve. The height of this intersection point read off on the distance scale then gives the range in miles and is in this particular case equal to 54.5 miles. If this procedure is reversed, Fig. 39 can be used for finding the power required for a given antenna height in order to cover a certain distance with a 50 μv/m level. It will be noted that these curves also enable us to make calculations for the 1,000 μv/m as well as for the 5 μv/m contours.

Moreover, with respect to the upper field intensity formula of Eq. (89), we have to remember that it is based on a half-wave dipole transmitter antenna. However, like the above, it is directly applicable to other antenna arrays when the field gain is known. Some manufacturers give the field gain and others give the power gain for their antennas. If the field gain is given, the factor is to be squared and multiplied by the true power value in order to obtain the effective value for P to be used under the square-root sign. If the power gain is given, the factor is to be directly multiplied by the true power rating in order to obtain the value for P to be used under the square-root sign. H. H. Beverage and M. G. Crosby[1] have extended the radiation formula in the ultrahigh-frequency range to distances beyond the horizon. The distance[2] d_h to the horizon in miles for the heights h_t and h_r in feet is given by the formula

$$d_h = 1.22(\sqrt{h_t} + \sqrt{h_r}) \quad \text{miles} \tag{95}$$

The upper formula of Eq. (89) is then

$$\varepsilon = 0.0103 \frac{h_t h_r d_h^{q-2} F \sqrt{P}}{d^q} \quad \text{uv/m} \tag{96}$$

where d is the distance in miles from transmitter antenna located h_t ft above the tangential plane to the receiver antenna of height h_r ft with respect to the tangential plane. The quantity d_h is the distance in miles from transmitter to the horizon, F is the carrier frequency in megacycles, and P is the effective wattage; i.e., the actual power in the antenna times the antenna power gain over one half-wave dipole. For a half-wave antenna at the transmitter, P will be equal to the true antenna power. If the distance d to the receiving antenna is smaller than the distance d_h to the horizon, then the exponent q is equal to 2 and the semiempirical formula (96) degenerates into Eq. (89). For present-day FM frequency allocations, we have q equal to about 3.5. This value is the outcome of experimental determinations.

[1] Beverage, H. H., *RCA Rev.*, **1**, January, 1937. Crosby, M. G., *RCA Rev.*, **4**, 349, 1940.

[2] For other details, consult "Phenomena in High-frequency Systems," p. 362.

CHAPTER II

AUXILIARY APPARATUS EMPLOYED IN FM SYSTEMS

Since frequency modulation is based on variations along the time axis of a current wave, we need not only devices for producing such effects but also devices for extracting signals at the receiver end. We also have to use apparatus for removing undesirable AM effects, which may be inherent to certain methods of producing FM or may be due to interference. As complicated as the production of an FM current may seem, it can be done at low power rating, *i.e.*, with tubes that are used in receiver engineering. Frequency multiplication is accomplished after the primary or "master" FM has been brought about and the final stages involve mere step-ups in power.

It should be realized that amplification of power in FM systems can be done efficiently with ordinary power amplifiers since the current level remains constant. This is a great inherent advantage with this type of modulation as compared with amplitude modulation.

26. Balanced Modulators.—Balanced modulators can be used for producing the amplitude modulation product, *i.e.*, the completely modulated portion of a carrier current. It is, then, the portion b in Eq. (2). The portion a, which is of carrier frequency F, is automatically suppressed.

The reason for suppressing the remaining unmodulated carrier component is that the modulation product can then be shifted in phase and, as is shown in Fig. 3, can be added geometrically with the a component in order to produce another type of modulation. We have then generally PM + AM.

One way of removing the carrier-frequency component of an AM wave is by "bucking" out the carrier component at the output side of an amplitude modulator. This is done by means of an induced voltage, which causes a current flow $(-)I_m \sin \Omega t$ in opposite direction to the component $a = (+)I_m \sin \Omega t$. This is comparatively easy to do since the a component has the original I_m level for any degree of AM and is of pure sine shape.

150

Superior methods for the elimination of the carrier component are the bridge and differential methods, since they are based on balance and will inherently cancel out the carrier-frequency component. A modified Wheatstone bridge circuit can be used. One branch of the bridge forms a series inductance-capacitance combination and is tuned to the carrier frequency F. The ohmic resistances of the other three branches are made equal to the effective resistance of the tuned branch. Hence, if the output

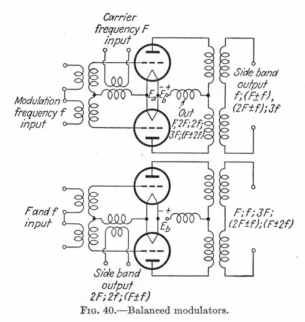

FIG. 40.—Balanced modulators.

voltage of an amplitude modulator is applied to any two diagonal bridge points, a load connected to the other two bridge points can experience only currents that are not of the frequency F for which the bridge is balanced.

Much more convenient are balanced tube circuits, such as are shown in Fig. 40. These circuits, well known in the art, are self-explanatory. The side-band output terminals are marked in this figure. It is the upper network that is of greatest use, since the signal voltage and the carrier voltage are applied through *separate* transformers and in such a way that no power transfer is possible between the carrier-frequency and the signal-frequency sources. For the upper network the signal voltage $e_m \cos \omega t$ acts in push-pull on the two grids while the carrier voltage $E_m \sin \Omega t$

acts in equal pull on these grids. Hence, when the voltage $E_m \sin \Omega t + e_m \cos \omega t$ is effective on one grid, we have a voltage $E_m \sin \Omega t - e_m \cos \omega t$ acting on the other grid, say on the lower one. The upper grid experiences, therefore, the amplitude effect of $E_m(1 + K \cos \omega t)$ where $K = e_m/E_m$ and the lower grid experiences the amplitude effect $E_m(1 - K \cos \omega t)$. The current variation in the upper tube is, therefore,

$$I_m \sin \Omega t + 0.5 K I_m [\sin (\Omega + \omega)t + \sin (\Omega - \omega)t];$$

for the lower tube we have

$$I_m \sin \Omega t - 0.5 K I_m [\sin (\Omega + \omega)t + \sin (\Omega - \omega)t].$$

But as far as the secondaries of the respective plate transformers are concerned, these current variations act in opposition and we have the effects

$$+I_m \sin \Omega t + 0.5 K I_m \sin (\Omega + \omega)t + 0.5 K I_m \sin (\Omega - \omega)t$$
$$-I_m \sin \Omega t + 0.5 K I_m \sin (\Omega + \omega)t + 0.5 K I_m \sin (\Omega - \omega)t$$

which, added together, show that $K I_m[\sin (\Omega + \omega)t + \sin (\Omega - \omega)t]$ remains. $(2K I_m \cos \omega t) \sin \Omega t$, the corresponding modulation product, is the *only* component that is effective in the output current. This modulation product has *twice* the amplitude value of the corresponding product in Eq. (2). This should not matter since this amplitude difference is due only to a constant of proportionality like the fixed mutual inductances that are instrumental in causing the output current of the modulation product in the secondaries of the plate transformers.

In FM systems we use, besides, balanced transformers, which cause balanced reactance injections as far as the steady reactance component is concerned. This is discussed in the sections dealing with reactance modulators.

27. Ring Modulators.—Ring modulators are important since they are used in connection with frequency division (consult pages 154, 242). Figure 41a shows a ring modulator, which is likewise a balanced modulator and produces only the modulation product; *i.e.*, it suppresses the carrier-frequency component. Since contact rectifiers are often used for the rectifiers 1, 2, 3, and 4 in Fig. 41a, such as the well-known cuprox dry-disk rectifier, the suitable type depending on the frequency range, there is also indicated in Fig. 41b the rectifier bridge circuit employed in alternating-current instruments in order to clear up any confusion that may arise about the differences between these two circuits. In the amplitude modulator network of Fig. 41a, the rectifiers are connected all in *direct series*, so to speak, "around a ring." A direct-current flow is then possible from A to C to B to D and back to A. In the rectifier connection of Fig. 41b, the polarity of the rectifiers 1 and 2 must be such that direct-current flow toward point C is possible, just as rectifiers 3 and 4 must also permit the return flow of the current $I_1 + I_2$. Hence, when an

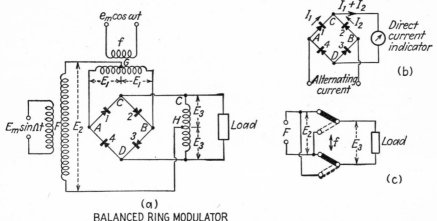

(a)
BALANCED RING MODULATOR
Fig. 41.—Connection and action of the ring modulator.

alternating voltage is applied to points A and B, a direct-current meter will experience a corresponding unidirectional deflection.

It is, of course, the ring modulator that concerns us. The connections of Fig. 41a bring about AM in the load branch if a carrier voltage $E_m \sin (6.28F)t$ and a signal voltage $e_m \sin (6.28f)t$ are applied as indicated. What happens in case of an abrupt or "keying-fashion" modulation instead of a smooth AM can be readily understood from Fig. 41c. Here a switch is used in place of the "electric-bridge" switch effective in Fig. 41a. Suppose that in Fig. 41c the reversing switch reverses the polarity of the applied voltage E_2 of carrier frequency F many times, say f times per second; then the voltage E_3, which is effective across the load, will key or modulate the current coming from the F source. Exactly the same thing will happen in Fig. 41a except that the keying is not abrupt but is according to the $e_m \cos \omega t$ law. During the positive half cycle of the signal current of frequency f, the bridge point A will be positive with respect to the bridge point B and the voltage $2E_1$ produces a direct-current flow in accordance with the time function $\cos \omega t$. During such a current flow, G is electrically connected with C so that the carrier-frequency source of voltage E_2 applies a voltage E_3 across C and H. When ωt is 90, 270, etc., deg, then $2E_1$ is zero and bridge points A and B are equipotential; hence, no carrier current can flow toward the load. But, when the voltage $2E_1$ passes through its negative cycle, the rectifiers 3 and 4 permit a direct-current flow since bridge point B is now positive with respect to bridge point A. Therefore, the

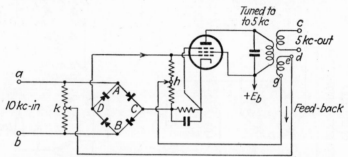

FIG. 42.—Frequency division by regenerative modulation.

carrier voltage E_2 is effective again and causes the corresponding voltage E_3 across H and D but with reversed polarity. Hence, the current of signal frequency f modulates the carrier current of frequency F with the carrier component of frequency F suppressed.

28. Frequency Division by Regenerative Modulation.—Figure 42 shows an application of a ring modulator for dividing the carrier frequency by means of regenerative modulation. As far as the modulation action is concerned, it is exactly the same as in Fig. 41a except that the current of frequency f is the outcome of the current of frequency F and bears a subharmonic relation to the F current. Suppose that a 10-kc voltage is applied across terminals a and b. The plate circuit of the tube is tuned to half the frequency for this particular numerical case, $i.e.$, to 5 kc. This 5-kc output is fed back by means of the secondary voltage produced across e and g to points k and h, thus causing a keying or modulation action which is at the same time in half-frequency step with the current to be modulated. The resulting output across terminals c and d is, therefore, a current of frequency which is only 5 kc.

Figure 43 shows a case where by means of two ring modulators, I and II, and only one tube, successive frequency halving is accomplished; *i.e.*, a final frequency equal to one-fourth of the original carrier frequency is obtained. Suppose a 10-kc voltage is again applied to the ring modulator I and the upper output tank is tuned to half the frequency value, *i.e.*, to 5 kc. A portion of the tank energy is fed back toward the other diagonal bridge point of the ring modulator I in order to cause modulation. The other

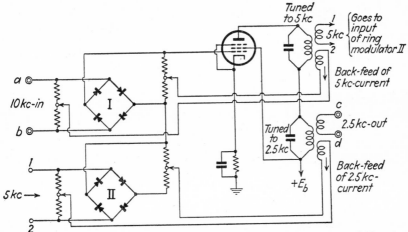

Fig. 43.—Cascaded frequency division employing two-ring modulators I and II and one and the same tube for regenerative modulation.

secondary of the 5-kc tank applies its terminal voltage across 1 and 2 to ring modulator II. The corresponding lower tank of the external plate circuit is tuned to 2.5 kc and a portion of the tank energy is fed back to the other diagonal bridge points in order to cause electric keying. Hence, at the output *c-d* a 2.5-kc current is finally obtained.

29. Reactance Tubes.—Reactance tubes have the object of injecting reactances into associated networks. If the associated network is an ordinary tube oscillator whose frequency is not stabilized, *i.e.*, "not stiff," then the reflected reactance will change the frequency of the oscillations that are generated. But if the frequency is stabilized, *i.e.*, "F is stiff," as in a piezo oscillator or in a carrier-frequency amplifier without sufficient back action, then the injected reactance will cause a corresponding phase shift. Hence, when the injected reactance swings or varies, FM will be caused in the former case and PM in the latter case.

The case of FM is of importance since some commercial FM transmitters are based on such modulators and considerable frequency deviations can be caused *directly* by this method.   Figure 44a shows a reactance or quadrature tube T_m which, with its plate load R_1C_1, causes reactance fluctuations in the oscillator frequency-determining CL branch, which is the plate load of the

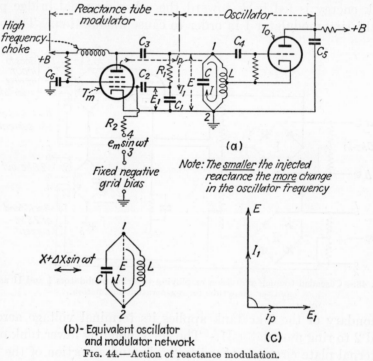

Fig. 44.—Action of reactance modulation.

oscillator tube T_0.   From the equivalent network of Fig. 44b we note that a reactance $X + \Delta X \sin \omega t$ is generally injected across terminals 1 and 2 of the frequency-determining network of the actual oscillator.   The portion X represents the steady or fixed reactance and the portion $\Delta X \sin \omega t$ represents the variable reactance component applied to 1-2.   It is the variable component $\Delta X \sin \omega t$ that brings about FM.   The fixed component X is also used in FM systems, but for stabilizing the center frequency of the master oscillator.   The fixed reactance X is affected by the fixed negative-grid bias of the modulator tube T_m.   This bias determines about which reference mutual conductance value the variations in the dynamic mutual conductance due to the signal voltage $e_m \sin \omega t$ take place.

Now any tube oscillator sustains oscillations on account of the energy fed back from the plate circuit into the grid circuit, which, in turn, due to the amplification property of the tube, causes the maintenance of the plate current variation. Hence, the feedback into the grid branch and the subsequent "through-grip" within the tube due to its grid-into-plate actions must be such that the plate current oscillations remain fixed not only in amplitude but also in phase. The latter is often overlooked since for amplitude modulation the phase does not matter and for customary a-f amplifications we have no perceptions as far as our ear is concerned when phase distortion occurs. The amplitude balance in an oscillator satisfies the energy balance requirement and the second condition satisfies the phase balance requirement. If, for instance, the energy balance requirement is not met, we should experience some sort of AM. What would occur in one case is that for subsequent grid-into-plate actions more variable plate current would be produced. Then the amplitude of the plate current would keep growing until the plate-current saturation limits the action, or until the increase in circuit losses just prevents a further amplitude growth. For the other case, if the energy due to the internal "through-grip" of the tube is not sufficient to supply the circuit losses, successive amplitudes in the plate-current variations will decrease until the oscillation stops altogether. Neither of these cases concerns us here. The only condition of interest, namely, that for growing oscillations, on account of ultimate energy balance or on account of plate-current saturation, whichever might be the case, would cause sustained oscillations in next to no time. But the inphase requirement is important since it can be used for causing useful PM as well as useful FM. Thus if, for instance, the subsequent plate-current variations during a certain period of time are advanced in phase with respect to the plate-current variations that are affecting the grid potential of the oscillator tube by feedback action, then the frequency of oscillation cannot remain constant since each following cycle speeds up somewhat more than the preceding cycle. In the same way, if the subsequent plate-current variations are lagging in phase, then the corresponding oscillation frequency must gradually drift to lower values. It is this undesirable feature in any ordinary tube oscillator which is made use of in *reactance modulators*. It is generally not done by a feedback within the oscillator, but in virtue of an injected out-of-phase current coming from an associated network. The associated network is known as the output branch of a reactance tube.

In Fig. 44a condensers C_3 and C_4 are coupling elements and condensers C_2, C_5, and C_6 are by-pass or isolation condensers. They can have, therefore, no frequency effect as long as their magnitudes are properly chosen. Condenser C_4 acts as a feedback coupling condenser toward the oscillator grid; condenser C_2 acts as a forward coupling condenser toward the control grid of the modulator tube T_m. The modulation action that takes place in the circuits of Fig. 44 is, then, as follows:

The tank voltage E across points 1 and 2 causes a corresponding current flow in the series combination of resistance R_1 and capacitance C_1. If R_1 is chosen at least five times the value of $1/6.28FC_1$, then this current can be considered as essentially in phase with the driving tank voltage E. Hence, I_1 is vertical in Fig. 44c as is vector E. The voltage E_1 across condenser C_1 caused by this current I_1, then lags I_1 by 90 time degrees and is, therefore, in quadrature. Hence, it is drawn to the right in the vector diagram of Fig. 44c. Essentially this voltage E_1 is applied to the control grid of the modulator tube T_m. It "triggers off" a corresponding plate current variation i_p, which essentially flows only to points 1 and 2 and back toward the cathode of tube T_m, since R_1 is high in comparison to the multiple reactance across points 1 and 2. Theoretically, this reactance would be infinite if parallel resonance could take place with no resistance effects. But in practice the parallel combination of C and L acts like an ohmic resistance which is much smaller than the R_1 value and very much smaller than the impedance offered by both R_1 and C_1. The i_p current is in phase with the voltage E_1 and causes, therefore, a superimposed current in the plate tank of tube T_0 which lags 90 deg behind the original tank current. This is the reason why for a 90-deg out-of-phase action, T_m can also be called a quadrature tube. Since we deal with a lagging current, the reactance across points 1 and 2 can no longer be infinite unless something happens. If I is the circulating tank current, what occurs is that the resultant current $I + i_p$ will change its original carrier frequency F_0 to another value until the total reactance across points 1 and 2 is again infinite. But this means that in equivalence a corresponding reactance X has been injected in parallel with both the tank condenser C and the tank inductance L.

This is exactly what happens when terminals 3-4 are shorted. Since the mutual conductance $g_m = \partial i_p / \partial E_1$, we note that the magnitude of the positive reactance X, which is injected across points 1 and 2, depends directly on the mutual conductance of the operating point on the modulator tube characteristic. Hence, the value of X can be controlled by varying the negative grid bias of the modulator tube. Therefore, when a variable signal voltage $e_m \sin \omega t$ acts across terminals 3 and 4, the corresponding impressed reactance across terminals 1 and 2 is $X_t = X + \Delta X \sin \omega t$ at any instant of time. If the voltage E_1 had been taken off across the resistance R_1 instead of across C_1 and $1/(6.28FC_1) \geqq 5R_1$, then the i_p current reflected back into the oscillator tank circuit would have been a leading current. Hence, a negative reactance would have been impressed across terminals 1 and 2; *i.e.*, a carrier-frequency increase would result as far as the steady component is concerned.

The action just discussed finds two important applications in FM systems. One is that we have a modulator that gives a means for translating signal voltages directly into corresponding carrier-frequency variations. The other application has to do with the steady component X in the value of X_t. This component gives a means for correcting any slow frequency drifts in the center frequency F by applying an appropriate grid bias to the modulator tube. This is done in the RCA as well as in the General Electric Company's FM transmitters (consult pages 128 and 236), where a frequency discriminator is used for translating any slow frequency drifts into either positive or negative voltages when the correct center frequency F is either exceeded or fallen short of. These output voltages are then made to act in proper polarity in series with the fixed grid bias of the reactance tube modulator. This modulator brings about FM and the reactance tube will then automatically correct the desired center frequency F by reflecting the proper reactance into the tank circuit of the master oscillator, owing to the grid bias change.

It should also be understood that the reactance tube does not necessarily have to be a quadrature tube in order to cause FM. By quadrature tube is meant a modulator tube that injects pure reactances due to plate currents i_p that are exactly 90 deg out of phase with the driving tank voltage E. Any reflected current i_p that is out of phase by an angle with respect to the phase of the tank voltage E will impress an impedance $Z = R \pm X$ across

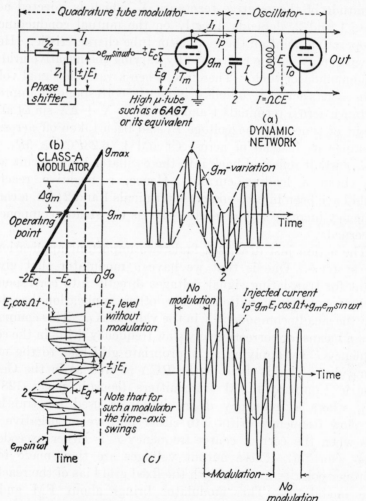

Fig. 45.—Performance in a class A frequency modulator.

terminals 1 and 2 of Fig. 44, and will cause FM. This is, however, not desirable since the resistance component is apt to cause appreciable dissymmetry with respect to the center-frequency position when large variations are involved as in wide-band FM.

What occurs in the general case can be readily understood from Fig. 45a, where only the dynamic network without any steady supply voltages is shown. We note from this figure that the reactance tube[1] T_m is dynamically directly across the oscillator tank circuit and, therefore, is also in multiple with the oscillator tube T_0. By tube is meant, in each case, the plate-to-cathode path of the particular tube. Hence, for a lumped dynamic tube voltage $e_l = e_p - \mu e_g$ we have the corresponding dynamic plate current $i_p = e_l/r_p$, where μ and r_p denote the dynamic amplification factor and the internal dynamic tube resistance, respectively, of the modulator tube T_m. It is really an internal tube *impedance* in this case instead of a dynamic tube resistance since e_p/i_p is, in the general case, an impedance with an active and a reactive component. Substituting m for e_g/e_p, we have

$$i_p = e_p \left(\frac{1}{r_p} - \frac{m\mu}{r_p} \right) = Y e_p$$

where $Y = i_p/e_p$ is the admittance. It must also be complex and when expanded is

$$Y = \frac{1}{r_p} (1 - m\mu \cos \varphi) - j \frac{m\mu}{r_p} \sin \varphi = A - jB \qquad (97)$$

The real part vanishes for $\cos \varphi = 1/(m\mu)$. Hence, generally the plate-to-cathode path of the modulator tube T_m acts as though an admittance of amplitude value $\sqrt{A^2 + B^2}$ with a phase $\tan^{-1}(-B/A)$ were connected across the tank circuit of the oscillator. The corresponding complex impedance in shunt with the tank impedance determines the effective oscillator frequency F_t, since to circulating tank currents the total reactance must vanish in case of natural tube oscillations. When the real term A vanishes, we have only a reactance

$$\Delta X = \frac{jr_p}{m\mu \sin \varphi} \qquad (98)$$

injected in the frequency-determining branch of the oscillator circuit.

Generally, it may be said that for larger L/C ratios in the tank circuit, the ΔX effect and the corresponding frequency deviation ΔF in the center frequency F will be larger, but at the expense of

---

[1] For the general case we deal with an impedance tube rather than with a quadrature tube or a reactance tube since i_p is no longer 90 deg behind or ahead of the driving tank voltage E.

less stable tube oscillations since for high L/C ratios the frequency stability is poorer. Equation (98) shows that ΔX is directly proportional to the dynamic plate resistance of the modulator tube T_m. Since low values of ΔX in parallel with the tank reactance across terminals 1 and 2 give more ΔF deviation, a power reactance tube is desirable since a power tube has a low dynamic plate resistance.

30. Design Formulas and Useful Quadrature Tube Modulators. In Sec. 29 we learned that either a leading or a lagging current may be superimposed on the normal tank current. The tank circuit in Fig. 44a consists of a condenser in parallel with an inductance. It is correct to assume that, in equivalence, a superimposed current, due to the action of a reactance tube modulator that is 90 deg leading with respect to the original tank voltage E, causes more condenser current since the superimposed current is in phase with the original condenser current. Hence, the superimposed current must cause an equivalent increase ΔC in the value of the normal capacitance C. This will then account for the corresponding ΔF decrease and the new oscillation frequency F. In the same way, a 90-deg lagging i_p current is in phase with the normal current through the inductance L of the tank. This must cause an equivalent decrease ΔL in the normal value of L. This will then account for the increase in the oscillation frequency. It can also be assumed that a 90-deg lagging i_p current with respect to the normal tank voltage E, since the current is in antiphase with the normal C current, must cause a decrease ΔC in C. Both assumptions are correct as long as they satisfy the actual frequency relation, which is $6.28(F + \Delta F) = [(L - \Delta L)C]^{-0.5} = [L(C - \Delta C)]^{-0.5}$.

Figure 45a shows the dynamic network of Fig. 44. Figure 45b shows the corresponding ideal linear mutual conductance characteristic with respect to the corresponding grid voltages of the modulator tube T_m. As far as the operating point is concerned, we deal with a class A modulator. The normal tank current is I since the grid exciter current I_1 is small in comparison with I. The fixed grid bias is $-E_c$. When the modulation voltage $e_m \sin \omega t$ is active, the applied carrier voltage of frequency $\Omega/6.28$ is either $+E_1 \cos \Omega t$ or $-E_1 \cos \Omega t$, causing a corresponding plate current variation $+i_p \cos \Omega t$ or $-i_p \cos \Omega t$, depending on whether the injected superimposed i_p current is leading or lagging the normal oscillator voltage E by 90 deg. We have, therefore, for the resultant tank current at any instant

$$I_r = \begin{cases} \Omega CE \sin \Omega t + g_m E_1 \cos \Omega t + g_m e_m \sin \omega t \quad i_p \text{ leading} \\ \Omega CE \sin \Omega t - g_m E_1 \cos \Omega t + g_m e_m \sin \omega t \quad i_p \text{ lagging} \end{cases} \tag{99}$$

where the i_p leads and lags refer to 90 time degrees. From Fig. 45*b* we note that when the signal voltage $e_m \sin \omega t$ is effective, the time axis for the superimposed i_p current "waves up and down" in accordance with variations of the $\sin \omega t$ function with an amplitude of $g_m e_m$. Hence, during the modulation cycle, we have three significant peak values P for the resultant condenser current I_c if i_p is leading E by 90 deg. These peak values are

$$P = \begin{cases} \Omega CE + g_m E_1 & \omega t = 0, 180, 360° \\ = \Omega CE + g_m e_m + g_m E_1 & \omega t = 90° \\ = \Omega CE - g_m e_m + g_m E_1 & \omega t = 270° \end{cases} \tag{100}$$

The amplitude value $p = \Omega CE + g_m E_1$ is *fixed* since it exists without any signal modulation $e_m \sin \omega t$ and we have the three significant cases

$$P = \begin{cases} p & 0, 180, 360 \\ p + g_m e_m & 90 \\ p - g_m e_m & 270 \end{cases} \tag{100a}$$

We have, therefore, a means of computing the order of magnitude of the equivalent reactance which is injected across terminals 1 and 2 in Fig. 45*a* due to the quadrature tube network for the condition when no signal voltage is present, *i.e.*, for $e_m \sin \omega t = 0$.

When E_1 is lagging the small exciting current $I_1 \sin \Omega t$ by an angle of 90 deg, we have the condition of Fig. 44 and the i_p current passing to the oscillator tank must also be lagging by such an angle. Hence, the total peak current through C is no longer ΩCE, but for zero signal voltage ($e_m \sin \omega t = 0$) is

$$I_c = \Omega CE - g_m E_1 = \Omega CE - g_m \frac{I_1}{\Omega C_1} \cong \Omega CE - g_m \frac{E}{\Omega C_1 R_1} \tag{101}$$

since for 90-deg lagging current in Fig. 44 we have, in Fig. 45*a* in the phase shifter, $Z_1 = 1/\Omega C_1$ and $Z_2 = R_1$, where $R_1 \geq 5/\Omega C_1$ so that I_1 is essentially equal to E/R_1. For the normal circulating tank current we have $I = \Omega CE = E/\Omega L$ because the current I is the same in the C as well as in the L branch of the tank. Hence, I leads E by 90 deg in the C branch and I lags E by 90 deg in the L branch. The 90-deg phase lag in the injected i_p current causes in the L branch the effect

$$I_L = \Omega CE + g_m E_1 \cong \Omega CE + g_m \frac{E}{\Omega C_1 R_1} \qquad (102)$$

It does not matter whether we use Eq. (101) or Eq. (102) since each expression accounts for the same injected i_p effect. But in either case we note that the normal branch current is either decreased by the amount $g_m E/\Omega C_1 R_1$ or is increased by this amount. The resultant current in the L branch can also be written as

$$I_L = E\left(\frac{1}{\Omega L} + \frac{g_m}{\Omega C_1 R_1}\right) = \frac{E}{\Omega}\left(\frac{1}{L} + \frac{1}{C_1 R_1/g_m}\right) = \frac{E}{\Omega L_e} \qquad (103)$$

which shows that an inductance $L_i = C_1 R_1/g_m$ is injected in *parallel* with L since the effective inductance L_e is

$$\frac{1}{L_e} = \frac{1}{L} + \frac{1}{C_1 R_1/g_m} \qquad (104)$$

The fixed bias E_c of the modulator tube results in an operating point having a dynamic mutual conductance g_m in mhos. For C_1 in farads and R_1 in ohms, we have for the injected inductance the formula

$$L_i = \frac{C_1 R_1}{g_m} \quad \text{henrys} \qquad (105)$$

For the values $g_m = 5 \times 10^{-3}$ mho, $R_1 = 50{,}000$ ohms, and $C_1 = 2 \times 10^{-12}$ farad, this expression yields $L_i = 2 \times 10^{-5}$ henrys or 20 microhenrys. Since the injected inductance L_i is in multiple with the tank inductance L, the smaller the value of L_i becomes the more it will decrease the effective tank inductance and, therefore, the more it will increase the value of the normal oscillation frequency F_0 which would exist if the reactance tube were removed. From Eq. (104) we find that the effective tank inductance L_e is

$$L_e = \frac{C_1 R_1 L}{C_1 R_1 + g_m L} \qquad (106)$$

and that the operating frequency F is

$$F = \frac{1}{2\pi \sqrt{CL_e}} \tag{107}$$

Hence, the frequency has been changed by the i_p injection which lags the normal tank voltage E by 90 time degrees. We have, therefore, for the case depicted in Fig. 44 no longer a frequency $1/(6.28 \sqrt{CL})$ but the frequency given in Eq. (107).

Equation (105) can also be confirmed if we realize that the superimposed i_p current causes the shunt impedance $Z_i = E/i_p$ across the terminals 1 and 2. Hence, $Z_i = E/g_m E_1$ and since $E_1 \cong E/\Omega C_1 R_1$ because $R_1 \geqq 5/\Omega C_1$, we find

$$Z_i = \Omega \frac{C_1 R_1}{g_m} = \Omega L_i \tag{108}$$

Therefore, L_i has the same value as already found in Eq. (105).

As mentioned before, the i_p current can also be considered as affecting only the C branch of the tank circuit, and we then obtain the difference relation of Eq. (101) instead of the addition relation of Eq. (102). The resultant C current can then be written as

$$I_c = \Omega E \left(C - \frac{g_m}{\Omega^2 C_1 R_1} \right) = \Omega E \left(C - \frac{g_m CL}{C_1 R_1} \right) = \Omega E C_e \tag{109}$$

Hence, the decrease in the value of C is $g_m CL/C_1 R_1$ and must produce the same resultant frequency F as above. Since in this expression we have $C_e = C - C_i$, the value $-C_i$ is the capacitance injected in multiple with the normal capacitance C of the oscillator tank. But $C_i = g_m CL/C_1 R_1 = 1/\Omega^2 L_i$ showing that $\Omega L_i = 1/\Omega C_i$. Therefore, L_i is the inductance injected in parallel with the oscillator tank and is of the same value as in Eq. (105).

Figure 46 shows four different quadrature tube arrangements where diagram (a) has reference to the case just derived. Figure 46b uses a resistance R_1, which is at least five times as large as the inductive reactance ΩL_1 in series with it. Hence, the output current I_1 due to the tank voltage E is essentially in phase with E and grid voltage E_1 must be essentially 90 deg ahead with respect to E. The corresponding plate current i_p is then $i_p = g_m E_1 = g_m j\Omega L_1 I_1 \cong jg_m \Omega L_1 E/R_1$. This means that i_p is in phase with E_1 or 90 deg ahead of the tank voltage E. But the normal tank current is $I = \Omega CE$ and it is likewise leading E by 90 deg. The current in the C branch is, therefore,

$$I_c = j\left(\Omega CE + \frac{g_m \Omega L_1 E}{R_1}\right) = j\Omega\left(C + \frac{g_m L_1}{R_1}\right)E = j\Omega C_e E \quad (110)$$

Hence

$$C_i = \frac{g_m L_1}{R_1} \quad (111)$$

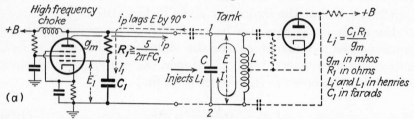

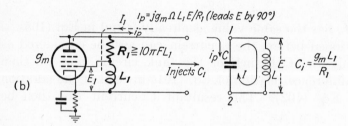

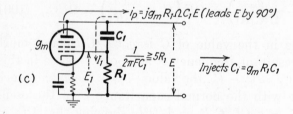

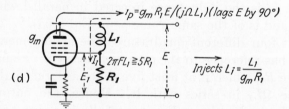

(Modulating $e_m \sin \omega t$ not shown but is in series with grid bias)

FIG. 46.—Quadrature networks.

is the capacitance injected in parallel with C, since C_e is the resultant or effective tank capacitance when the quadrature circuit acts. Also, in this case we can imagine that the injected i_p current flows in the L branch, but is in antiphase with the normal circulating current I in this branch. This is indicated in Fig. 46b. We then have

$$I_L = \frac{E}{j\Omega L} + \frac{j g_m \Omega L_1 E}{R_1} = \frac{E}{j\Omega L} - \frac{E}{j R_1 / g_m \Omega L_1} = \frac{E}{j\Omega}\left(\frac{1}{L} - \frac{1}{L_i}\right) \quad (112)$$

for $1/L_i = \Omega^2 C_i$. Hence, $(-L_i)$ is injected across L, which means that a negative reactance $(-\Omega L_i)$ is injected across the positive reactance ΩL of the normal tank inductance L. A negative reactance is, however, due to a condenser, and since in the last expression of Eq. (112) we have $\Omega L_i = 1/(\Omega C_i)$, we note that again an injected capacitance C_i as in Eq. (111) is obtained. It does not matter, therefore, how we derive the expression for the injected reactance as long as we look out for the sign of the reactance. In Fig. 46c we have a large value of the high-frequency reactance of C_1 with respect to the ohmic resistance R_1. Hence, the current I_1 of frequency F must be leading the tank voltage E by 90 deg. But the grid voltage is now $E_1 = I_1 R_1$ and also must be leading E by 90 deg. Hence, the corresponding injected plate current variation $i_p = g_m I_1 R_1$ must also lead E by 90 deg. But for such a large capacitance reactance in comparison with the R_1 value we have $I_1 \cong j\Omega C_1 E$ and $i_p = j g_m R_1 \Omega C_1 E$. We have a $(+j)$ term in this case and the reactance injection belongs, therefore, to the C branch of the tank. This can also be seen from

$$X_i = \frac{E}{i_p} = \frac{1}{j\Omega g_m R_1 C_1} = \frac{1}{j\Omega C_i} \quad (113)$$

which is the injected reactance across the tank circuit. We have, therefore, a capacitance

$$C_i = g_m R_1 C_1 \quad (114)$$

injected across the normal capacitance C.

For Fig. 46d we have essentially $I_1 = E/j\Omega L_1$. This is a current that lags the tank voltage E by an angle of 90 deg and, therefore, E_1 and i_p likewise are lagging E by such an angle. We have then $i_p = g_m R_1 E/j\Omega L_1$ and in turn an input reactance

$$X_i = \frac{E}{i_p} = j\Omega \frac{L_1}{g_m R_1} = j\Omega L_i \quad (115)$$

The injected inductance is, therefore

$$L_i = \frac{L_1}{g_m R_1} \tag{115a}$$

All cases shown in Fig. 46 have been derived for static reactance injections. Such injections exist only when the signal voltage is zero; *i.e.*, $e_m \sin \omega t$ in Fig. 45 is zero and the corresponding terminals are short-circuited. But Figs. 45*b* and 45*c*, as well as Eqs. (100) and (100*a*), show that for a signal voltage $e_m \sin \omega t$, also acting on the control grid, the i_p current, which is injected in either the C or the L branch of the oscillator tank, has a "wavy" time axis. This means that we have a "wavy" reference axis that varies in accordance with the modulation swing. At instants of time when $\omega t = 0, 180, 360$, etc., deg, we have the static or fixed reactance injections corresponding to the C_i and L_i values of Fig. 46.

Suppose we are dealing in Fig. 45*a* with a phase shifter which causes an injected i_p current which leads E by 90 deg. The voltage on the grid of the modulator tube is then jE_1; *i.e.*, it is a cos Ωt function if the tank voltage E is a sin Ωt function. Since we assume a linear g_m characteristic in Fig. 45*b*, we note that the time axis swings in the i_p current produced by the signal voltage $e_m \sin \omega t$ are no longer $g_m E_1$ but are $g_m E_1 \pm g_m e_m$ for such a condition when maximum values of $e_m \sin \omega t$ prevail. We have, therefore, a peak voltage $E_1 \pm e_m$ on the grid which also accounts for the "wavy" grid voltage time axis. We have seen, that the current injected into the L branch of the tank for a 90-deg phase advance is $g_m E_1$, if E_1 is the h-f voltage affecting the grid without the signal voltage $e_m \sin \omega t$ acting. Since optimum condition obtains when $E_1 = e_m = 0.5E_c$, we see that at 1, as well as at 2 in Fig. 45*b*, the effective grid voltage of the modulator tube T_m is $1.5E_1$ instead of E_1 as for the condition with no $e_m \sin \omega t$ voltage acting. This grid voltage corresponds, then, to the peak conditions 1 and 2 in the corresponding i_p variations since $1.5g_m E_1$ is now active. With no modulation, *i.e.*, when $e_m \sin \omega t = 0$, the effective oscillator frequency F according to Fig. 46*b* is due not only to C and L, but also to $(C + C_i)$, as well as L, and can be computed from

$$F = \frac{1}{2\pi \sqrt{\left(C + \dfrac{g_m L_1}{R_1}\right) L}} \tag{116}$$

where all quantities are in practical units, *i.e.*, in cycles per second, farads, henry, ohms, and mhos. Since our oscillator works at all times in conjunction with the quadrature tube T_m, the frequency F is fixed and the portion $C_i = g_m L_1/R_1$ must be considered as a part of the frequency-determining elements. This is always true for a *single* tube modulator. When the instantaneous frequency deviations were cosine functions, we had, according to Eq. (7), the instantaneous oscillator frequency $F_t = F + \Delta F \cos \omega t$ where $e_m \cos \omega t$ was the modulation stimulus. Hence, the peak swing ΔF in the frequency deviation must be caused by the difference voltage $1.5E_1 - E_1$ or $0.5E_1$ acting on the modulator grid. Therefore, the portion $0.5g_m E_1$ with respect to the normal circulating tank current $I = \Omega C E$ must represent the fractional change of current from zero to maximum deviation. Because $\Delta F/F$ is a very small quantity, even for wide-band FM in case of present-day FM allocations (since, for instance, $F = 44.5$ Mc and ΔF is equal to only 75 kc), we have for $\Omega = 6.28F$, the ratio

$$\frac{\Delta F}{F} \cong 0.5 \; \frac{0.5g_m E_1}{I} = 0.0398 \; \frac{g_m E_1}{CEF}$$

and

$$\Delta F = 0.0398 \; \frac{g_m E_1}{CE} \tag{117}$$

where the quantities are again in cycles per second, mhos, farads, and volts. This formula holds for all cases of quadrature tube modulations, irrespective of whether the injected i_p current is leading or lagging the tank voltage E by 90 deg. The reactance modulator constant of 0.0398, which is the result of $1/8\pi$, is correct only for a linear g_m characteristic corresponding to the peak-to-peak swing $2\Delta F$. If no true linearity exists, this factor will be considerably smaller. Since a frequency modulator, like a frequency demodulator, depends on the peak-to-peak deviation, the total band width w is $2\Delta F$ and we have for g_m in micromhos and C in micromicrofarads, the formulas

$$w = 79.7 \; \frac{g_m E_1}{CE} \quad \text{kc/sec} \left.\rule{0pt}{16pt}\right\}$$
$$\Delta F = 39.83 \; \frac{g_m E_1}{CE} \quad \text{kc/sec} \left.\rule{0pt}{16pt}\right\} \tag{118}$$

The units of the voltages need not be known since we deal only with the ratio E_1/E, which is numerical.

The function of the quadrature tube is to cause directly large ΔF swings around the center frequency F. This can happen only when *small* reactance variations are injected in multiple with the tank of the oscillator. This becomes clear if we realize that for injections of $X_i = \infty$, *i.e.*, reactances that are infinitely large, the tube oscillator would not be affected at all by the quadrature network and would have a frequency of $F = 1/(6.28\sqrt{CL})$ in cycles per second for C in farads and L in henrys. This would, therefore, occur if the ratio $E/i_p = \infty$, *i.e.*, if the injected current $i_p = 0$. Hence, we require relatively large injected current values for i_p which, on account of the relation $i_p = g_m E_g$, means that either E_g or g_m, or both, should be large.

E_g and g_m are the grid voltage and mutual conductance, respectively, of the modulator tube. The value of E_g is practically limited for two reasons. One is that E_g can be increased by increasing the current I_1, which in Fig. 45a passes over the Z_1, Z_2 phase shifter, since this increases the component E_1 of the effective grid voltage E_g. But we must realize that the magnitude of I_1 is limited by the fact that I_1 should be small only in comparison to the useful circulating tank current I, so that the voltage E, which drives I as well as I_1, remains essentially constant. If E did not remain essentially constant, we would also cause superimposed AM. Removing the superimposed AM with an amplitude limiter would be only an apparent remedy since, according to Sec. 12, some of the cross-spectrum modulation energy would be lost. Since the other possibility for increasing E_g consists in increasing the value of g_m, it is important to use a tube that has a high dynamic g_m value. The limitation that exists in this case is that g_m should change linearly with effective grid voltage variations for the entire peak-to-peak frequency swing.

At this point it should be realized that a good tube for such work should show also good power amplification. A mere voltage step-up is not necessarily power amplification, otherwise we could use ordinary transformers. It is the magnitude of the i_p current that determines the effectiveness of the frequency modulation.

Since the T_m tube is a linear amplifier, which must have also g_m linearity with respect to E_g variations, we should realize that in such amplifiers we have $g_m = \mu/r_p$, where the mutual conductance

g_m, the amplification factor μ, and the plate resistance r_p are all dynamic values. Hence,[1] a high g_m value can be obtained if the value of the dynamic amplification factor μ is large compared with the value of the dynamic plate resistance r_p. Customary types of three electrode tubes with cathode, plate, and only one grid would not provide a good modulator design. Customary types of double-grid tubes or tetrodes are better by far, since the grid-voltage–plate-current characteristic can be made much steeper in these tubes. The grid next to the plate, besides causing a large g_m value, has the advantage of making the plate current *independent* of the plate voltage as long as the positive screen-grid voltage is smaller than the positive plate voltage. The tetrode has a further advantage over the triode in that for screen-grid tube operation the plate current depends to a large degree only on the screen-grid voltage. Hence, the screen grid can also be used for impressing the modulation voltage $e_m \sin \omega t$. When operated as a screen-grid amplifier, the back actions from the plate into the control grid branch are also small.

Since the shield or screen-grid tube connection gives a very high value for the dynamic plate resistance r_p, we have to use a tube that combines the features of the space-charge connection in a tetrode and the screen-grid connection in a tetrode, so that a high μ value obtains for comparatively low plate potentials. Such a tube is the well-known pentode tube. A pentagrid tube such as the 6SA7 or its equivalent represents a very good reactance tube. If a power pentode is used as a modulator tube for producing large ΔF excursions in the oscillator frequency F, the dynamic plate resistance r_p of the modulator tube can reach very low values for large positive grid swings on the modulator tube. This would not be desirable if an impedance $R_i \pm X_i$ were injected across the oscillator tank since, according to Eq. (97), this would cause severe AM in addition to FM. But if the real part of the injected impedance is suppressed, we have only reactance injections as in all cases shown in Fig. 46 and limit the r_p effect in Eq. (97), thus essentially avoiding superimposed AM.

The application of Eqs. (118) is simple and in some instances leads to further simplifications in these formulas. Suppose we use a quadrature tube network as shown in Fig. 46b. In this

---

[1] For other details, consult "Phenomena in High-frequency Systems," pp. 12–15, 28–32, McGraw-Hill Book Company, Inc., New York.

case the injected i_p current is leading the tank voltage E by 90 deg. This current will, therefore, add directly to the I current in the C branch, and for zero modulation voltage will cause the C_i injection in parallel with the tank circuit. The resultant capacitance is then $C + C_i$ instead of C and the oscillator frequency at any instant is $F_t = 1/[6.28 \sqrt{(C + C_i)L}]$. This is a smaller value than the frequency that would exist if the quadrature tube were not active, *i.e.*, if C_i were not injected. Since for this network the h-f voltage is $E_1 = \Omega L_1 I_1 \cong \Omega L_1 E/R_1$, we have for the corresponding ΔF swing in Eq. (117)

$$\Delta F = 0.0398 \frac{\Omega L_1 g_m}{CR_1} \quad \text{cycles per second} \tag{119}$$

if all quantities are in practical units of mhos, ohms, farads, henrys, and $\Omega = 6.28F$ cycles per second.

This result can also be checked by comparing the resultant tank current for maximum e_m swing on the modulator grid with the case when $e_m \sin \omega t = 0$. We then have in the C branch

$$I_c = \begin{cases} \Omega CE + 1.5 g_m E_1 = \Omega CE + 1.5 g_m \dfrac{\Omega L_1 E}{R_1} \\ \qquad = \Omega \underbrace{(C + 1.5 C_i)}_{\substack{\text{effective} \\ \text{capacitance}}} E \quad \text{for } e_m \sin \omega t = e_m \\[2em] \Omega CE + g_m E_1 = \Omega CE + g_m \dfrac{\Omega L_1 E}{R_1} \\ \qquad = \Omega \underbrace{(C + C_i)}_{\substack{\text{effective} \\ \text{capacitance}}} E \quad \text{for } e_m \sin \omega t = 0 \end{cases} \tag{120}$$

Hence, the instantaneous oscillator angular velocity Ω_t is

$$\Omega_t = \begin{cases} \dfrac{1}{\sqrt{(C + 1.5 C_i)L}} \cong \dfrac{1}{\sqrt{CL}} \dfrac{1}{\sqrt{1 + 1.5(C_i/C)}} \quad \text{for } e_m \sin \omega t = e_m \\[2em] \dfrac{1}{\sqrt{(C + C_i)L}} \cong \dfrac{1}{\sqrt{CL}} \dfrac{1}{\sqrt{1 + (C_i/C)}} \quad \text{for } e_m \sin \omega t = 0 \end{cases}$$

But C_i/C can be only a very small quantity compared with unity. This is also the case for $1.5C_i/C$. Hence, by applying the approximation for a small value s in $1/\sqrt{1 + s} = (1 + s)^{-0.5} \cong 1 - 0.5s$, we find the approximations

$$\Omega_t \cong \begin{cases} \Omega \left(1 - \dfrac{1.5C_i}{2C}\right) & \text{for } e_m \\[2ex] \Omega \left(1 - \dfrac{C_i}{2C}\right) & \text{for } e_m = 0 \end{cases}$$

with the corresponding instantaneous carrier frequencies

$$F_t = \begin{cases} F \left(1 - 0.75\,\dfrac{C_i}{C}\right) & \text{for } e_m \\[2ex] F \left(1 - 0.5\,\dfrac{C_i}{C}\right) & \text{for } e_m = 0 \end{cases} \tag{121}$$

Subtracting the lower value from the upper value must yield the maximum frequency deviation ΔF, and we find

$$\Delta F = 0.25\,\frac{C_i F}{C} \tag{122}$$

where, according to Fig. 46b, we have $C_i = g_m L_1 / R_1$ and

$$\Delta F = 0.25\,\frac{g_m L_1 F}{C R_1} \tag{123}$$

This is exactly the expression that was found in Eq. (119), if we realize that $\Omega = 6.28F$ and that $0.25/6.28 = 0.0398$.

As is seen from Fig. 45c, the effective h-f grid voltage of frequency F in presence of the signal voltage $e_m \sin \omega t$ is, so to speak, "waved up and down" without changing its carrier level with respect to the "wavy" reference time axis. It has already been seen that this "wavy" time axis is caused by the modulation voltage component $e_m \sin \omega t$. This "wavy" action also occurs in the i_p current for a linear modulator,[1] since linear-grid-voltage into plate-current translation takes place, and not AM effects, as would occur with a curved translation characteristic.

From these derivations it can be seen that not only can we bring about proportional FM by means of reactance tubes, but that the static injections, as explained in connection with Fig. 46, give also a means for stabilizing the center frequency about which proportional frequency deviations are taking place. The fixed injections can be changed to other values by using another operat-

---

[1] For details, consult "High-frequency Measurements," Fig. 300 on p. 353, McGraw-Hill Book Company, Inc., New York.

ing point (consult Fig. 45).   This means that the center frequency
can be changed by employing another fixed negative grid bias.
This is done in automatic frequency control systems by having
any drifting carrier frequencies affect a frequency discriminator
that will not apply an output voltage to the modulator tube if the
center frequency is correct.   For a carrier-frequency drift toward
a somewhat higher frequency value, a corresponding, say positive,
output voltage is superimposed on the modulator grid; for a drift
toward a lower carrier-frequency value, the discriminator will
superimpose a corresponding negative potential on the modulator
grid.   In each case the discriminator will just cause compensation
of the center-frequency drift.   This is shown in Figs. 35, 73.

31. Useful Frequency Modulators.—From Eqs. (117) and
(118) we note that for a *class A modulator*, which has a linear g_m
characteristic as in Fig. 45b, we have a sensitivity of $2 \Delta F/E_c$
kc/volt, where E_c denotes the negative grid bias that determines
the operating point.   For any other bias, even for class B modulator operation, which would be advisable only in push-pull modulators, it is only necessary to use the corresponding g_m and E_c
values in these expressions.   For two class A modulators in push-
pull, the total sensitivity is $4 \Delta F/E_c$, since twice the peak-to-peak
swing of a single class A modulator can be obtained.

As far as useful circuits[1] are concerned, they are mostly based
on a 90-deg phase shift.   We deal, therefore, with quadrature
tubes, although there exists also a procedure whereby FM is
produced without a phase-shifting network.   The circuit then
consists of a capacitance, resistance, and inductance in parallel.
The inductance is inductively coupled to the frequency-determining branch of a tube oscillator.   Variations in the parallel resistance then reflect variable impedances into the oscillator branch.
As a matter of fact, most reactance-tube modulators reflect a
certain resistive component into the oscillator branch unless
resistance neutralization is provided.   If E_b and I_b are the direct-

[1] With respect to many other commercial details on reactance tubes reference is
made to C. Travis, Automatic Frequency Control, *Proc. IRE*, **23**, 1125, 1935; D. E.
Foster and S. W. Seeley, Automatic Tuning, Simplified Circuits, and Design Practice,
Proc. IRE, **25**, 289, 1937; I. R. Weir, Field Tests of Frequency and Amplitude Modu-
lation with U.H.F. Waves, *Gen. Elec. Rev.*, **42**, 188–191, 270–273, 1939; C. F. Sheaffer,
Frequency Modulator, *Proc. IRE*, **28**, 66, 1940; M. G. Crosby, Reactance Tube
Frequency Modulators, *RCA Rev.*, **5**, 89, 1940; B. E. Montgomery, An Inductively
Coupled Frequency Modulator, *Proc. IRE*, **29**, 559, 1941.

current supply voltage and current in the plate branch of a
reactance tube, for resistance neutralization the power dissipated
over the carrier-frequency cycle is only $E_b I_b$ while, for an impedance
injection into the oscillator branch, the average power is $E_b I_b +$
$0.5 E_p I_p \cos \varphi$, where the last term vanishes for $\varphi = 90$ deg. This
term is additive to $E_b I_b$ for $\varphi < 90$ deg, and is negative for angles
above 90 deg within the second quadrant with a simultaneous
decrease in the value of I_b. The plate dissipation of the reactance
tube varies considerably, especially when the phase shift is approximately 90 deg.

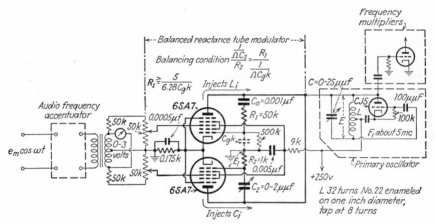

FIG. 47.—Balanced-reactance frequency modulator.

Figure 47 shows a balanced reactance-tube modulator affecting
the frequency of a tube oscillator having a center frequency in the
neighborhood of 5 Mc/sec. This is an order of magnitude that is
often used for the center frequency of the primary or master
oscillator of an FM transmitter. By primary oscillator is understood the source in an FM transmitter that is modulated in frequency before frequency multiplication is applied in order to
obtain still larger frequency excursions as well as to secure the
final much higher center frequency F. Since for direct FM the
center frequency is varied, the carrier frequency can not be
"stiff" as in a piezo source or in some kinds of electron-coupled
oscillators, especially when the cathode of the oscillator is dynamically at a high potential and the plate is dynamically at ground
potential.

A 6J5 tube or its equivalent will do well as an oscillator tube.
Using 6SA7 tubes, or their equivalents, for the modulator, gives

the advantage of having available an additional grid electrode for applying the signal voltages. The upper modulator tube injects a lagging i_p variation into the oscillator tank; hence, a variable L_i is effectively across the tuning coil of the oscillator. The lower modulator tube injects a leading i_p variation into the tank and causes, therefore, a variable C_i effect in multiple with the tank condenser. On account of using two modulator tubes, the peak-to-peak swing of the primary modulation is doubled.

The L_i and C_i injections can be readily understood from the following: The phase-shifting network in the upper modulator branch is composed of a series combination of the resistance $R_1 = 50,000$ ohms and the control grid to cathode capacitance of the upper modulator tube. It is understood that C_{gk} also includes the wiring capacitance of the control grid branch toward ground. Since R_1 is chosen well in excess of a value equal to five times the capacitive reactance $1/(\Omega C_{gk})$, the corresponding primary carrier voltage E_u applied to the upper control tube lags the tank voltage E by essentially 90 deg as will also the corresponding plate current variation $i_p = g_m E_u$. Hence, L_i is injected in multiple with L. The condenser C_0 which is of about 0.001 μf capacitance is merely an isolation condenser and may be considered as a short circuit as far as the primary carrier-frequency current is concerned. With respect to the lower tube, we note that the effective control grid voltage E_l is produced by the voltage drop in the low resistance $R_2 = 1,000$ ohms, and that in series with this resistance R_2 is a very small capacitance C_2, which can never be larger than $2\mu\mu$f. Hence E_l, as well as the injected i_p variation due to the lower modulator tube which is $g_m E_l$, must lead the tank voltage E by 90 deg and C_i variations are operative across the tank condenser C.

The combined modulation action is then simple. Suppose a positive increase of the modulation voltage $e_m \cos \omega t$ on the upper tube increases the L_i injection. Since this injection is in multiple with the tank inductance L, we have an effective tank inductance L_e which is given by $1/L_e = (1/L) + (1/L_i)$. Therefore, a value of L_e results, which must be smaller than the normal inductance L of the tank. This means that the primary carrier frequency is accordingly increased. Simultaneously the lower modulator tube injects an apparent fixed capacitance C_i in multiple with the tank condenser C. But at a moment when $e_m \cos \omega t$ is positive, as above on the upper tube, there must be applied an *equal negative* modulation voltage on the lower tube; *i.e.*, instantaneously the fixed C_i injection *decreases*. This decrease will also increase the primary carrier frequency.

At this point it should be understood that the fixed L_i and C_i injections, together with the true or normal C and L values of the tank, determine the primary center frequency F. For an ideal modulator of this type, the center frequency F should also be equal to $F = (6.28 \sqrt{CL})^{-1} = (6.28 \sqrt{C_e L_e})^{-1}$, where $C_e = C + C_i$ and $L_e = LL_i/(L + L_i)$. The quantities C_i and L_i are the instantaneous injections in multiple with the oscillator tank. Such an ideal circuit adjustment is, however, not strictly required since any unsymmetrical balance, because there is more frequency increase due to the L_i effect than frequency decrease due to the C_i effect, will only shorten the peak-to-peak frequency swing and can be made symmetrical by means of automatic center-frequency stabilization. Normally, we call, therefore, the frequency that occurs for fixed C_i and L_i injections together with the existing C and L values, the center frequency F.

Inasmuch as we have found that in effect we have push-pull modulation during the positive modulation cycle acting on the upper modulator tube at times when the negative modulation cycle is operative on the lower modulator tube, it is evident that the same thing happens when the upper tube is exposed to negative modulation swings and the lower tube to corresponding positive modulation swings.

For the symmetrical modulation about the center frequency, we can, besides changing the L/C ratio, also change the tap points on the 50,000-ohm potentiometers in Fig. 47 in order to obtain the best operating condition.

Figure 48 shows how plate-resistance neutralization is accomplished in a reactance-tube modulator. Such neutralization not only reduces distortion but also permits larger frequency deviations since the shunting effect of the plate resistance of the reactance tube on the tank of the oscillator is reduced. The normal reactance-tube connection would be with the switch S on 1, which connects to the plate of the oscillator. Since the grid of a 1F4 tube, or its equivalent, receives its voltage through the grid-to-cathode interelectrode capacitance, the resistance R has to be chosen quite high, at least five times $1/(6.28C_{gf})$ in order to cause a voltage E_1 on the control grid, which lags the tank voltage E by about 90 deg. But when the switch S is closed on 2, the phase will be greater than 90 deg and will approach the value of $\varphi = 180$ deg as the value of resistance R is reduced. It is then possible to find an R setting that satisfies the condition of cos $\varphi = 1/(m\mu)$ of Eq. (97), where μ is the dynamic amplification factor of the tube and $m = e_g/e_p$. This is evident if it is realized that for cos $\varphi = 1/(m\mu)$ the real term A in Eq. (97) will vanish; *i.e.*, the plate-resistance effect of the modulator tube is neutralized and can, therefore, cause no parasitic AM. Such neutralization seems

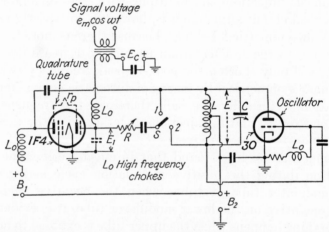

Fig. 48.—Frequency modulator with neutralized r_p of the quadrature tube.

especially advisable when pentodes with low plate-resistance values are functioning as modulator tubes.

Figure 49 shows a balanced reactance-tube modulator where a phase inverter replaces the push-pull input transformer. Since amplification in this inverter also takes place, a crystal microphone can be directly connected at the input side of the inverter. A 6SC7 tube, or its equivalent, is used. The balanced modulator is essentially the same as shown and described in connection with Fig. 47, except that a somewhat lower value grid resistor of $R_2 = 300$ ohms is used. Such a system then applies, according to Crosby, for an FM having a center frequency of about 14 Mc. A circuit of this type is convenient when frequency accentuation is of no concern as in speech transmission.

32. Balancing of a Two-tube Frequency Modulator.—Generally, push-pull modulators, such as the network shown in Fig. 47,

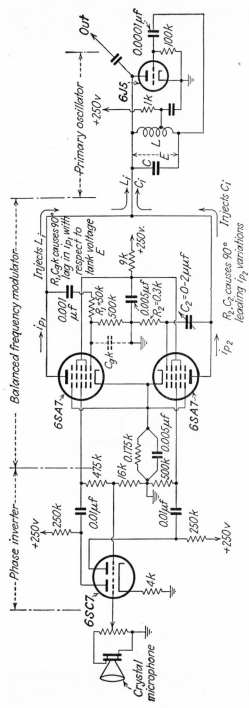

FIG. 49.—Balanced modulator with phase inverter.

have, the advantage of giving twice the frequency swing and also the advantage that any voltage fluctuations occurring in the power-line supply voltage can be made ineffective as far as the stabilization of the center frequency and all the important side frequencies are concerned. This is accomplished by superimposing on the push-pull modulator action a small and suitable push-push modulator action. Such a superimposed action can be made to offset any reaction between the oscillator frequency and the power-supply voltage. The superimposed push-push action is effected by a small off balance of the respective modulator sections.

To do this we first obtain modulator balance such as is required by the balancing condition given in Fig. 47. Since the C_{gk} capacitance is small and rather indefinite, as far as the actual measurement is concerned, it seems best to use a value for the series resistor R_1 large enough so that essentially only the resistor is responsible for the magnitude of the current flow I_1 due to the tank voltage E. A value of $R_1 = 50,000$ ohms will accomplish this. Using a 1,000-ohm resistor from the control grid of the lower modulator tube to ground and a two-plate midget condenser of 0-2 $\mu\mu$f in series with it provides a ready means for adjusting the balance. For no signal voltage $e_m \cos \omega t$ acting, the primary center frequency F should result. Suppose we want to use the balanced modulator in connection with a transmitter, where eightfold frequency multiplication follows the primary FM and the assigned carrier frequency of the radiated wave is 44.5 Mc. We have, then, a primary center frequency $F = 44.5/8 = 5.5625$ Mc. The next step in the adjustment of the modulator is to vary the variable condenser C of the tank until no beat note is obtained against a standard frequency source which has an integral relationship with respect to 5.5625 Mc. This is done with the midget condenser C_2 at its mid-capacitance setting. If the supply voltage is varied, say over ± 10 per cent of its normal value of 115 volts, and a beat note is heard again, then a value of the C_2 setting is found for which F remains essentially fixed. This adjustment may be called the unmodulated carrier-frequency stabilization toward line-voltage fluctuations. To meet also the actual FM condition, we have to apply FM for maximum permissible frequency deviations and repeat the procedure by beating against the carrier.

A maximum voltage e_m in $e_m \cos \omega t$ is impressed on the balanced modulator of Fig. 47, such that e_m corresponds to a maximum frequency swing of ± 75 kc in the radiated wave. This leads to β values, even for the maximum audio frequency $f_{max} = 15$ kc, as large as $\beta = {}^{75}\!/_{15} = 5$, and eight significant side currents on each side of the carrier frequency appear. This can be seen from Table III on page 33. This table also shows that the amplitude of the carrier frequency is only 17.7 per cent of the unmodulated carrier I_m; some of the side currents have much larger amplitudes. It seems, therefore, more convenient to work with a reduced carrier frequency, such as the primary center frequency of 5.5625 Mc in this particular example. There is then a corresponding maximum permissible frequency excursion of only ${}^{75}\!/_8 = 9.375$ kc. For the highest signal frequency $f_{max} \equiv 15$ kc, there is a β value of only $9.375/15 = 0.623$ radian. According to Table III, essentially only two additional side currents on each side of the center frequency then exist. According to Table I on page 20, we now have a center-frequency amplitude of essentially 90 per cent of the unmodulated carrier level. It is, therefore, much easier to make the center-frequency check directly on the primary FM current modulated to the largest permissible frequency swing. It is to be understood that any resetting of the small condenser C_2 requires also a slight readjustment of the tank setting of C.

If it is of concern only to balance the modulator of Fig. 47, irrespective of any frequency drifts due to line-voltage drifts of the supply voltage, it is only necessary to tune in with an FM receiver on the radiated wave to be tested with respect to modulator balance. We have then two possible procedures. One is to operate the transmitter with the modulator in the normal condition, *i.e.*, with the normal connection in push-pull. When the C_2 setting is varied for an e_m amplitude corresponding to the highest permissible frequency deviation in the radiated wave, then the greatest FM, *i.e.*, the loudest reception, will be noticed in the receiver for correct balance. But as far as the sensation in the human ear is concerned, it is quite difficult to distinguish between loud and somewhat louder sounds. This is especially true when a certain pronounced loudness exists. The second procedure avoids this difficulty since for it the respective modulator grids are connected together; *i.e.*, they act in parallel. This yields a push-push modulation for which the injected i_p variation due to the upper modulator tube tends to cancel the effect of the simultaneous injected i_p variation due to the lower modulator tube. Hence, when this modulator connection is used during the modulator adjustment, the setting of the C_2 condenser is varied until minimum sound is noticed in the FM receiver. Theoretically, no FM should exist. Thereafter, during normal operation the modulator is connected with the control grids as indicated in Fig. 47.

33. Phase Modulators.[1]—Generally, it may be said that in FM we have higher plate efficiencies in the respective power stages than for AM systems, on account of the feature of constant carrier level I_m. This is, of course, also true for PM systems. The modulation apparatus required in PM systems is simpler than that used in AM systems. It is also possible to produce PM at low-power levels since amplitude linearity in the power stages is of no concern for phase variations. Even though the main purpose of this treatise is to describe systems for FM, it must be recalled that, in indirect FM, phase modulation is instrumental in bringing about all the features of direct FM. Such features exist as far as the final stages in the transmitter are concerned as well as in the entire FM receiver.

With respect to the description given in connection with Fig. 3, we understand that PM can be accomplished with a network such as is shown in Fig. 50. In Fig. 50a, two equal tubes are connected in parallel, as far as their plate outputs are concerned, with respect to the common external plate load, which is a CL tank tuned with respect to the carrier frequency F. It will be noted that the modulating or signal voltage $e_m \cos \omega t$ drives the two tubes in algebraic push-pull. As far as the respective control grids are concerned, the tubes are driven in geometric push-push with respect to the voltage $E_m \sin \Omega t$ of carrier frequency F. By algebraic push-pull is meant the customary push-pull input voltage where at any instant equal but opposite voltages act on the respective grids. Owing to the $C_1 R_1$ network across the carrier-frequency source as well as across the respective control grids,

[1] Armstrong, E. H., A Method of Reducing Disturbances in Radio Signaling by a System of Frequency Modulation, *Proc. IRE*, **24**, 689, 1936. Lautenschlager, F., Phase Modulated Oscillators, *ENT*, **11**, 357, 1934. Crosby, M. G Communication by Phase Modulation, *Proc. IRE*, **27**, 126, 1939 (this paper gives about the best account on useful devices in PM). Yocum, C. H., Frequency Modulation, Part II, *Communications*, **19**, p. 14, December, 1939, (this article describes also the R. E. Shelby phase modulator). Sabaroff, S., New System of Frequency Modulation, *Communications*, **21**, p 8, September, 1941.

the control grid-to-cathode path of one tube is exposed to an applied voltage q_1, which is a sine function of carrier frequency. The control grid-to-cathode path of the other tube is exposed to a voltage q_2, which is a cosine function of the carrier frequency. Therefore, the respective tubes are driven in quadrature push-push. On account of the chosen reactance value of condenser C_1 at the carrier frequency F, there are at any instant quadrature voltages of equal values acting on respective control grids.

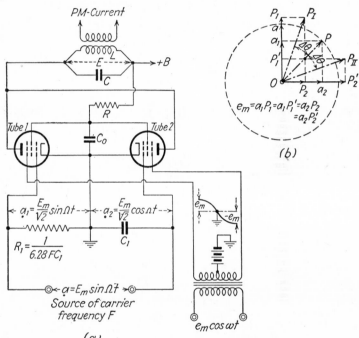

(a)

(b)

Fig. 50.—Production of phase-modulated currents.

As far as the input is concerned, we have the vector Oa for zero modulation voltage in Fig. 50b for the voltage $E_m \sin \Omega t$ of the carrier-frequency source. The applied control voltage $(E_m \sin \Omega t)/\sqrt{2}$ on tube 1 must be in phase with vector q and is indicated by vector Oa_1; the equal quadrature voltage applied to the other tube is the vector Oa_2. The resultant of vectors q_1 and q_2 is the vector OP. This vector must have the same scalar value as vector Oa. The 45-deg time delay of OP with respect to the voltage Oa of the supply is not *directly* active at the input side, but for a unity grid-into-plate branch action, on account of the parallel connection, would represent the resultant tank voltage E.

Voltage E would generally be proportional to voltage OP. Therefore, we may take the vector OP as the measure for E with respect to size as well as with respect to relative position when *no* modulation is taking place.

Now suppose that the signal-voltage $e_m \cos \omega t$ is acting at an instant when $\omega t = 0$. This is the instant of time indicated by the cosine trace in Fig. 50a. Then e_m will add algebraically to a_1 in tube 1 and e_m will subtract algebraically from amplitude a_2 in tube 2. Then we have in Fig. 50b the respective instantaneous carrier voltages OP_1 for tube 1 and OP_2 for tube 2. The resultant voltage, as far as the output network is concerned, is OP_I. After $1/2f$ sec, $-e_m$ is superimposed on the control voltage of tube 1 and $+e_m$ adds on the control grid of tube 2. This causes the instantaneous voltages OP_1' on tube 1 and OP_2' on the control grid of tube 2, with the resultant vector OP_{II} which causes the value of the tank voltage E. Hence, the effect in the output branch of the modulator tubes is a phase fluctuation $\pm \Delta \theta$ and the peak-to-peak phase swing equal to the time delay of OP with respect to the supply voltage $E_m \sin \Omega t$.

It will be noted that for such large $\Delta \theta$ swings as are shown in Fig. 50b, a certain amount of harmonic distortion must be expected. Simultaneous AM occurs because the extreme vectors OP_I and OP_{II} are somewhat longer than the correct vector size given by the radius of the circle. To remove the superimposed AM at the output side of the phase modulator by means of an amplitude limiter would also remove some of the useful modulation energy as is explained on page 59. It is, therefore, better engineering practice not to work with the equal amplitudes a_1 and a_2 at the input side, but with amplitudes that cause an angle aOP of not more than about 23 deg. Then $\Delta \theta \leq 11.5$ deg or about ≤ 0.2 radian for which values the extremities of vectors P_I and P_{II} will remain on the circle of radius a.

Figure 51 shows a block diagram of a phase modulator where the modulation product $k_1(KI_m \cos \omega t) \sin \Omega t$ is produced by a balanced amplitude modulator (page 187). The sinusoidal output current of a fixed carrier frequency F divides itself between a buffer amplifier and a balanced amplitude modulator which is also affected by a signal current $i_m \cos \omega t$. The constant k_1 takes care of the modulator efficiency and K is the degree of amplitude modulation obtained. A 90-deg phase shifter causes a modulator output current of $k_1(KI_m \cos \omega t) \cos \Omega t$. The output of the buffer amplifier delivers a current $a = kI_m \sin \Omega t$, where k stands for the gain of this amplifier. Since the two instantaneous

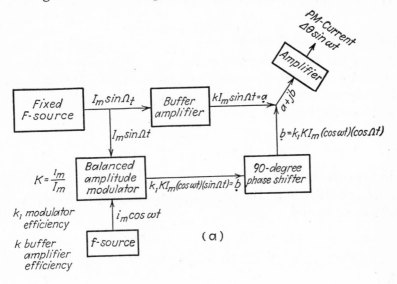

(a)

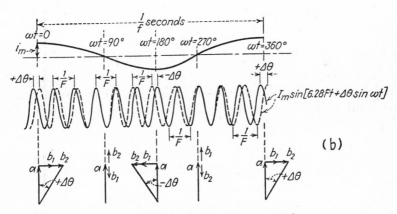

(b)

$a = kI_m$ of frequency F; b_1 portion of b of frequency $F+f$;
b_2 portion of b of frequency $F-f$; $b_1 = 0.5 k_1 i_m = b_2$

Fig. 51.—True phase modulation with maximum deviations $\pm \Delta \theta$ and modulation index $\beta = \Delta \theta$ radians.

currents are in time quadrature at any moment, they must be added vectorially at the mixer of the input of the last amplifier. Hence, the current $a + jb = \sqrt{a^2 + b^2}$ flows into the mixer with an instantaneous relative phase $\tan^{-1}(b/a)$. Since $\cos \Omega t \cos \omega t$

$= 0.5[\cos{(\Omega + \omega)t} + \cos{(\Omega - \omega)t}]$, we have for $k_1 K = k_2$ the instantaneous mixer current

$$I_t = kI_m \sin{\Omega t} + 0.5k_2 I_m \cos{(\Omega + \omega)t} + 0.5k_2 I_m \cos{(\Omega - \omega)t}$$
$$= \quad a \quad + \quad b_1 \quad + \quad b_2 \qquad (124)$$

As far as the modulation is concerned, we are interested only in the cycle of the modulation frequency f, and not in the cycle of the instantaneous carrier frequency F_t, which for amplitude modulation happens to be equal to the center frequency F. We have, therefore, the expressions

$$\left.\begin{array}{l} b_1 = 0.5k_2 I_m \cos{(\Omega t + \omega t)} \\ b_2 = 0.5k_2 I_m \cos{(\Omega t - \omega t)} \end{array}\right\} \qquad (125)$$

which at the instant $t = 0$, for the signal frequency f, yield $b_1 = 0.5k_2 I_m \cos{\Omega t} = b_2$. But $k_2 = k_1 K = k_1 i_m/I_m$; hence $b_1 = b_2 = 0.5k_1 i_m \cos{\Omega t}$ and

$$I_t = I_0 = kI_m \sin{\Omega t} + 0.5k_1 i_m \cos{\Omega t} + 0.5k_1 i_m \cos{\Omega t}$$
$$= \quad a \quad + \quad j(b_1 \quad + \quad b_2) \qquad (126)$$

where $b_1 = b_2 = 0.5k_1 i_m$. Equation (126) also shows that there is a phase deviation $\Delta\theta = \tan^{-1}{[(b_1 + b_2)/a]} = \tan^{-1}{(k_1 i_m/kI_m)} = \tan^{-1}{(k_1 K/k)}$. Therefore, if the modulator efficiency were 100 per cent and no buffer amplifier were used, we would have $\Delta\theta = \tan^{-1}{K}$, where the argument K is the degree of AM in the balanced modulator. For 20 per cent AM we would have $\Delta\theta = \tan^{-1}{0.2} \cong 0.2$ radian, or about 11.5 deg. The corresponding vector addition is shown in Fig. 51b at the instant when $\omega t = 0$.

For $\omega t = 90$ deg we have, then,

$$I_t = I_{90} = kI_m \sin{\Omega t} + 0.5k_1 i_m \cos{(\Omega t + 90)} + 0.5k_1 i_m \cos{(\Omega t - 90)}$$
$$= kI_m \sin{\Omega t} - 0.5k_1 i_m \sin{\Omega t} + 0.5k_1 i_m \sin{\Omega t}$$
$$= \quad a \quad - \quad b_1 \quad + \quad b_2 \quad = a \qquad (127)$$

since $b_1 = b_2 = 0.5k_1 i_m$. We have, therefore, no phase swing at this instant of time as can also be seen in Fig. 51b. The effects of the upper and lower side currents of respective frequencies $F \pm f$ cancel because they are in antiphase and in phase with the carrier-frequency amplitude $a = kI_m$. At the moment for which $\omega t = 180$ deg, we find

$$I_t = I_{180} = kI_m \sin{\Omega t} - 0.5k_1 I_m \cos{\Omega t} - 0.5k_1 I_m \cos{\Omega t}$$
$$= a - j(b_1 + b_2) \qquad (128)$$

and we have a negative phase swing in Fig. 51*b*.   We have for this
swing $\Delta\theta = \tan^{-1}[-(b_1 + b_2)/a]$.   For $\omega t = 270$ deg, we find

$$I_{270} = a + b_1 - b_2 = a \tag{129}$$

which means that again this is an instant of time on the signal-
frequency cycle for which no modulation can occur. I_{360} is
naturally the same case as I_0.

We note, therefore, that linear PM occurs, since the instantaneous phase swings during the modulation cycle are directly

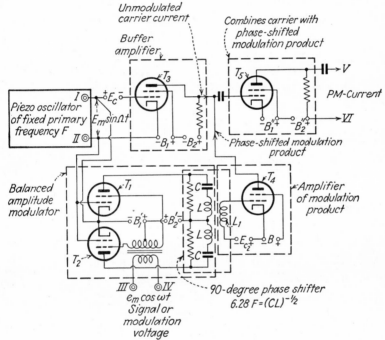

FIG. 52.—Generator for a true PM current with a modulation index $\beta = \Delta\theta$.

proportional to the instantaneous value $i_m \cos \omega t$ of the signal
current which causes the modulation. Also here the limitation
applies that, for distortion-free PM, the maximum $\pm\Delta\theta$ swings,
occurring when the maximum values i_m of $i_m \cos \omega t$ act, should
not exceed 0.2 radian.

Figure 52 shows an actual network based on the block diagram
of Fig. 51 where, in addition, an amplifier for the modulation
product is used, which also acts as a buffer stage.   We note that a
piezo oscillator of stabilized primary or master frequency F feeds
into the buffer tube T_3, as well as in push-push to the control grids

of like modulator tubes T_1 and T_2 while the output plates of these tubes are connected in push-pull. Hence, no carrier current can flow in the output coil L_1 in absence of a signal voltage $e_m \cos \omega t$. The signal voltage affects the second set of modulator grids in push-pull, and must, therefore, produce the modulation product. The inductive reactances of the primary output coils L in the respective modulator plate branches are neutralized by means of the capacitive reactances of the condensers C, with respect to the carrier frequency F. Hence, the plate variations due to the carrier-frequency source must be in phase with the driving carrier-frequency voltages acting on the respective grids of the modulator tubes T_1 and T_2. The natural period of the secondary L_1, which applies its voltage to the control grid of tube T_4, is very short compared with the period of $1/F$ sec of the carrier current. Hence, voltages induced in L_1 must be either 90 deg ahead or lagging, and the modulation product coming from the two L coils is shifted 90 deg in phase as far as the input and output actions of the amplifier with tube T_4 are concerned. Hence, at the input side of the mixer amplifier we combine again $a \pm jb$ and cause PM as explained in connection with Fig. 51.

The network of Fig. 52 is the network used by Armstrong, except that a voltage which is proportional to $(e_m \cos \omega t)/f$ is applied at terminals III and IV. Therefore, the current emerging from terminals V and VI is not a true PM current at all, but is in effect an FM current since it has a maximum phase shift that is proportional to $\Delta\theta/f$. This has exactly the form of $\Delta F/f$. When $\Delta\theta$ in radians is numerically equal to ΔF, we shall have the same number of side currents in either case and for any signal frequency f the identity $\Delta\theta/f \equiv \Delta F/f$ holds.

In the commercial Armstrong transmitter not only does a correcting network for the $1/f$ effect precede the input terminals III and IV, but also a correcting network for a-f preaccentuation having a time constant of about 100 μ sec. This latter correcting network should follow directly the microphone since its purpose is to offset any of the undesired noises in the upper a-f range of frequencies.

We note, therefore, that in the Armstrong system there is primarily balanced AM. In virtue of the 90-deg phase shifter in the output branch of the balanced modulator, the modulation product adds itself, at any instant, in quadrature with an unmodu-

lated current of carrier frequency F. The effect is that PM is
produced. But, owing to the amplitude e_m/f of the signal current,
the PM experienced has all the features of direct FM. This
means that the same energy distributions exist in the frequency
spectrum for the entire a-f range as though FM were operative.
We obtain, therefore, indirect FM. The primary indirect FM is,
however, very small[1] since the corresponding extreme phase
swings for allowable values of distortion should never exceed
values of about 0.2 radian. Allowing only a small amount of
harmonic distortion in indirect FM, phase swings larger than
about ±30 deg should be avoided.

At this point it should be understood that, when PM is caused
by the addition of two out-of-phase currents, such a limitation of
maximum phase swings also must be met, if distortion is to be kept
low. But if the relative phase θ of the unmodulated current
$I_m \sin(\Omega t + \theta)$ can be changed *directly*, and not by geometric
addition, then large phase swings can cause PM without harmonic
distortion since simultaneous AM is avoided. It does not seem
helpful, therefore, to consider schemes where large phase swings
result and geometrical addition is instrumental in bringing about
wide-phase swing modulation. It is, however, true that we can
cause wide-phase swing modulation, even in the Armstrong
system, as long as we *keep together*, in the transmitter as well as at
the reception end, the AM and the PM or the FM, whatever may
be the combination. The only drawback in such a doubly modulated system would be that, at first, in the power amplifier stages
there would not be such high plate efficiencies as with pure FM

---

[1] There seems to be much confusion in current literature about the concept of PM
in the Armstrong system. Some writers give the impression that we deal at first
with PM because the FM is so small that we actually have only small phase liberations.
It should, therefore, be clearly understood that the order of magnitude does not and
cannot make of an FM effect a PM effect. If it is an FM effect for wide-band FM, *i.e.*,
after frequency multiplication, then it is also an FM effect for a very narrow band FM.
It has been brought out in Chap. I over and over again that there is a great difference
between PM and FM. For PM the number of significant side currents is, for a fixed
maximum phase swing, independent of the order of the signal frequency f. This is
not true for FM since for a fixed maximum frequency swing the number of significant
side currents decreases as the signal frequency f increases. In other words the distribution of the modulation energy for FM is generally different from the energy
distribution for PM. It is the energy distribution of the modulation energy that
counts. Since in the Armstrong system, after combination of the carrier current
with the phase-shifted modulation product, the inverse $1/f$ effect also exists, we have
throughout an FM *effect*, no matter how small it is to begin with.

or with pure PM systems. Secondly, the very feature of high signal-to-noise ratio characteristic of FM would be defeated, since amplitude limiters could not be used.

When the output of an oscillator, whose frequency F is "stiff," is affected, for instance, by a reactance tube, the result will be a PM with quite large phase swings instead of direct FM. The reason for this is that a stabilized frequency F, as in a piezo source, will not allow phase balance and the resultant oscillator current will so to speak "give way" and will yield to periodic phase shifts. What will occur then is an oscillator current which "as a whole" shifts forward and "as a whole" shifts backward without changing the number of cycles within the current wave, which is shifted "as a whole." In other words the entire current wave shifts to and fro along the time axis and, as such, is kinetic with modulation energy that can be separated by phase demodulation. It is true that we have equivalent frequency variations, but we should not confuse equivalent frequency modulation with real changes in the carrier frequency where the time intervals between successive current maxima are not equal as in PM.

Hence, one way of causing PM would be to apply a voltage of a stabilized frequency F to the grid of a pentode tube and to tune the plate output tank circuit to the carrier frequency F with a quadrature tube network in parallel with the plate tank circuit. This assumes that the modulation voltage is not acting. But when the signal voltage $e_m \cos \omega t$ is also present, the plate tank current will be modulated in phase since the frequency F is "stiff." A coupled circuit feeding into a load experiences, therefore, a PM current.

It was shown[1] how a cathode-ray tube acted upon by two high-frequency voltages, which are in space quadrature as well as in time quadrature and affecting a cathode ray, can be made to show a spiral fluorescent pattern if the two voltages are modulated in amplitude. Using such an arrangement, we have the illustration of Fig. 53a where a piezo generator of stabilized carrier frequency F feeds into a modulator which, on account of the signal voltage $e_m \cos \omega t$, causes AM. The output of the modulator feeds into a 90-deg phase shifter and then affects the respective deflection plates P_1P_2 and P_3P_4 of a cathode-ray tube. Figure 53b shows

---

[1] "Phenomena in High-frequency Systems," pp. 146, 157; "High-frequency Measurements," pp. 373–374.

that a circular fluorescent cathode-ray trace is obtained when no modulation voltage $e_m \cos \omega t$ is present. For a certain degree K of amplitude modulation, a concentric fluorescent ring of width W appears on the screen of the cathode-ray tube. In reality the fluorescent ring is a spiral trace which shrinks and grows according

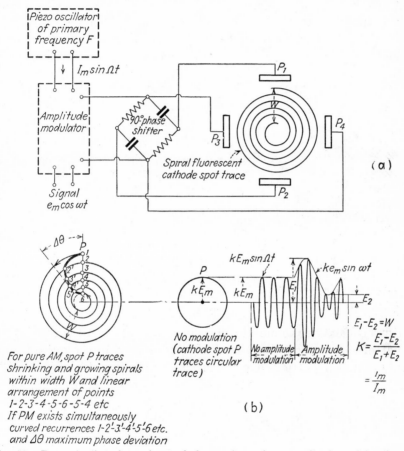

Fig. 53.—Determination of superimposed phase swing $\Delta\theta$ in an amplitude-modulated current with parasitic PM.

to the signal-frequency modulation. At any instant the vector of the trace, which rotates with the angular velocity $6.28F$, has a length that is proportional to $E_m(1 + K \cos \omega t)$, the constant of proportionality being k. Since, for pure AM the extremities 1, 2, 3, 4, etc., of the rotating vectors, which occur $1/F$ sec apart, must lie on a radius as OP, we have a means for finding out experimentally when PM also exists in addition to AM. If PM exists also, then the respective vectors that occur after consecutive intervals of $1/F$ sec no longer grow from a minimum value along OP toward a maximum value along OP, then decrease again but always along OP, but are 01′, 02′, 03′, 04′, OP, 05′, 06′, 07′, 08′, and 01′ during a complete modulation cycle of $1/f$ sec. The extremities of these vectors then lie on the curved locus and a maximum phase excursion of $\pm\Delta\theta$ occurs as is indicated in Fig. 53b. The experimental method is described in the cited publications but is not necessary for understanding the application mentioned now.

Inasmuch as in Fig. 53 we have a means for *detecting* PM, we must also have here a means for *causing* PM as we have only to

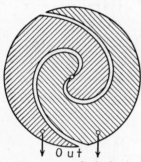

reverse the action. This brings us, then, to a method due to R. E. Shelby where the entire network of Fig. 53 can be used as a phase modulator if output terminals are provided where the cathode-ray trace impinges. This is accomplished by properly shaped collecting targets. There is, then, in place of the fluorescent screen a mica target on which a conducting Archimedean spiral ribbon is deposited, as shown in Fig. 54. Such a mathematical shape is needed in order to obtain a linear PM at the output because if the metal ribbon on the screen were, for instance, a pattern of straight lines, no PM would occur in the output current. Such a pattern would correspond to the straight line OP in Fig. 53. Maximum phase deviations $\Delta\theta$ of several hundred degrees are then possible. The output power is, of course, very much smaller than that obtained in balanced phase modulators. It is also of importance that the voltages impressed on the respective deflection quadrants of the cathode-ray tube are in exact time quadrature. At any instant of the modulation cycle they also must be of exactly the same value. This may give rise to engineering difficulties.

Inasmuch as the circuit shown in Fig. 53a can be used in connection with any intermediate carrier frequency, the cathode-ray scanning on the target of Fig. 54 can be accomplished. A spiral scan is employed and is due either to the actual carrier frequency F or to any submultiple thereof, as long as the corresponding fixed angular velocity 6.28F can accommodate the signal modulation speed of 6.28f. It is this speed that causes the circular cathode-ray trace periodically to increase or decrease in diameter as the vector, due to the carrier angular velocity 6.28F, spins around. Even though such a system may give rise to practical difficulties as far as the balancing of the deflection voltages is concerned, it may be said that a more true PM can be produced when such difficulties are overcome. The reason for this is that the cathode-ray tube gives a very good buffer action toward the source that excites it.

We have to realize that we are interested in pure PM and not in PM with partial superimposed FM. Now, the producing of a modulation along the time axis of a current wave can do both; it can change the carrier frequency directly or only the phase. It can also affect both types of time axis modulations. Pure PM without direct FM effects is possible only when the sinusoidal wave train is moved to and fro about its fixed relative phase position without, so to speak, "squeezing" or "stretching" the consecutive current waves together or apart during to-and-fro oscillations of the entire wave train. In this system we have to begin with a "stiff" frequency F, since it is due to a piezo source, and we can hardly imagine any back action on the magnitude of F from the collector electrodes on the mica screen. Hence, we may assume that no superimposed FM can exist.

At this point it should be realized that even though any frequency demodulator can be readily converted into a correct phase demodulator, and vice versa, by adding a simple correcting network (described in Sec. 34), this remedy cannot be used when both types, *i.e.*, FM and PM, act *simultaneously*.

34. Commercial Demodulators.—In Sec. 15 dealing with the translation of FM into AM, the fact was discussed that a frequency discriminator will translate FM variations as well as PM variations into corresponding AM variations. These amplitude variations will, in turn, give also an inherent a-f output, owing to the amplitude demodulator action of the rectifiers used in the discriminator.

The fact that a discriminator can translate either FM or PM into a-f variations does not mean at all that the audio output is correct as far as the relative amplitudes of the various audio frequencies f at the transmitter end are concerned. The separation of the various audio components in a *frequency* discriminator is correct for impressed FM voltages, since the discriminator is designed for reversing the action of the FM caused in the transmitter. It is not correct, however, when PM voltages are impressed on a frequency demodulator since the translation is not due to phase discrimination but to equivalent frequency discrimination. From Eq. (6) we learned that the equivalent frequency deviation about the true and fixed carrier frequency F is $f \Delta\theta \cos \omega t$. Hence, it increases with the pitch of the sound heard or causes a-f accentuation toward the higher audio frequencies.

This can be readily remedied by connecting, between the audio output of a frequency discriminator and the a-f amplifier of an FM receiver, a correcting network which compensates for the f effect by means of a $1/f$ effect. All that is necessary is to connect a series combination of a resistance and a condenser across the output of the discriminator and to apply the condenser voltage to the a-f amplifier. That a $1/f$ effect is produced thereby is seen from the fact that the uncompensated $f i_m \cos \omega t$ current is proportional to the amplitude $f i_m$ instead of only to i_m and flows through both the resistance R and the condenser C. It causes a voltage across the terminals of the condenser which is proportional to $i_m \int \cos \omega t \, dt$, the constant of proportionality being $1/C$. The integration gives a value that is inversely proportional to the signal frequency f and cancels the f effect in $f i_m$. A voltage that is proportional only to i_m is, therefore, applied to the a-f amplifier.

A direct phase-to-amplitude translation can be obtained by reversing the action illustrated in Fig. 3. In connection with this figure, we learned that PM can be caused by adding in quadrature to the unmodulated vector a the modulation product b obtained in AM. The product b of Eq. (2) can, according to Eq. (3), be split up into the upper and lower side currents of respective frequencies $F \pm f$ if the maximum phase deviation is not much more than about 11.5 deg. Otherwise, an AM effect due to the other side currents given in Eq. (3) would also exist. Since phase demodulation is the opposite action to that shown in Fig. 3, it is only necessary that the PM demodulator shift the phase of the carrier with respect to the side currents by 90 deg, or vice versa, in order to obtain AM. Customary amplitude demodulation then follows in order the extract the a-f currents. When, for instance, a crystal filter is used without completely neutralizing the crystal-holder capacitance, then PM into AM translation takes place.

35. Actions in Frequency Discriminators.—Since frequency discriminators are used not only as FM-AM converters, but also for center-frequency stabilization in FM transmitters, a brief description of the actions in such apparatus is given here.[1] Frequency discriminators are more or less adaptations of the well-known Seeley type of a-f-c discriminator. They are, therefore, basically a primary branch, which is tuned to the center frequency F, and a secondary system, which gives no unidirectional output voltage if the desired center frequency F prevails. It gives, how-

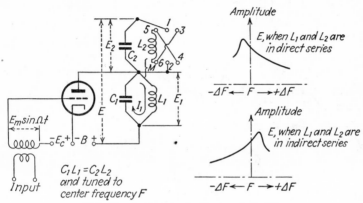

Fig. 55.—Actions in doubly tuned circuits.

ever, either positive or negative output voltages for all instantaneous carrier frequencies F_t that are close to F and within the peak-to-peak frequency swing for which the discriminator is designed. For frequency demodulation the design has to be for a width of at least 150 kc. There are also other types of FM to AM converters but they are not in common use.

Generally, when an emf is induced in a loosely coupled tuned secondary circuit, owing to a resonance current flowing in a tuned primary circuit, the voltages across the respective primary and secondary coils are 90 deg out of phase. When such circuits are connected in the output branch of a vacuum tube, as in Fig. 55, L_1 is the primary coil and L_2 is the secondary coil. Since E_1 is

[1] Travis, C., Automatic Frequency Control, *Proc. IRE*, **23**, 1125, 1935. Foster, D. E., and S. W. Seeley, Automatic Tuning, Simplified Circuits, And Design Practice, *Proc. IRE*, **25**, 289, 1937. Grammer, G., and B. Goodman, Wide Band Frequency Modulation in Amateur Communication, *QST*, January, 1940. Crosby, M. G., Reactance Tube Frequency Modulators, *RCA Rev.*, **5**, 89, 1940. Weiss, W., Detection in FM Receivers, *Communications*, **21**, p. 16, March, 1941. Levy, M. L., Frequency Modulation Receivers, *Communications*, **21**, p. 5, March, 1941.

the driving voltage that causes the resonance current flow I_1 of frequency F, a voltage E_2 which is 90 deg out of phase is produced in the loosely coupled secondary coil L_2. The absolute magnitude of the resultant total voltage E in the neighborhood of the resonance frequency F is then as indicated by the E curve. We have to distinguish between two relative coil connections. In one connection, the double-pole double-throw switch 1-2 is on 3-4 and the fields of coils L_1 and L_2 are additive; for the other connection, 1-2 is on 5-6 and the inductances act in indirect series. The fields are, therefore, subtractive. For this reason, the respective E curves are in a mirror symmetry with respect to the amplitude reference axis.

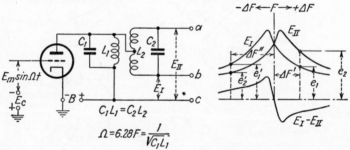

FIG. 56.—How a frequency-discriminator characteristic can be obtained.

Hence, if we desire a system that reacts only when frequency deviations ΔF occur about the center frequency F but does not respond at its output when a center-frequency voltage is applied, we have only to use a differential action in a network that is driven by the voltages E_1 and E_2. This is indicated in connection with the network of Fig. 56, where we likewise obtain symmetrical output voltages E_{I} and E_{II} and the difference voltage E_{I}-E_{II} gives the desired characteristics. Since in Fig. 55, for one switch connection, we have a positive coupling and, for the other switch connection, a negative coupling between primary and secondary tuned circuits, the potential at either end of the secondary winding with respect to the center tap of this winding must be 180 deg out of phase. For this reason the center tap, instead of one end of the secondary, is connected to the primary in Fig. 56. With such a direct connection from primary to secondary, the respective output voltages E_{I} and E_{II} give likewise maximum values on each side of the "mirror or amplitude axis." We note, therefore, that for the center frequency F, the voltages E_1 and E_{II} have equal amplitude values.   Also for frequencies that are deviated by the same amount $\pm\Delta F$ above the center frequency F and below it, we have equal E_I and E_{II} values.   Even though the difference effect E_I-E_{II} could be obtained directly in a network properly connected to terminals a, b, and c of Fig. 56, a preferred form is to apply the respective voltages E_I and E_{II} to two like and separate rectifiers and then to add the resultant direct voltages at the output side in *opposition*.   In this way there can be no direct output voltage at the center frequency F, while at frequencies $F \pm \Delta F$, equal direct voltages of opposite polarity occur at the output side of the

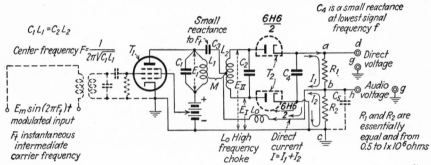

Fig. 57.—Frequency discriminator for obtaining direct output voltage as well as audio-frequency recovery.

discriminator.   The polarity for the resultant output voltage for a frequency $F + \Delta F$ is then in opposition to the polarity of voltage for frequency $F - \Delta F$ since we are dealing now with a *balanced* frequency discriminator.   It can be shown that in tuned coupled circuits such as are used here having the same Q value in the primary as in the secondary, when coupled critically together, the best discriminator condition obtains if the secondary inductance is *twice* the value of the primary inductance.   For such a condition the greatest rate of change occurs in the absolute magnitude of the resultant of two voltage components, which are 90 deg out of phase, when small changes in the angle between the components occur.   Hence, the largest possible difference voltage will be obtained at the output.

   Figure 57 shows how the difference effect is obtained.   Tube T_1 serves the purpose of producing a driving voltage E_1 across primary inductance L_1 of the double-tuned transformer L_1, L_2. This voltage is then affected when the instantaneous carrier frequency F_t changes.   The coupling condenser C_3 is the direct connection to the center tap of the secondary; hence, it must be dynamically a short circuit to currents of frequencies F_t. Since the center tap of L_2 connects to the mid-point of the respective external rectifier resistors R_1 and R_2, a rectified current must flow from b toward the center tap of L_2. The resistances R_1 and R_2 have large values and are usually equal to about 0.1 to 1 megohm for essentially equal tube halves of a 6H6 twin rectifier. Hence, the rectified current must divide itself equally, flowing through the linearity resistance R_1 from the cathode of the upper tube half and through the linearity resistance R_2 from the cathode of the lower tube half. Since the purpose of the condenser C_4 is to connect the respective cathodes dynamically together with respect to F_t frequencies, we note that the h-f voltages E_I and E_{II} have such effects on the direct potential at point a with respect to ground that for the center frequency we have $E_I = E_{II}$. Hence, this potential vanishes because the direct current flow through R_1 and R_2 is in opposition and causes equal and opposite direct voltages across terminals ab and bc.

But when the instantaneous carrier frequency has a value $F_t = F + \Delta F'$, we note in Fig. 56 that E_{II} is larger than E_I and we have the corresponding values e_2 and e_1 acting at the input side of the discriminator shown in Fig. 57. This means that the direct current flow I_1 through R_1 is now larger than the direct current flow I_2 through resistor R_2. Since the values of R_1 and R_2 are essentially equal, a certain *positive* potential results at terminal d with respect to ground. If the instantaneous frequency had had a value $F_t = F - \Delta F''$, we note from Fig. 56 that $E_{II} = e_2'$ would be smaller than $E_I = e_1'$. Hence, in Fig. 57 the drop in R_1 would be smaller than the negative drop in R_2, leaving a certain negative potential at terminal d with respect to ground. Hence, the output terminals d and g of the discriminator will give direct voltages with a polarity positive or negative, according to whether the instantaneous carrier frequency F_t is larger or smaller than the center frequency F. The terminals d and g are used when the discriminator is employed for stabilization of the center frequency F, since the output voltages can be made to change the fixed grid bias of a reactance tube. When the fixed bias of such a modulator tube is changed, the fixed reactance injection into an oscillator can be made to compensate the center-frequency drift of this oscillator.

Inasmuch as in this network rectifiers are used, we have also inherent amplitude demodulation after FM-AM conversion has taken place. Since in Fig. 57 the condenser C_4 has a reactance that is small, even for the lowest audio frequency of interest, both rectifier cathodes are essentially at ground potential as far as the useful a-f and h-f voltages are concerned. In this network the condenser C_5 is needed only when a h-f choke is employed between the center tap of L_2 and mid-point b. The use of such a C_5 con-

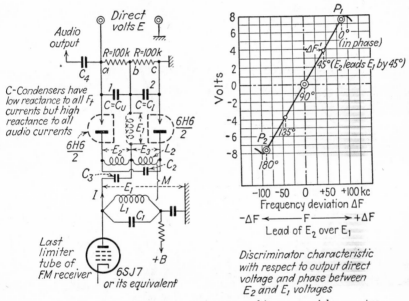

FIG. 58.—Discriminator connections as used in commercial apparatus.

denser and a h-f choke coil will decrease the effect of the resistors R_1 and R_2 on the Q value of the C_1L_1 branch. The magnitude of condenser C_5 is so chosen that it has a high impedance even at the highest audio frequency of 15 kc, but a low impedance for any instantaneous carrier frequencies F_t. Hence, h is a potent a-f pole and terminals h and g will give directly an a-f output. The a-f output could also be taken off across terminals d and g if condenser C_4 by-passes only h-f carrier currents and acts as a high reactance for the entire a-f range.

Figure 58 shows a symmetrical discriminator. Its actions are as shown in Fig. 59. In Fig. 58 the output of the two rectifier halves not only work into equal high resistances R but also use equal condensers C which behave as low reactances at all carrier frequencies F_t but as high reactances at all audio frequencies. The a-f output is taken off through an isolation condenser C_4 from the cathode that is dynamically high or potent with respect

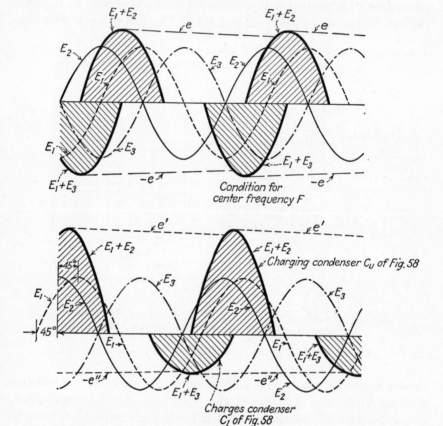

(a)-Voltage E_2 leads voltage E_1 by 90 degrees, e = –e , positive (E_1+E_2)-caps cancel effects of negative (E_1+E_3) caps

(b)- Voltage E_2 leads voltage E_1 by 45 degrees, e'>–e'', positive (E_1+E_2)- caps larger than effect of negative (E_1+E_3)-caps, hence direct output voltage which is positive

Fig. 59.—Explanation of the cause of an output voltage.

to the other cathode, which is at ground potential. We have twofold power transfer from an i-f stage into the discriminator. One transfer is by means of the coupling condenser C_3, which has a negligible reactance at all F_t frequencies. The other power transfer is by means of the mutual inductance of the discriminator transformer L_1, L_2. Since the reactance of C is negligible at all occurring carrier frequencies F_t, the primary voltage E_1 acts essentially also across the h-f choke. Hence, we have generally the voltages E_2 and E_3 across the halves of the L_2 inductance. The high resistors R make point a a potent potential point with respect to ground, not only as far as the output direct voltages are concerned, but also as far as the audible-frequency output voltages play a part. Rectification takes place at very high frequencies, customarily at 4.3 Mc. To such frequencies the condensers C act as large electric storage tanks. This is all the more pronounced since the resistors across them cannot cause much drainage. Hence, these condensers will essentially hold constant direct voltages, which are equal to the peak values of the voltages that charge them.

The h-f choke is connected to the mid-point of L_2 and we have equal and opposite h-f voltages E_2 and E_3. Owing to the explanation given, in Fig. 59a the voltage E_2 leads E_1 by 90 deg. As far as the output currents and the output voltages of the rectifiers are concerned, only positive voltages on the respective rectifier plates can be instrumental. For the upper rectifier, the driving voltage caps are marked $E_1 + E_2$ and the upper condenser C_u will charge up to essentially the peak value of these caps and will discharge but little in potential during the negative-cap cycle. The negative-cap cycle is not shown, but the slight discharge is indicated by the somewhat slanting peak-value line. During the following positive-cap action, the small discharge loss in the condenser potential will be compensated, and essentially the peak value of the $E_1 + E_2$ caps prevail. Hence, we preserve a positive potential e on the upper condenser plate 1 of condenser C_u. With respect to the lower rectifier, we note that the caps $E_1 + E_3$ cause the same positive potential e on the lower plate 2 of condenser C_l. Since the voltages across C_u and C_l are "bucking" each other, there can be no direct as well as no a-f output voltage at the center frequency F.

If we apply an FM voltage at a certain moment for which the instantaneous frequency F_t is somewhat deviated from the center frequency F, then the phase relationship shown in Fig. 59a no longer holds. Suppose that the ΔF deviation causes E_2 to lead E_1 by 45 deg instead of by 90 deg as is the case for the center frequency. Hence, E_3 lags behind E_1 by 135 deg instead of by 90 deg.

We have, then, the conditions depicted in Fig. 59b and note that the voltage caps $E_1 + E_2$ affecting the magnitude of the positive potential of the upper plate 1 of C_u give rise to a much larger e' value than the voltage caps $E_1 + E_3$ which cause the positive value e'' on plate 2 of the lower condenser C_l. The result is that point a is at a higher potential than ground, and a *positive* direct potential, as well as an audio signal, can be taken off at pole a with respect to ground.

In connection with this discussion it will be noted that the discriminator characteristic of Fig. 58 is limited, even though high linearity resistors R are being used in the respective load branches of the rectifiers. The limitation is due to the fact that at resonance, *i.e.*, when both the primary and secondary circuits are tuned to the center frequency F, a 90-deg phase shift occurs between the primary voltage E_1 and E_2 as well as E_3. This is seen in Fig. 59a, where E_2 leads E_1 by 90 deg and E_3 is 90 deg behind E_1. But for any instantaneous carrier frequency such as $F_t = F + \Delta F'$, we still have antiphase relationship between E_2 and E_3, since the secondary coil L_2 is center-tapped, but E_2 leads E_1 only by 45 deg. For a frequency deviation corresponding to the upper bend P_1 of the discriminator characteristic, the voltages E_2 and E_1 are in phase and E_3 and E_1 are in antiphase, and vice versa, at the lower bend P_2 of Fig. 58.

This can be realized from the fact that for all frequency values of F_t, the primary voltage E_1 is, after all, responsible for any actions in the discriminator. The condenser C_3 represents essentially zero reactance at all F_t values, and, therefore, $E_1 + E_2$ acts as the driving voltage on the upper rectifier. But at resonance frequency F, the secondary is tuned and must behave like a *resistance* load, which accounts for the quadrature addition $E_2 + jE_1$. If, therefore, the carrier frequency F is increased by an amount $\Delta F'$, the reactance of C_2 decreases while the reactance of L_2 increases and the net effect is that the C_2L_2 branch no longer behaves like a resistance load. The C_2L_2 branch acts now more like a capacitance load since more current passes through C_2 than through the L_2 branch. Hence, the resulting current flowing toward the parallel C_2 and L_2 branches is no longer in phase with the voltage across C_2, but is leading this voltage by a certain angle. This causes in turn a phase of E_2 with respect to the primary driving voltage E_1 which is less than 90 deg leading, 90 deg being the angle of lead for the resonance frequency F. The very opposite occurs if an instantaneous carrier frequency F_t lower than F prevails and the lead of E_2 over E_1 becomes more than 90 deg. Between the limits corresponding to points P_1 and P_2 we have, therefore, phase angle leads of from zero to 180 time degrees. Beyond these points, for instance, beyond point P_2 of Fig. 58, we will have more than 180-deg lead of E_2 with respect to E_1 but at the expense of reduced output voltages. In addition, the linearity with respect to ΔF changes is lost when we go beyond such points

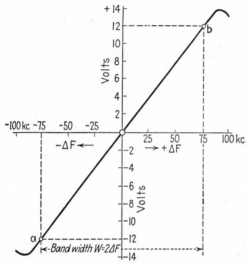

FIG. 60.—Characteristic of a frequency demodulator (note that band width W refers only to the linear portion of the characteristic and is not necessarily equal to the band width for which transfer network is to be designed).

as P_1 and P_2 of Fig. 58. The discriminator should not be operated beyond such limits although some sort of frequency demodulation still takes place on respective branches beyond points P_1 and P_2.

36. Band-width Design of Discriminators.—The problem of band width in the design of discriminators has reference to the linear portion a to b of the discriminator characteristic of Fig. 60. Generally, the linear portion should cover somewhat more frequency space than 150 kc as required by the maximum permissible peak-to-peak frequency swing. If only the portion a-b is taken into account, $2\,\Delta F$ is the total band width and is equal to 150 kc. If Q_1 and Q_2 denote the Q values of the primary $C_1 L_1$ and the secondary $C_2 L_2$ branches of the discriminator, where $C_2 L_2 = C_1 L_1 = CL$, we have for the center frequency F in the kilocycles, as well as for the desired band width W in kilocycles, the relations

$$\left. \begin{array}{c} F = \dfrac{1,592 \times 10^2}{\sqrt{CL}} \\[2mm] W = \dfrac{F}{\sqrt{Q_1 Q_2}} \end{array} \right\} \tag{130}$$

where the capacitance C is in micromicrofarad and the inductance L in microhenrys.

At this point it should be realized that the center frequency F affecting the discriminator in FM receivers is the intermediate frequency, which is usually 4.3 Mc. For discriminators used in transmitters for center-frequency stabilization, the center frequency F has other values, for instance, 1 Mc as in the RCA transmitter shown in Fig. 35. The center frequency could also be in the neighborhood of intermediate frequencies such as are used in ordinary AM superheterodynes.

Tuned circuits used in FM receivers, as well as in transmitters, cannot be made very selective since they have to pass all important side currents without frequency attenuation. The tuning must be broader the larger the very maximum frequency swing ΔF. This swing changes in an FM transmitter from a narrow band to a wide band as the instantaneous carrier frequency is multiplied in order to obtain the final-frequency swing. The networks in the i-f stages of an FM receiver generally use a suitable ohmic resistance R across the parallel combination of C and L of a tuned circuit in order to cause broader tuning. When, therefore, such a circuit through magnetic coupling energizes a Crosby discriminator as shown in Fig. 61, we have, for instance, for the Q value of the primary network with C, L, and R in multiple, the empirical design formula

$$Q = \frac{1}{6.28 FCR} = \frac{6.28 FL}{R} = \frac{F}{1.5W} \tag{131}$$

where the band width W and the frequency F are in cycles per second, C in farads, L in henrys, and R in ohms.

37. Useful Discriminator Networks.—Figures 35 and 73 show discriminators used in the RCA and the General Electric FM transmitters for the stabilization of the center frequency. Figure 61 shows how a Crosby discriminator brings about center-frequency stabilization. It will be noted that no condenser coupling between

the primary discriminator coil L and the input coil $L_1 + L_2$ is
employed as is done in the Seeley discriminator. The primary
C, L, R branch is tuned to the center frequency F and for a Q
value as is given in Eq. (131). The secondary coil $L_1 + L_2$
forms input branches C_1L_1 and C_2L_2. The C_1L_1 input tank is

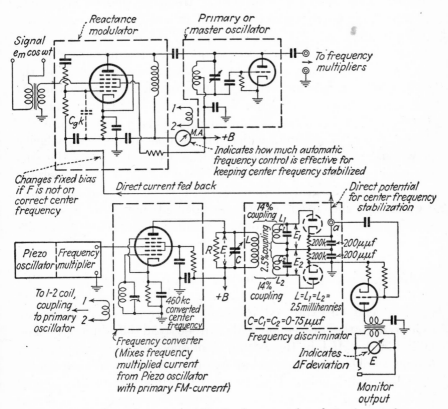

Fig. 61.—Center-frequency stabilization by means of an electronic control.

tuned somewhat above and the C_2L_2 branch somewhat below the
center frequency. These resonance frequencies are often chosen
near the upper and the lower cutoff frequency of the pass band.
The Q value of either input tank is made *twice* the Q value of the
primary C, L, R tank. The symmetrical off-tuning of the respective input tanks depends on the maximum frequency deviations
effective in the FM voltage E. This frequency deviation is not
necessarily 2×75 kc since for practical center-frequency stabilization we affect the primary or master center frequency of the oscil-

lator shown in this figure. In this network, a small amount of the primary oscillator energy is fed by means of the 1-2 link into the mixer of the frequency converter. The output current of a multiplied frequency of a stable piezo source, together with the superimposed current due to the 1-2 coupling, produces then a difference frequency. The difference frequency has an intermediate center frequency much lower than the primary center frequency, say about 460 kc against a value of about 5,000 kc, as is often used for the primary center frequency of the master oscillator. The respective maximum-frequency deviations will still be the same as they were in the primary center frequency. Since the FM voltages E_1 and E_2 act on the respective rectifiers having linearity resistors of 200,000 ohms, we obtain at terminal a a direct potential with respect to ground, which has a magnitude and polarity depending on the magnitude as well as the direction of the corresponding center-frequency drift. Hence, if this direct voltage is applied to the grid of the reactance tube, the tube will shift accordingly the fixed reactance injected into the associated oscillator branch when the primary center frequency is not at its correct value.

Since in this network the desired FM is also active, it can be taken off over the output condenser C_0 from terminal a and be amplified. By means of a suitable voltmeter E, the voltage readings can be expressed in terms of corresponding frequency swings and the degree of FM can be read off directly. The milliammeter MA in the B supply of the reactance tube gives a means of determining to what extent the control of the center frequency takes hold. For the correct primary center frequency this meter will give a certain reading. The meter will give a higher reading if the center frequency is off in one direction and a lower reading if it is off in the other direction.

Inasmuch as the controlling action of the drift in the center frequency is more effective the narrower the band width of the discriminator, and because the desirable FM deviations cause also instantaneous potentials, a filter has to be provided to prevent the FM variations from affecting the reactance tube. This is shown in connection with the General Electric FM transmitter in Fig. 73. It is the C_3R_3 filter that permits only currents of frequencies lower than the lowest desirable a-f f to pass toward the grid branch of the reactance tube. Only such currents are needed in the center frequency control since the center frequency drifts only slowly as a rule.

Figure 62 shows how a discriminator is connected to the final i-f stage of 4.3-Mc center frequency, which is designed for a band width of about 225 kc, while the discriminator covers a linear peak-to-peak swing characteristic of somewhat more than 150 kc. Figure 63 illustrates a similar arrangement of a discriminator and shows how the discriminator characteristic depends on the applied voltage.

In the design of the output network of a discriminator, we choose the high linearity resistance R_l about equal to 100,000 ohms

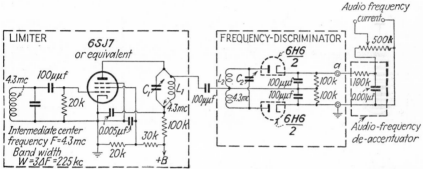

Fig. 62.—Frequency demodulator as a coupling between the last i-f stage (final limiter) and the recovered audio-frequency output.

in Fig. 63. The respective condensers C_l in parallel with each linearity resistor are so chosen that their reactance at the highest desired audio frequency is approximately equal to the value of each linearity resistor, or $1/(6.28f_{max}C_l) = R_l$ where f_{max} is usually taken as 15 kc.

38. Tests on Discriminators.—Commercial FM receivers use a fixed L_1, L_2 transformer. The small condenser C_1 and C_2 in the primary and secondary of this transformer, indicated in Fig. 62, are the only parts of discriminators that require adjustment. There are many ways of measuring the linearity of a discriminator but the most straightforward method seems to be to use a high-resistance voltmeter and to measure the output direct voltage between point a and ground, while varying the applied intermediate frequency in known steps. Suppose all i-f stages are aligned and that the output condenser C_1 of the last i-f stage, which is also a limiter stage, has the correct setting. A voltage of the center intermediate frequency is applied to the grid of the mixer tube[1] and the setting of the secondary condenser C_2 of Fig. 62 is varied until zero output voltage is noted between point a and ground. It is of importance to realize that both terminals of this condenser are above ground potential and, therefore, a well-insulated screw driver is needed for the adjustment. The adjustment is, besides, rather critical since it balances the discriminator. Equal voltages are then applied from the signal generator of frequencies, say, 75 kc above and the same below the intermediate center frequency. The high-resistance voltmeter should indicate

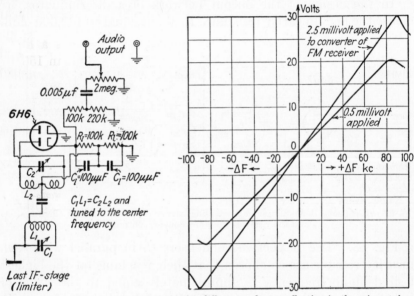

FIG. 63.—Discriminator characteristics for different voltages effective in the mixer tube of an FM receiver.

equal but opposite direct voltages. If unequal voltages are obtained, this is an indication that the primary condenser setting is not correct. By changing the setting of condenser C_1 equality can be secured. It is then best to check again the C_2 setting with the center frequency to determine if zero output voltage is still obtained. This is about all that can be done with a commercial receiver, although the linearity over the entire range can be determined in the same way by using, say, signal frequencies which are ± 10, ± 20, ± 30, etc., kc off the intermediate center frequency of 4.3 Mc. The output voltage of the signal generator should be constant or at least so that the limiter applies equal

[1] Of receiver (not shown).

voltages to the discriminator for all intermediate carrier frequencies used in the test.

39. Useful Amplitude Limiters.—In FM receivers, amplitude limiters are needed in the last i-f stage, or in the last two stages that precede the discriminator. Amplitude limitation or saturation can be accomplished by grid limiting, screen limiting, plate limiting, or any combination of these methods. The limiter of

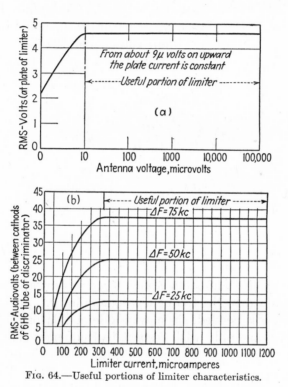

FIG. 64.—Useful portions of limiter characteristics.

Fig. 62 uses a pentode tube 6SJ7 or its equivalent. It saturates with effective input voltages of about 10 volts. Since it has essentially unity gain at the start of saturation, the output voltage is also about 10 volts. Inasmuch as we have to transmit currents of signal frequencies up to about 15 kc, the time constants should be short compared with a time interval of 1/15,000 sec. Generally, sharp cutoff tubes make the best limiters. The use of tubes having large g_m values will increase the output voltage that is applied to the discriminator. Grid leaks cause plate-current limitation, and low screen and plate supply voltages produce plate-voltage limiting. When two limiter stages are used, a gain of about 2 to 5 is obtained.

Figure 64a shows how the input antenna voltage, which is a measure for the received field intensity ε in $\mu v/m$, is related to the output voltage of the last i-f stage which acts as a limiter. This output voltage should remain essentially constant since it is the voltage effective at the input side of the frequency discriminator. We note, therefore, that a high-gain i-f amplifier is essential in FM reception since we have to saturate the last i-f tube with the lowest possible antenna input voltage in order to avoid disturbing peak interference. For the static limiter characteristic of

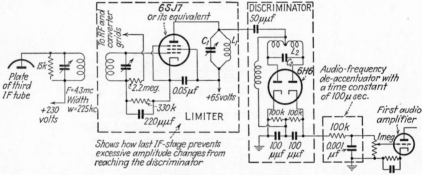

FIG. 65.—Limiter with suitable values.

Fig. 64a, we note that from about 9 μv on upward, a constant voltage is applied to the frequency demodulator. Such an amplitude constancy is needed, since even a demodulator that produces an output voltage only with respect to frequency changes is still in some way dependent on the amplitude of the impressed intermediate frequency voltage. This can be seen from the two discriminator characteristics of Fig. 63. Figure 64b shows the a-f rms voltage given off between the respective rectifier cathodes with respect to the limiter current for different frequency excursions. The *horizontal* portion of these ΔF characteristics is employed for undistorted frequency demodulation.

Usually 6SJ7 tubes or their equivalent, operated without bias and with about 330,000 ohms in the grid circuit with reduced plate and screen voltages, as shown in Fig. 65, act as good limiters. When the voltages in the antenna exceed the threshold point, then the increasing grid bias, together with the plate current cutoff, prevents the plate current from increasing. With some tubes the knee or threshold point on the limiter characteristic is as high as 200 μv, while with other tubes, it may be only 25 μv. When an 1852 tube or its equivalent is used in the h-f stage, the knee can be brought down to about 8 μv.

Figures 66a and b compare one and two stages of amplitude limiters and the corresponding characteristics are given in Fig.

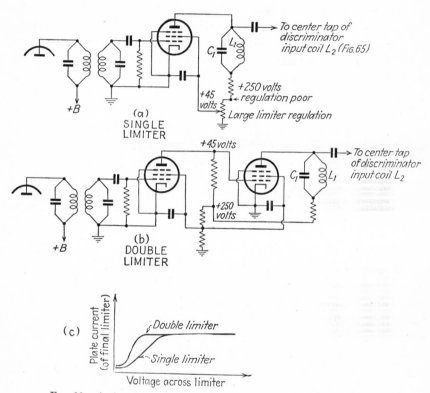

FIG. 66.—Actions in single and double stages of amplitude limitation.

66c. For properly designed FM receivers, *two* stages of amplitude limitation are *desirable*. It should be understood that the limiter must provide at its limiting voltage enough carrier level to drive properly the first a-f amplifier. Hence, limiting the output voltage of the last i-f stage, as well as the corresponding output current, to too small values, may cause insufficient a-f recovery for weaker degrees of FM. We have, therefore, the same problem as with AM where, for instance, for $K = 10$ per cent AM we should still produce maximum a-f output with moderate field intensities affecting the first tube of the FM receiver. Hence, it is most important that the FM receiver have a high gain before the amplified i-f voltages are applied to the amplitude limiter.

The more the degree of amplitude limitation, the more sensitive the FM receiver has to be. From the theory of random or fluctuation noise in an antenna network, we know that the sensitivity should not be increased beyond the point where the random noise produces saturation in the limiter stage. For a maximum frequency swing of ± 75 kc and about 100-ohm antenna impedance, this noise has approximately 1-μv effective value and is considered to have a corresponding peak value of 4.5 μv. Good present-day FM receivers are designed, therefore, to produce complete limiter action when the applied FM voltage at the input side of the receiver is somewhere between 10 and 50 μv. The margin requirement of the FCC is 50 μv/m field intensity. Hence, for an effective length of a receiver dipole of 2 m, the applied FM voltage is about 100 μv. A 10,000,000-fold gain is needed to cause a voltage saturation of 10 effective volts at a limiter.

Even though the limiter action can be tested statically by obtaining experimental characteristics as shown in Figs. 64a and 66c, a dynamic test seems a better procedure. In the dynamic test an i-f current with 50 per cent AM is applied to the limiter with a voltage level for optimum limiter saturation. The AM remaining in the output should be decreased at least 20 db if the limiter functions properly. By this is meant that if K_1 is the degree of input AM and K_2 the degree of output AM, then

$$20 \log_{10} (K_1/K_2) \geqq 20 \text{ or } K_1/K_2 \geqq 1.$$

40. Time Constants in FM Networks.—The trend in FM receivers is to increase the sensitivity in order to avoid static interference. It used to be customary to work down to about 25 to 50 μv when amplitude limitation is used. Values from 5 to 10 μv are not uncommon sensitivities today.

The static limiter characteristics shown in Sec. 39 have reference only to desired output relations of the limiter stage as experienced at the input side of the frequency demodulator. The time constants may also play a part if it is important that undesirable signals, such as interfering noise, be kept from essentially affecting the output of the discriminator. The reason for this is that the time lag introduced by any of the stages preceding the discriminator may affect the voltages that arrive at the input side of the discriminator. This becomes clear if we realize that the time constant of any band-pass filter must be short in comparison with the time it takes to cause useful FM changes. Hence when, for instance, a desired frequency change occurs so fast that the automatic grid bias due to a condenser charge across a cathode resistor cannot check the corresponding plate-current flow fast enough, distortion must be caused. For instance, when a sharp interfering impulse occurs faster than CR sec, then the cathode bias due to R with its by-pass condenser C will not check the pulse fast enough and will emphasize the pulse interference.

Generally, we have to deal with three types of time constants, since we have fundamentally three different networks.

Any of these networks has a certain effective resistance R. If, therefore, our FM current passes through a coil of inductance L, at the first moment, *i.e.*, at $t = 0$ sec, there can be no effect of the resistance since no voltage drop occurs before current flows. The same is true as far as the inductance L is concerned at this time. During the first few moments only a portion of the inductance seems active, because it takes time to build up the magnetic field to the full value. This means that unless all the lines of magnetic force are established, the counter emf of the coil cannot cause the full choking action that we would expect from the value of L. Theoretically, the magnetic field of a coil builds up according to an exponential function when a fixed voltage is suddenly applied, and collapses according to such a function when the supply no longer acts. Since such functions call theoretically for an infinite duration of time, because of the asymptotic approaches for the charge as well as the discharge, from an engineering point of view we may resort to a growth as well as to a decay constant. Such constants indicate how fast the growths or decays are taking place for fixed R and L values. We have then the well-known damping constant α due to the damping factor $\epsilon^{-\alpha t}$.

The three fundamental networks are (1) a coil (L, R) such as is used for transferring power from one stage of a network to the next stage; (2) a condenser C that has either its own effective series resistance R or such a resistance in the branch that feeds power to another network; and (3) a circuit that contains a capacitance C, an inductance L, and exhibits an effective resistance R. The time constants in seconds then are

$$\tau = \begin{cases} \dfrac{L}{R} & \text{for } L \text{ and } R \\ CR & \text{for } C \text{ and } R \\ \dfrac{2L}{R} & \text{for } C, L, \text{ and } R \end{cases} \tag{132}$$

where C is in farads, L in henrys, R in ohms, and $\tau = 1/\alpha$. That the time constant of the third network does not show C directly does not mean that it is not functional since, when the natural frequency of this network is taken into account, we note that $f \cong 1/(6.28\ \sqrt{CL})$ cycles per second and C can be expressed in terms of f and L.

Taking $\tau = CR$ sec we know from transient-current theory that during this time a condenser C reduces its charge to 37 per cent of its original value, when a discharge takes place over R ohms.

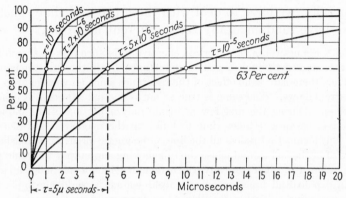

Fig. 67.—Time-constant characteristics.

This constant also indicates that during CR sec the terminal voltage of a condenser rises to a value that falls short of its final value by 37 per cent. Hence, a well-defined and convenient reference level is obtained by using such time constants. From Eq. (132) we note that in a C, L, R circuit the rise as well as the decay occurs half as fast as in an L, R circuit. Moreover, it does not matter whether we think in terms of growth or in terms of decay as far as the speed of the corresponding electrical action is concerned. Plotting then the growth factor $\epsilon^{\alpha t}$, we have curves as shown in Fig. 67, which hold for all three expressions of Eq. (132). From these formulas we note that for the L, R case it does not matter at all what the value of L is if R can be properly chosen, or what the value of R is as long as L is properly chosen. Only the ratio L/R determines the speed of the corresponding electrical action. In a similar way, for a condenser-resistance coupling it is only the magnitude of the product CR that counts as far as the speed of the action is concerned.

It is true, in actual circuit design, that there are other com-
promises to be met besides the speed of electrical actions. For
instance, if we use a network where R is a cathode resistor and C
is a by-pass condenser that must pass all currents down to, say,
50 cycles per second essentially like a very low impedance, then
we may not reduce the value of C very much. In such a case it
may be possible to change the value of R somewhat in order to
produce the desired minimum speed action. But also here there
is little leeway for changing R, as in cases where R should cause
linearity, where R produces the desired bias, or where R determines
the gain partly. Fortunately, in such cases the functional values
of at least one of the two circuit constants are such that generally
a permissible speed can be obtained. From the curves of Fig. 67,
we note also that the intersection of the 63 per cent line with the
respective curves determines directly the corresponding time
constants τ in seconds.

When several i-f stages precede the discriminator, as in an FM
receiver, then the network of each section exhibits a certain time
delay and interactions of such delays can take place if such networks are coupled to each other, unless a high-resistance coupling
is provided between the two networks so as to prevent these
interactions. When a tube is used as a separator of two networks,
it may be assumed that the interactions are essentially only small.

A network having a time constant $\tau = 1/\alpha$ when exposed to a
sudden steep voltage impulse that changes abruptly from zero
to a maximum E value in volts, experiences, therefore, at the
output of this network a voltage $E\epsilon^{\alpha t}$. For a C, L, R network the
α value is $(R/2L)$. For an a-f emphasizer, where a resistance R
is connected in series with an inductance L, we would have an α
value of $(-R/L)$. In such a network a signal voltage $e_m \cos \omega t$
is applied across the series combination of L and R. The voltage
developed across L acts between the grid and the cathode of an
audio amplifier, the output of which actuates the reactance tube
of a frequency modulator. But if we have a network of time constant τ_1 on the grid side of a vacuum tube and a network of time
constant τ_2 on the plate side, then a sudden voltage dip occurring
at the input side of the first network would apply to the grid a
voltage $E\epsilon^{-\alpha_1 t}$, where E is the level of the voltage before the dip
takes place. Suppose $\alpha_1 = 1/\tau_1$ is due to a condenser C_1 across
a grid-cathode path and a resistor R_1 which is in series with the

grid. The voltage E is then applied across the series combination of C_1 and R_1. Then $E\epsilon^{-t/c_1R_1}$ is impressed on the grid. Suppose further that the plate-to-cathode path is bridged by a condenser C_2 and a resistor R_2 acts towards the B source and includes also the resistance effect of this source. Then, as far as the effective resistance value of the plate side is concerned, we have also the dynamic plate resistance r_p acting in parallel with R_2. The effective resistance on the plate side is then $R_e = r_pR_2/(r_p + R_2)$, giving a time constant $\tau_2 = C_2R_2$ for this network. The voltage across the condenser C_2 is then

$$E_c = E\left(\frac{1}{1 - (\alpha_1/\alpha_2)}\,\epsilon^{-\alpha_1 t} + \frac{1}{1 - (\alpha_2/\alpha_1)}\,\epsilon^{-\alpha_2 t}\right) \qquad (133)$$

Since in this formula either the time constant $\tau_1 = 1/\alpha_1$ or the time constant $\tau_2 = 1/\alpha_2$ is smaller, one term must be negative. Suppose $\alpha_1 = 10^{-5}$ and $\alpha_2 = 2 \times 10^{-5}$, then $\alpha_1/\alpha_2 = 0.5$ and $\alpha_2/\alpha_1 = 2$ and we find

$$E_c = E(2\epsilon^{-0.00001t} - \epsilon^{-0.00002t}) = 2E\epsilon^{-0.00001t} - \underbrace{E\epsilon^{-0.00002t}}_{\text{decays faster}}$$

For equal time constants $\tau_1 = \tau_2$ we have also $\alpha_1 = \alpha_2 = \alpha$ and the evaluation of Eq. (133) does not give a determinate solution. However, it can be shown that we have then a formula $E_c = (1 + \alpha t)E\epsilon^{-\alpha t}$.

The time constant $\tau = 1/\alpha$ is made up of at least two electrical constants, such as C and R, or L and R. It gives, therefore, a means for designing networks that have definite phase characteristics with respect to different frequencies. This can be understood if we realize that a series combination of, say, a condenser C and a resistance R has a displacement current through C of exactly the same magnitude as the current through R. But as far as the voltages across C, across R, and across the series combination of C and R are concerned matters are different, since the time delay of the entire RC combination must show up as far as the terminal voltages are concerned. In a similar manner when C is in parallel with R, as far as the voltages across C and R are concerned, they must be identical, since we deal with one and the same terminals. But in this case the branch currents must be affected, as well as the total current which flows to the parallel combination, since the time delay must cause such actions. In other words the time delay causes corresponding amplitude changes.

The simplest way of examining the time-constant effect is, in case of harmonic currents, for instance, for a sinusoidal current flow. Suppose we are dealing with a coil and a resistance in series. The coil has essentially only an inductance L in comparison with the magnitude of the series resistance R. We know that we have a time constant $\tau = R/L$ sec where L is in henrys and R in ohms. We also know that the impedance to a sinusoidal current flow is $Z = \sqrt{R^2 + X^2}$ with a phase angle $\tan^{-1}(X/R)$ between Z and R, where $X = 6.28fL$ and f is in cycles per second. For a series combination of this type we also know that the voltage across the series combination makes a phase angle with the voltage across R. The reactance X depends on the rate of variation of the current flow and increases, therefore, directly with the frequency f, and the phase angle must change accordingly. The relative magnitudes of the coil voltage, terminal voltage across the resistor, and the applied voltage across the series combination must change also. Hence, even when the applied voltage is kept fixed, the terminal voltage across each circuit element, namely across L and R, must show a dependency with respect to f and must bear a definite relation to the time constant $\tau = L/R$. Using this substitution in the expression $Z = \sqrt{R^2 + \omega^2 L^2}$, we find

$$Z = \left\langle \begin{array}{l} R\sqrt{1 + \tau^2\omega^2} \\[2ex] L\sqrt{\omega^2 + \tau^{-2}} = mL \end{array} \right\} \tag{134}$$

Calling E the effective voltage impressed on the series combination and E_1 and E_2 the effective voltages across R and L, respectively, we may write

$$E = \left\langle \begin{array}{l} E_1\sqrt{1 + \tau^2\omega^2} \\[2ex] IL\sqrt{\omega^2 + \tau^{-2}} \end{array} \right\} \tag{135}$$

since for a current I we have $E = IZ$ and $E_1 = IR$. Each expression yields $E = \sqrt{E_1^2 + E_2^2}$, i.e., expresses the same thing. Since in the first expression two different voltages E and E_1 appear and the remaining voltage E_2 is $\sqrt{E^2 - E_1^2}$, i.e., it is obtainable by geometrical quadrature subtraction, we have

$$\sqrt{1 + \tau^2\omega^2} = \begin{cases} \text{either} & \dfrac{E}{E_1} \\ \\ \text{or} & \dfrac{Z}{R} \end{cases} \tag{136}$$

Hence, we are in a position to compare the two voltages and can write for the ratio E/E_1 the relation

$$\text{db} = 20 \log_{10} \sqrt{1 + \tau^2\omega^2} = 10 \log_{10} (1 + \tau^2\omega^2) \tag{137}$$

which defines the amplitude-frequency characteristic in terms of the time constant $\tau = L/R$. When expressed in f cycles per second, we have the important formula

$$\text{db} = 10 \log_{10} (1 + 39.45f^2\tau^2) \tag{138}$$

where the number of decibels is either positive or negative depending on whether the ratio $Z/R = E/E_1$ is larger or smaller than unity.

Hence, as far as the amplitude-frequency characteristic is concerned, the time constant $\tau = L/R$ sec determines what we may expect. Even though for a fixed time constant τ we have one and the same decibel characteristic with respect to the frequency f, there are many possibilities for keeping τ unchanged and yet dealing with entirely different L and R values. For instance, an inductance of 100 henrys and a series resistance of 10^6 ohms give a time constant $\tau = 100 \times 10^{-6} = 10^{-4}$ sec or 100 μ sec. The same time constant, as well as the same decibel characteristic, would exist for $L = 50$ henrys and $R = 500,000$ ohms, or for 1 henry and 10,000 ohms. What absolute value of L to choose to obtain a given value of τ with a desired performance with respect to the operating frequencies depends upon where the series combination is to be used. If it is to be used in a power circuit, then a small value of L has to be chosen, since otherwise the R value would be large and lead to prohibitive circuit losses. But if the combination is to be used in a customary low-level tube circuit, as in the preliminary stages of FM transmitters where signal voltages are applied to tubes having a power rating like tubes in receivers, relatively large values of L are chosen. For instance, when the series combination acts in the plate branch of a tube where a signal voltage is active on the control grid and the voltage drop across the impedance $\sqrt{R^2 + \omega^2L^2}$ is used for activating a grid of a succeeding tube, it must be realized that dynamically this combination is also across the grid-cathode gap of the succeeding tube, even though an isolation condenser is employed between the stages. Since for the low-frequency range, say 25 cycles per second, R is effective essentially only in the square-root value, this resistance must be high in order to cause sufficient voltage drop on the grid. Hence, a value of about 1 megohm seems suitable. But this requires for a fixed τ value, a large value for L also. In a similar way, if the series combination is to be used

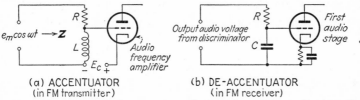

(a) ACCENTUATOR
(in FM transmitter)

(b) DE-ACCENTUATOR
(in FM receiver)

FIG. 68.—Networks for audio-frequency preemphasis and audio-frequency deemphasis in the upper audio-frequency range of signal currents.

directly in the input side of a tube as in Fig. 68a, then the voltage drop across the inductance drives the grid and we have to use sufficient inductance to cause a desired frequency accentuation in the upper a-f range. This will be brought out in more detail in Sec. 41.

When we deal with a series combination of a condenser C and an ohmic resistance R, we have the impedance $Z = \sqrt{R^2 + 1/(\omega C)^2}$ and in terms of the time constant $\tau = CR$ sec, the expression

$$Z = \begin{cases} R\sqrt{1 + \omega^{-2}\tau^{-2}} = pR \\[2ex] \dfrac{1}{C}\sqrt{\tau^2 + \omega^{-2}} = \dfrac{q}{C} \end{cases} \qquad (139)$$

For an effective voltage E across the series combination, a voltage drop E_1 across R due to the current flow I, and a voltage drop E_2 across C, we have

$$E = \begin{cases} pE_1 \\[2ex] \dfrac{qI}{C} \end{cases} \qquad (140)$$

Hence, if we compare E and E_1, we have

$$db = 20 \log_{10} \frac{Z}{R} = 20 \log_{10} q \tag{141}$$

or

$$db = 10 \log_{10} \left(1 + \frac{1}{\omega^2 \tau^2}\right) \tag{142}$$

But quite often we utilize the condenser voltage $I/\omega C$ for causing the frequency characteristic and we require then the ratio E_2/E, which would lead to negative decibel values. If expressed as E/E_2, we obtain the answer in positive decibels. By dividing the second expression of Eq. (139) by ω on each side, we finally obtain for the comparison of E against E_2

$$db = 20 \log_{10} \frac{E}{E_2} = 20 \log_{10} (\omega C Z) = 20 \log_{10} (q\omega)$$

$$db = 20 \log_{10} \frac{E}{E_2} = 10 \log_{10} (1 + \omega^2 \tau^2)$$

$$= 10 \log_{10} (1 + 39.45 f^2 \tau^2) \tag{143}$$

This is apparently the same expression obtained in Eq. (138), but with the difference that the time constant is now $\tau = CR$ sec and we utilize the reactive drop E_2 across the condenser C for causing the frequency characteristic. The frequency f in this formula is again in cycles per second.

If we also use in Fig. 68a the reactance drop E_2 that exists across L, we can find the solution by multiplying the second expression of Eq. (134) on each side by ω and taking the ratio $Z/\omega L = E/E_2$. We then have

$$db = 20 \log_{10} \left(\frac{E}{E_2}\right) = 20 \log_{10} \left(\frac{Z}{\omega L}\right) = 20 \log_{10} \left(\frac{m}{\omega}\right)$$

where $m = \sqrt{\tau^{-2} + \omega^2}$. Hence

$$db = 20 \log_{10} \left(\frac{E}{E_2}\right) = 10 \log_{10} \left(1 + \frac{1}{\omega^2 \tau^2}\right) \tag{144}$$

This result looks like the result of Eq. (142), but we have to realize that we are dealing now with the inductive drop E_2 and with a time constant $\tau = L/R$ sec. We note, therefore, that the decibel expressions in terms of time constants are, so to speak, interchangeable when having a resistor R in series with an inductance L, instead of in series with a capacitance C.

All cases just treated are of importance when dealing with corrective networks for a-f preemphasis and deemphasis and will be applied now.

41. Networks for Audio-frequency Accentuation and Deaccentuation.—Networks for a-f accentuation and deaccentuation are also known as circuits for a-f preemphasis and deemphasis, respectively. The former network is used in the FM transmitter and *requires*, therefore, the latter network in an FM receiver in order to offset the preemphasis action so that sounds with the correct relative amplitudes in the a-f spectrum will be heard. The reason for using such networks is that most disturbing a-f noise in a transmitter, irrespective of whether modulated in amplitude, frequency, or phase, seems to lie somewhere between 5 and 15 kc. Since the useful relative amplitudes of the desired a-f signals are generally small in the upper a-f range, preaccentuation is provided in the upper a-f range for the desired signal currents, with respect to desired signal currents in the lower a-f range. Electrically, such preaccentuation can be accomplished with simple circuit elements as well as the equivalent deaccentuation in the FM receiver.

Figure 68 shows such networks, where the network used in the transmitter consists of a suitable resistance R in series with a suitable inductive reactance ωL; in the FM receiver a suitable resistance R in series with a suitable reactance $1/\omega C$ is employed. In each case the reactance drop is applied to the grid branch of a class A amplifier and the respective input voltages act across the series combination of the correcting networks. When no other correcting network, such as a $1/f$ corrector, is employed in a transmitter, then this correcting network precedes the modulator; *i.e.*, the output of the tube of Fig. 68a causes the signal voltage which affects the frequency modulator. If additional stages of a-f amplification are employed after the microphone, then the correcting network should be located right after the sound pickup. The preaccentuator can also be used in the plate branch of a tube as in the transmitter of the General Electric Company (Fig. 73). The R_2, L_2 network then acts as the accentuator and the effective voltage variations across the impedance $Z_2 = \sqrt{R_2^2 + (\omega L_2)^2}$ cause preemphasized amplitudes in the upper a-f range and are applied to a single quadrature tube.

Accentuators as well as deaccentuators are apparatus where the time constant τ has to be chosen so as to obtain the correct desired amplitude-frequency characteristic. A time constant of $\tau = 100$ μ sec is considered good engineering practice. Hence, for the case of the accentuator R_2, L_2 shown in Fig. 73, we have $\tau = L_2/R_2 = 100$ μ sec and we obtain the transmission characteristic of Fig. 69 by means of Eq. (138). In Fig. 73 it will be noted that the voltage drop across both L_2 and R_2 is applied toward the grid of the reactance tube. Hence, a high impedance branch has to be chosen so that the grid voltages will be appreciable. Choosing $L_2 = 100$ henrys and R_2 equal to 1 megohm yields the

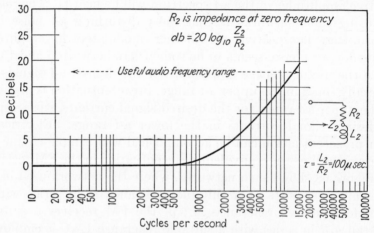

Fig. 69.—Response characteristic in decibels.

requirement $\tau = 100/10^6 = 100$ μ sec, and it is, therefore, only necessary to use in the receiver a deemphasizer which also has a time constant of 100 μ sec. The ratio of the effective impedance Z_2 to the series resistance R_2 is used in obtaining the decibel characteristic of Fig. 69, since the L_2, R_2 emphasizer in the plate circuit of Fig. 73 applies its series terminal voltage toward the modulator grid. As far as the audio frequency is concerned, the voltage drop across resistance R_2 is essentially responsible for the lower a-f range; at the upper a-f range the inductive drop accounts essentially for the applied a-f voltage. Hence, comparing the impedance $Z_2 = \sqrt{R_2^2 + (\omega L_2)^2}$ at any frequency with the lowest impedance which can ever occur, and which is equal to R_2, must give the proper frequency characteristic for the entire audio range.

Figures 70a and b show CR type a-f accentuators and deaccentuators each having a time constant of 100 μ sec. In the FM transmitter of the RCA shown in Fig. 35, the drop across a series combination of an inductance L and a resistance R is used as an a-f preaccentuator. It will be noted that an adjustment is provided for bringing about the best upper a-f emphasis. We note that an a-f response flat within 2 db from the value of 1,000 cycles per second can be expected from 50 to 15,000 cycles per second.

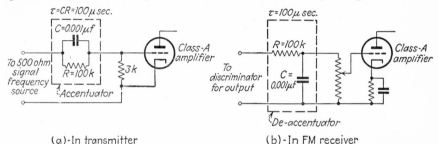

(a)-In transmitter   (b)-In FM receiver

FIG. 70.—Accentuator and deaccentuator for a time constant t = 100 microseconds.

This flatness requires, of course, that a deemphasizer of the same time constant be employed in the FM receiver.

42. Networks for Producing Inverse Frequency Effects.—As has been discussed at several places in this text, for indirect FM we have to apply to the balanced amplitude modulator not a voltage $e_m \cos \omega t$ but a voltage that is proportional to $(e_m/f) \cos \omega t$, in order to cause subsequent phase swings that are proportional to $\Delta\theta/f$ instead of to $\Delta\theta$ as in customary PM. Figure 71 shows the

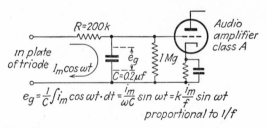

$$e_g = \frac{1}{C}\int i_m \cos \omega t \cdot dt = \frac{i_m}{\omega C} \sin \omega t = k\frac{i_m}{f} \sin \omega t$$

proportional to $1/f$

FIG. 71.—Network for producing inverse audio-frequency effect.

predistorter that produces the inverse frequency effect. This is the predistorter in the block diagram of the Armstrong transmitter shown in Fig. 33. It is connected between the line amplifier and the a-f preaccentuator. The $1/f$ network consists of a high resistance R in series with a condenser C, the reactance of the condenser being relatively small at the lowest desired signal frequency f in comparison with the R value. R = 200,000 ohms and C = 0.2 μf are accepted values giving a time constant τ =

$CR = 0.04$ sec. The decibel characteristic for comparison of the total applied signal frequency voltage to the corresponding condenser voltage can be expressed by means of Eq. (143). If the above value for the time constant τ is inserted, we have db $= 10 \log_{10} (1 + 0.0361f^2)$ where f is in cycles per second.

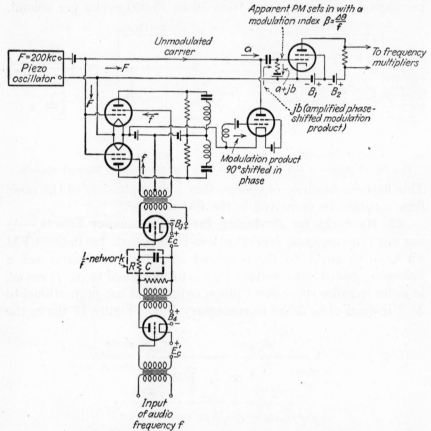

FIG. 72.—Application of an inverse audio-frequency network.

The derivation in Fig. 71 shows that the voltage applied to the amplifier is proportional to the amplitude i_m and is inversely proportional to the signal frequency f where k is the constant of proportionality. When the a-f accentuator is omitted we have then the circuit of Fig. 72. We note that when the modulation product b, which was shifted in phase by 90 deg, is combined with the unmodulated carrier component a, we have $a + jb$ with a maximum phase swing which is now $\Delta\theta/f$ and this has all the features of the value $\Delta F/f$ previously obtained for direct FM.

When a PM is changed into AM by a frequency discriminator, the translation is due to the equivalent frequency swing $f \Delta\theta \cos \omega t$. The same network as shown in Fig. 71 can be used after the frequency discriminator in order to cancel the f effect in the equivalent maximum frequency swing $f \Delta\theta$. A customary FM receiver with an additional 200,000-ohm resistor and a 0.2-μf condenser will then work also on PM waves.

CHAPTER III

TRANSMITTERS FOR FREQUENCY MODULATION

Unlike the usual practice in AM transmitters, most of the essential operations in FM transmitters are accomplished at low power levels, as a matter of fact with power levels as customary in receiver tubes. We may, therefore, divide a high-power FM transmitter into three essential parts: one part that causes primary or master frequency modulation, a second part that deals with frequency multiplication, and a third part that involves power step-up. For direct FM, the primary FM would take place about a center frequency which is either one-eighth or one-ninth of the center frequency of the radiated electromagnetic FM wave. An eightfold frequency multiplication, for instance, is employed in the Western Electric FM transmitter, and a nine-fold frequency multiplication is present-day practice in the General Electric and the RCA FM transmitters. Hence, with present-day FM allocations, the Western Electric transmitter would use primary or master FM about a center frequency of approximately 5 Mc/sec.

The second part of an FM transmitter deals with the frequency multiplication of the primary FM in the case of direct FM. For indirect FM, as used in the well-known Armstrong system, a very large order of frequency deviation multiplication is required; as a matter of fact, so large that the ratio of the final frequency deviation to primary frequency deviation is much larger than the ratio of the final center frequency to the primary center frequency.

The third part of the FM transmitter involves a mere power step-up. It may, therefore, be said that a 250-watt FM transmitter is more or less the same as the 250-watt transmitter section in a 50-kw FM transmitter.

43. FM Transmitters.—With respect to the above statements a 1-kw FM transmitter consists of a 250-watt transmitter stage which is followed by a final 1-kw power stage. This final stage could also be a 3-kw unit. For a 10-kw FM transmitter, we would have the 250-watt FM stage followed by an intermediate power stage of 1 kw which, in turn, drives the final 10-kw output stage. For a 50-kw transmitter the 250-watt exciter works into a 3-kw intermediate power stage and this stage works into the 50-kw output stage. For still higher output power, we would have after the 250-watt FM exciter two successive intermediate power stages, one of 1 kw and the other of 10 kw, the latter stage driving the final power stage of, say, 100 kw. Such successive power progressions may not be followed exactly by all manufacturers but is, for instance, the case in present-day General Electric equipment.

Normally, the first power unit, in the above examples the 250-watt unit, is adjusted to conform to good engineering practice in regard to noise level, frequency stability, and fidelity. In some transmitters inverse feedback is also employed in the last power stage.

The output of the transmitter, when calculated by the indirect method, is 0.6 times the product of the plate voltage and plate current of the last transmitter stage. According to present-day practice, the mean frequency or center frequency of the radiated FM wave must remain within ± 2 kc of the assigned megacycle center frequency. Generally, it may be said that in FM transmitters the frequency stabilization problem is more difficult from an engineering point of view than it is in AM systems, since in *direct* FM it is the *frequency* that is being varied by the modulating current. Even in indirect FM there is some difficulty, though the primary center-frequency source is a stabilized piezo generator. The reason is that in this system another stable reference frequency is employed and the frequency stability of the center frequency of the radiated FM wave is a function of the stability of two independent piezo standards. Yet, it appears that with the indirect FM system the stability should be equal to, if not better than, systems whose center-frequency stabilization depends on some sort of mechanical or electronic control.

It may be said that the design for low noise level and modulation linearity is accomplished better in an FM than in an AM transmitter. This seems to be true also with respect to a-f response. The distribution of the modulation energy in the frequency spectrum seems to be the *secret* that accounts for the inherent low noise-to-signal ratio in FM work. It cannot be stressed too much that the effectiveness in FM exists on account of the Bessel distribution of the many side currents and their relative phase relations. No random distribution of energy will ever produce such an efficient spread of the modulation energy in the frequency spectrum as does FM.

This is explained in detail in the text and has been proved in many numerical examples. For instance, it was shown that if all significant side currents are added with their actual magnitudes and correct instantaneous phase relationship, we shall *always* obtain for the resultant vector a constant length that is equal to the unmodulated carrier level. But, if we miss some significant side currents, then AM is also superimposed on the desired FM. These statements hold, of course, also for PM energy distributions. Now, random energy distributions have no definite phase relationships; they have also no definite frequencies in the spectrum, and undefined amplitude values. The resultant effect as extracted in the frequency discriminator of a receiver cannot, therefore, be efficient. The reason for this is that frequency demodulators are specially designed for *reversing* the modulation actions caused in a true FM transmitter, and accomplish, therefore, this task most efficiently.

That we have to use wide-band networks is rather favorable as far as noise suppression is concerned. The useful side currents distribute the FM energy over wide limits, say 100 kc above and 100 kc below the assigned center frequency F. For some FM conditions the frequency spread on each side of the center frequency is *more* than the maximum permissible frequency swing of $\Delta F = \pm 75$ kc and the circuits are usually designed for a band width of 225 kc. But in the same band width many random noise distributions are spread also, even though due only to sharp input impulses. As amplification takes place in the several i-f stages, the combination of the "erratic" random distributions due to noise and the desired and efficient Bessel distributions due to useful FM would give a very strange picture if it were viewed on the screen of a cathode-ray tube. But this picture is, fortunately, *not* what the human ear hears, since even with a wide-range a-f amplifier, say of 225-kc band width instead of the 30-kc maximum width for AM, we would still not hear what goes on, say, above 16 kc and below 16 cycles per second. This is because the human ear can perceive sound sensations only between the limits of 16 cycles per second and about 16 kc.

The frequency discriminator of the receiver recovers the modulation energy due to conversion of FM into AM. Hence, the discriminator characteristic converts the frequency swings $\Delta F \cos \omega t$, which are never larger than ± 75 kc, into amplitude variations that can never exceed signal frequencies higher than the a-f values of f used in the transmitter. The useful a-f recovery after demodulation of the FM-to-AM translation is, therefore, in the audible-frequency range, which is about 15 kc wide for good a-f amplifiers. Hence, the recovery of the intelligence or modulation is only 15 kc wide. The energy distribution in the entire frequency spectrum is, therefore, just as much "squeezed together" by the FM-to-AM translation of the discriminator as it was "spread out" in the transmitter when frequency modulation took place. The random noise distributions cannot be Bessel distributions but are spread out in virtue of the available band width of the transfer networks. Hence, the very opposite occurs since the *cause* and the *result* in case of FM are *reversed in case of noise*. This means, in other words, that the band width of the transfer networks has to be designed to accommodate all the significant side currents caused by FM. It also means that the wider the transfer networks have to be designed, the more the energy of an interfering noise can and will spread over the frequency spectrum due to the band width. Since only a 15-kc width can be recovered after the final amplitude demodulation, not all noise energy will be recovered in the a-f end. This proves that the discriminator is not efficient at all for modulation spreads due to noise components arriving at the input of the discriminator. It is true that some of these features would also exist if we should use networks in AM reception which are 225 kc wide, so that an a-f frequency recovery of only 15-kc width would be effective. Also, here the noise energy would, in many cases, spread itself over the entire 225-kc width, since this is the property of all wide-band networks, and only the energy components in the audible range could affect the loud speaker. It is, of course, understood that, if the noise distribution over the entire band width has large components in the audible spectrum in comparison with the desired a-f recovery, then the noise will "badly" mask the desired intelligence.

With respect to power measurements, the indirect method mentioned above, by means of the plate voltage and the plate current of the last power stage of the FM transmitter, is probably a good procedure if the radiation efficiency from this plate end toward radiation space satisfies the value assumed in the formula given. It is difficult to think of a real reliable method of power measurement at such high frequencies as the 40- to 50-Mc range and the even higher frequencies around 300 and 350 Mc as used for FM relay transmissions.

Up to about 1 kw of power, we can use incandescent lamps that have insignificant reactance effects. A lamp of such a size should be used that it is lighted to considerable brightness when acting as the load of the FM transmitter to be tested. The brightness is noted with a photometer. Afterward the lamp is brought to the same brightness by a 60 cycles per second current and the corresponding power read off with a commercial wattmeter. It is true that at frequencies such as are used in the FM range, skin effect causes the filament to carry current only near the surface of the incandescent filament. The error is, however, not serious since the brightness of the incandescent lamp depends only on the *actual* power dissipated in the filament. It does not matter much whether the dissipation is close to the surface or all over the cross section of the filament. The photometer registers essentially the entire effect as expressed by the radiation from the surface of the filament. It is, however, essential to use a photometer or a photo tube that registers all effects of the heat radiations.

A calorimetric method would be more accurate but much slower. A lamp or some other suitable heat dissipater, which acts essentially as a resistance (dissipater in a tuned load branch), is immersed in a calorimetric liquid. If water is used for the liquid and is made to flow by having an inlet and an outlet, and v is the rate of flow in gallons per minute, and τ the centigrade difference between the temperature of the water at the outlet and the temperature at the inlet, then the kilowatt power absorbed by the flowing water is $P = 0.263v\tau$.

The transmission-line method, using the line surge impedance, which is a resistance $R_0 = \sqrt{L/C}$ ohms at such frequencies, gives the power as R_0I^2 if a special ammeter is constructed and used for the determination of the effective current I flowing into the surge impedance experienced at the entrance of a properly terminated line. The termination has to be such that no standing waves exist along it. It seems better to use a diode voltmeter and to compute the power from E^2/R_0.

44. The Armstrong Indirect FM Transmitter.—Since it was E. H. Armstrong's important engineering developments that paved the way for frequency modulation in broadcasting, it may not be out of place to present first his type of transmitter.

Some of the important theoretical contributions that were made prior to any important engineering applications did not exactly predict great advantages for FM over AM. The reason for this was, perhaps, that general solutions of just one phase, *i.e.*, of FM by itself, without taking the difference between wide-band and narrow-band FM into consideration, did not show any particular advantages for FM. Naturally, any system of modulation, if ideally applied, should do the same as any other system of modulation. A modulated current does not realize, if it could, whether it is deformed in amplitude, phase, or in frequency. But when we choose suitable carrier-frequency allocations for which even wide-band transmissions are small in percentage compared with the narrow-band transmissions for customary AM allocations, then the argument of the discussion may be somewhat different. If we also take into consideration that at certain frequency allocations certain noises do not show up as much as for other allocations and that in virtue of wide-band transmission some of the noise energy when existing can be spread partly into a frequency region that will not affect the a-f output of a receiver, then we begin to realize that FM, as well as PM, may give better receptions than AM.

It was due to E. H. Armstrong's demonstration of the real merits of FM in his famous paper presented at an IRE meeting in 1935, and to the stirring up of interest in the minds of other engineers who have also contributed to the present art of frequency modulation, that the capabilities of FM transmission were eventually recognized.

Inasmuch as the individual apparatus used in the Armstrong transmitter has been described already, it is now of interest to learn how it is arranged in a transmitter. It is also of interest to learn what other ingenious means are employed in order to change the very small primary time axis swing modulation into wide-band FM, which behaves as though direct FM were instrumental in producing the action.

The block diagram of Fig. 33 shows the case for a center frequency $F = 43.2$ Mc of the radiated FM wave. A stabilized primary frequency $F_1 = 200$ kc is taken from a piezo oscillator and fed first into a buffer amplifier. It then divides itself into two parts. One part feeds into a balanced amplitude modulator, and the other part passes toward a carrier-frequency amplifier. The balanced modulator is affected by a signal current that brings about AM. On account of the predistorter, the signal current has an amplitude that is proportional to i_m/f instead of to i_m only. The preaccentuator emphasizes the amplitudes of the signal currents in the upper a-f range, while the line amplifier brings about proper primary signal-level voltage and proper matching. The output of the balanced amplifier is the modulation product with the unmodulated carrier portion suppressed. Hence, the output contains only the side-current pair of respective frequencies $F_1 \pm f$.

The output coupling of this modulator is such that the side-band modulation product is shifted in phase by 90 deg, and combined with the amplified unmodulated carrier. This results in a PM current with a maximum phase swing of $\pm\Delta\theta/f$. The phase swings are limited to values that never exceed ± 30 deg in order to preserve good linearity. The PM experienced in the succeeding buffer amplifier is, therefore, small and never more than one-twelfth of a single complete h-f cycle of frequency F_1. This so-called "PM" has now a modulation index $\beta = \Delta\theta/f$. When compared with the modulation index $\beta = \Delta F/f$ for direct FM, this shows that even though PM is instrumental in producing the present result we have numerically for the *entire* a-f or signal-frequency range the same conditions in either case. Hence, in effect, the current in the second buffer amplifier can be taken as an FM current since the number of significant side currents is exactly the same as if direct FM had been instrumental in producing the modulated output. There is actually an additional feature to this type of FM effect. The feature consists in the fact that the center frequency F_1 is *fixed*, not modulated at all, and yet the number of side currents is as though this frequency were oscillating up and down about F_1 with maximum frequency swings of $(\Delta\theta/f)f = \Delta F$ since, according to Eq. (6), the equivalent frequency swing for PM is f times the maximum phase swing $\Delta\theta/f$. We note, therefore, that for maximum phase swings of $\Delta\theta/f \leq 30$ deg, or $\leq 30/57.3 \leq 0.524$ radian, we have for a signal current of frequency $f = 50$ cycles per second the corresponding maximum frequency excursions of $0.524 \times 50 = 26.2$ cycles per second.

This is a very small frequency excursion even for a carrier frequency as low as $F_1 = 200$ kc. We have to deal, therefore, with a very large frequency multiplication in order to produce the final ± 75-kc frequency excursions. If we assume, for instance, that the largest frequency excursion is ± 25 cycles per second, instead of 26.2 cycles per second, the required deviation frequency multiplication would be $75,000/25 = 3,000$. Hence, if cascaded frequency multipliers were used, this degree of multiplication would also produce a final center frequency of $3,000F_1 = 3,000 \times 200,000 = 6 \times 10^8$ cycles per second or 600 Mc/sec. This value falls *completely* out of the present-day carrier frequency allocations for commercial FM. Hence, we have to resort to a scheme that brings about in the multiplied value of the original small frequency deviation an increase much larger than that in the corresponding center frequency. This is accomplished by inserting also a stage of frequency conversion between stages of frequency multiplication.

The frequency-conversion principle is well known from the superheterodyne technique. It is based on mixing two currents of different carrier frequencies and utilizing the beat or difference frequency of the respective carrier frequencies as the carrier frequency of the converted output current of the mixer. The only difference that exists here, in comparison with the conversion in customary superheterodyne operation, is that in the latter, one carrier current is modulated in AM and in the present case it is modulated in frequency. Hence, the beat frequency of the converted FM current, when beating with an unmodulated current of oscillator frequency F_0, is now $(F_3 \pm \Delta F_3) - F_0$ in case we have reference only to the maximum frequency swings $\pm \Delta F_3$ of the current of center frequency F_3, which mixes with the piezo current of frequency F_0. Hence, the difference frequency reduces only the center frequency but preserves the magnitude of the frequency excursions $\pm \Delta F_3$.

The primary equivalent frequency deviation ΔF_1 is dependent on the signal frequency f since $\Delta F_1 = 0.524f$ cycles per second. For a maximum phase swing limitation $\Delta \theta/f$ of ± 30 deg or ± 0.524 radian, we have to assume the value of the lowest signal frequency f for which we still expect to obtain full frequency swings of ± 75 kc in the final output current of the transmitter. We found that for 50 cycles per second the deviation ΔF_1 would be 26.2 cycles per second.

Consulting the block diagram of Fig. 33 we note that we have three groups of frequency multipliers. Each group consists of several stages of frequency multiplication in cascade. The first group multiplies the primary center frequency F_1 by 16 and produces the new center frequency $F_2 = 16F_1$. The second group causes fourfold frequency multiplication and produces a center frequency of $F_3 = 4F_2$. The last group employs a frequency multiplication of 48 with an output center frequency $F = 48F_4$. Here it must be understood that F_4 is much lower than F_3 on account of the center-frequency conversion from center frequency F_3 to center frequency F_4. The frequency multiplication due to all frequency multipliers is, therefore, $16 \times 4 \times 48 = 3{,}072$; this must also be the *over-all* frequency multiplication of the primary frequency swing $\pm \Delta F_1$. As explained above, on account of the center-frequency conversion, the over-all center-frequency increase is less than the increase of the corresponding ΔF_1 swing. As a matter of fact, even though the ratio of the final-frequency swing ΔF to the original-frequency swing ΔF_1 is a whole number, namely, 3,072, the corresponding center-frequency ratio F/F_1 does not have to be a whole number, but happens in this numerical illustration to be so and is $43{,}200/200 = 216$. The reason a whole number is not essential is that in the beat method any difference is possible, just as we can generate currents not only of frequencies that are a whole number when related to the time of 1 sec but also a number like 43.26 cycles per second. This is another desirable feature of this method. We can start out with any convenient primary frequency F_1 that looks promising with respect to the corresponding deviation frequency multiplication in order to provide full ± 75-kc deviations in the final center frequency F, and yet the exact value of F can be fractional, *i.e.*, not a whole number.

Since we have found that the over-all deviation-frequency multiplication is $\Delta F/\Delta F_1 = 3{,}072$ in this particular numerical example, we have a means for finding out what is the lowest audio frequency that, for the adopted 3,072 fold multiplication, results in full ± 75-kc swings in the radiated electromagnetic wave without exceeding maximum phase swings of ± 30 deg in the primary PM. We find then $75{,}000/3{,}072 = 24.4$ cycles per second for ΔF_1. This means that for audio frequencies below $24.4/0.524 = 46.6$ cycles per second we cannot expect to obtain

full frequency modulation.   It is true that this puts a limitation
to this system, but it does not seem serious.   Audio frequencies
in this neighborhood, and below it, are not always desired since
they are in the region of "hum" frequencies, which should be
avoided anyhow.   That a large number of tubes of the receiver
type are required and that careful shielding is necessary should
be understood.   But this has been successfully taken care of from
an engineering point of view.

Since the primary phase swing is $\Delta\theta/f$ in the original PM, we
note that the upper limit of ±30 deg can be kept correct only if
the $1/f$ effect in $\Delta\theta/f$ is properly compensated.   Otherwise the
maximum desired phase swing of ±30 deg in case of the loudest
signal transmissions would fall off toward larger f values.   The
a-f accentuator will take care of this, since it causes larger i_m
amplitudes of the modulating currents toward the higher audio
frequencies.

It will be noted that stages of power amplification follow the
arrangement shown in Fig. 33.   They have to be designed the
same way as for direct FM and for band widths of about 225
kc.

45. The FM Transmitter of the General Electric Company.—
The General Electric Company's FM transmitter, shown in Fig.
73, is based on direct FM; *i.e.*, the primary center frequency F_1,
which is in this case not stabilized or "stiff," is varied about its F_1
value.   An ordinary tube oscillator having a characteristic C, L
network brings about primary FM in conjunction with a reactance-
tube modulator.   The primary center frequency F_1 is, on account
of the application of only one quadrature tube, due to C, L as well
as to a fixed C_i injection in multiple with C.   This is because
the voltage of the high frequency applied to the grid of the modulator tube is leading the tank voltage of the oscillator by 90 deg.
Since the quadrature tube can cause considerable linear frequency
swings about the primary center frequency F_1, only a ninefold
deviation frequency multiplication is required.   It is, therefore,
possible to use two cascaded-frequency triplers in order to obtain
ninefold center-frequency multiplication as well.   Hence, if the
primary maximum-frequency excursions are $\pm\Delta F_1$, we have in
the antenna current of the transmitter an FM of center frequency
$F = 9F_1$ and the corresponding frequency swings $\Delta F \cos \omega t =
9 \Delta F_1 \cos \omega t$.

Inasmuch as in such a system ordinary tube oscillators have to be used in order to deviate the oscillation frequency *freely*, it is necessary to stabilize the center frequency of the radiated FM wave. This is accomplished with a great resolving power by means of frequency conversion and a frequency discriminator for affecting the fixed bias of the modulator tube. The frequency conversion takes place in the mixer tube whose output is tuned to

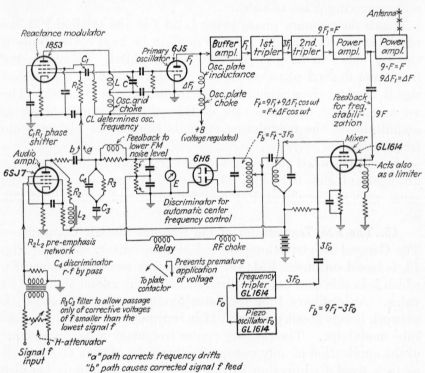

Fig. 73.—Essential sections of the FM transmitter of the General Electric Company.

a frequency F_b much lower than the final center frequency $F = 9F_1$. This is done by combining in this tube a small portion of the useful FM current of instantaneous carrier frequency $9(F_1 + \Delta F_1 \cos \omega t)$ with an unmodulated current of frequency $3F_0$, where F_0 is the primary stabilized frequency of a piezo oscillator. The output of the mixer or frequency converter has then an instantaneous intermediate frequency of $9(F_1 + \Delta F_1 \cos \omega t) - 3F_0$, which is also $F + \Delta F \cos \omega t - 3F_0$. Hence, the final frequency variation $\Delta F \cos \omega t$ is preserved, and the new center frequency $F - 3F_0$ is many times smaller than the center frequency F of the radiated wave and several times smaller than the primary center frequency $F_1 = 1/[6.28 \sqrt{(C + C_i)L}]$ of the master or primary FM oscillator.

We have, for instance, for a carrier frequency assignment of $F = 47.7$ Mc, a primary center frequency of $F_1 = 47.7/9 = 5.3$ Mc, and a beat frequency $F_b = F - 3F_0 = 1$ Mc, any center-frequency drifts d of the frequency F being preserved in the output current of the mixer. The percentage drift in the final FM current is much smaller than the corresponding off-drift in the beat current which is applied to the frequency discriminator. Hence, very small center-frequency drifts in the antenna current will greatly affect the discriminator. The discriminator would, for the foregoing numerical example, be tuned to 1 Mc/sec and would, therefore, be so balanced that at this instantaneous carrier frequency of 1 Mc no output voltage is possible. Hence, the stabilized piezo frequency F_0 is so chosen that $9 \times 5.3 - 3F_0 = 1$ Mc, or $F_0 = 46.7/3$ Mc/sec.

According to the theory of the discriminator, for any other carrier-frequency values that are not exactly equal to the assigned center frequency $F = 47.7$ Mc we obtain either a positive or a negative output voltage on the discriminator. This is because the balance of this apparatus is based on a 1-Mc tuning, which can prevail only when F is exactly 47.7 Mc. For any off balance of the discriminator, a corresponding direct current will flow along path a in Fig. 73 and will affect the fixed negative bias of the modulator tube. This affects the g_m value of this tube and consequently the magnitude of the injected capacitance C_i, which adds to the value C of the oscillator. If, therefore, the discriminator is so connected toward the grid of the modulator tube as to cause a decrease in the mutual conductance g_m when the center frequency F of the antenna current drifts toward a lower carrier frequency value, then the fixed C_i injection will also be lowered, since the injected leading i_p current from the modulator is lowered. The result is that the primary center frequency F_1 must increase its value correspondingly. In turn, also $9F_1$ will correspondingly increase and can be made just to compensate the frequency drift. Exactly the opposite occurs when the center frequency F drifts toward a higher value and causes an increase of the g_m value of the modulator tube. A larger C_i value is, therefore, injected in parallel with the capacitance C of the oscillator and the value of F_1

is increased until the correct primary center frequency is obtained. The corresponding effect in the $9F_1$ action will then compensate the frequency drift d in the center frequency F, which caused the discriminator to operate. We have, therefore, an "electronic" automatic center-frequency control.

There is another provision made in connection with the center-frequency regulation. From Fig. 73 it is seen that along path b the signal current, which brings about the useful FM in the primary carrier frequency, is also active. Hence, in the instantaneous intermediate frequency, which is applied from the mixer to the frequency discriminator, we shall also pass on the demodulated FM in terms of audio currents. If it were not for the C_3R_3 filter, which passes to ground any appreciable audio currents that are higher than the lowest signal frequency f of interest, the direct current along path a would have also audio currents flowing along the same path. These currents would more or less cancel the useful FM in the primary FM source. If this C_3R_3 filter by-passes, for instance, all audio currents above 40 cycles per second, the grid of the modulator tube will experience only superimposed biasing effects which are essential in the automatic center-frequency stabilization.

Figure 73, as well as the block diagram of Fig. 74, shows other details in the transmitter. The voltmeter E connected across the output branch of the frequency discriminator indicates directly the magnitude of any frequency drifts since a linear relation prevails between output volts and the change in the instantaneous beat frequency $F_b = F_t - 3F_0$. The $\Delta F \cos \omega t$ variations in the value of F_t are about the center frequency F of the output current of the transmitter. As far as the direct voltage indicated by the voltmeter E is concerned, it is in linear relationship with respect to the difference frequency $F - 3F_0$ since the voltmeter action is based on a small direct-current flow and the deflection indicates the *average* effect. In the General Electric transmitter, provision for a less sensitive scale for the E meter is made so that the meter can also be used when tuning up the transmitter. Large center-frequency discrepancies are then possible, which would give considerable output voltages on the discriminator.

All other details in Figs. 73 and 74 are self-evident. The a-f amplifier, which contains the preaccentuator R_2L_2 in the plate branch, serves primarily for obtaining preemphasis in the upper

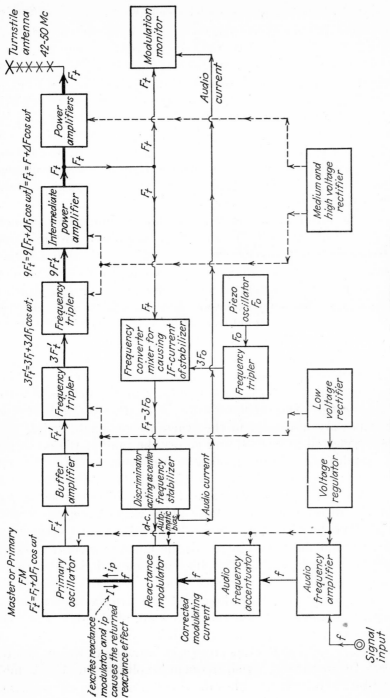

FIG. 74.—Block diagram of a direct FM-transmitter.

a-f range. The modulation monitor or indicator shown in Fig. 74 is based on the combined action of both FM current and audio current, the latter coming from the output branch of the discriminator. It gives, therefore, indications that can be directly expressed in terms of ΔF swings. Since swings of ± 75 kc are taken as the full permissible modulation, any correspondingly smaller swings give less than full deflections. The piezo oscillator of standard reference frequency F_0 is self-contained; *i.e.*, its supply power as well as the power needed for automatic temperature correction are independent of all other voltage supplies. Automatic relay action is also provided in order to avoid severe overloading and premature application of plate voltage.

46. The FM Transmitter of the Radio Corporation of America. The RCA transmitter is likewise based on direct FM and uses electronic center-frequency control as well as a reactance tube modulator. The wiring diagram is shown in Fig. 35. On account of a reactance modulation, we obtain again considerable primary FM, *i.e.*, large frequency excursions that have a linear relationship with respect to the signal-frequency voltage that causes FM. Hence, only ninefold center- as well as deviation-frequency multiplication is employed. An electron-coupled primary or master oscillator of center frequency F_1 is made use of. This oscillator frequency would be 5.3 Mc for a frequency allocation $F = 47.7$ Mc, since $F = 9F_1$. The oscillator tube is an RCA 807 tube. Two such tubes are also used in the reactance modulator with their plates connected in parallel and across the tank of the oscillator. The modulator grids are supplied with r-f voltage from the oscillator, not by direct connection but *inductively*. Since these grids are driven in push-pull, we have a phase difference of 180 deg from grid to grid, but 90 deg out of phase with respect to the tank voltage E of the oscillator. It will be noted that the phase of the h-f currents in the plate circuits of the modulator tubes are controlled by the grid tank. The link coupling and the adjustment are so made that the h-f currents are exactly 90 deg out of phase with respect to the tank voltage E. The two modulator output branches look, therefore, to the plate tank of the oscillator tube like reactive loads, the degree of the injected reactance depending on what happens in the respective grid branches of the modulator tubes. In absence of signal-frequency voltages on the modulator grids, the modulator tubes draw equal and oppositely phased currents and the injected reactance effects cancel. But, as soon as the signal voltage of frequency f interferes with such a balance, one modulator tube will draw more current and the other modulator tube less current. This causes an effective positive and negative reactance across the oscillator tank. We have, therefore, a differential modulator with twice the frequency-swing ability found in one modulator tube only. Two modulator tubes give besides the advantage that circuit irregularities can be canceled out.

It will be noted that a Crosby type of frequency discriminator is employed for the center-frequency stabilization in order to keep the mean frequency within about 0.0025 per cent of the assigned value. A separate piezo source of stabilized frequency F_0 affects one grid of a mixer tube; the other grid is supplied with energy from the RCA 807 amplifier, which follows the primary oscillator of center frequency F_1. For this particular numerical example the plate branch of the mixer is tuned to a difference frequency $F_0 - F_1 = 6.3 - 5.3$ or 1 Mc/sec. The output of the mixer is then coupled to the 6H6 rectifier tube through a discriminator circuit. The direct current of this rectifier is, in turn, fed into the grid branches of the two modulator tubes in order to provide a differential correction bias. Also, in this transmitter no output voltage is obtained from the discriminator when the instantaneous beat frequency is exactly 1 Mc. But when the primary oscillator frequency F_1 drifts, a differential voltage will result on the respective modulator grids and tend to counteract the frequency drift. The control ratio is such that the net frequency change is only a very small fraction of the change that would have resulted if the center frequency F_1 were not being corrected.

A 6J5 tube or its equivalent, not shown in Fig. 35, is also used in the interlock circuit which is so arranged that failure of any component in the automatic-frequency control unit actuates a relay. This can be used either to take the transmitter off the air or to sound a bell or to do both. The R, L branch acts again as an a-f preaccentuator.

47. The FM Transmitter of the Western Electric Company.— The FM transmitter of the Western Electric Company also produces direct FM by means of a balanced reactance tube. Unlike the RCA and the General Electric transmitters, we note from the block diagram of Fig. 34 that only eightfold center-

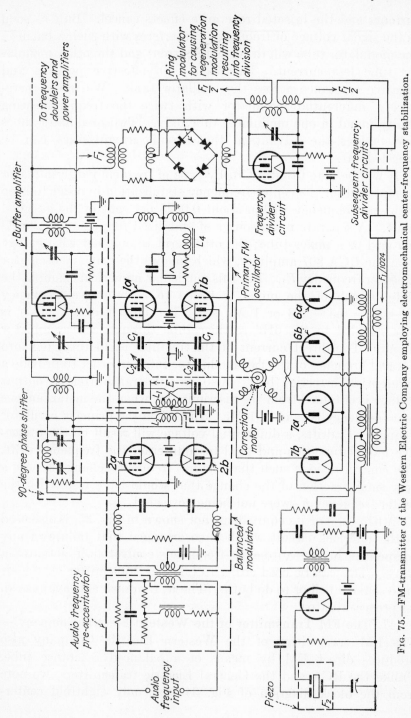

FIG. 75.—FM-transmitter of the Western Electric Company employing electromechanical center-frequency stabilization.

frequency multiplication, as well as deviation frequency multiplication, is employed in order to obtain the final wide-band FM. Automatic center-frequency control is not electronic, but is electromechanically accomplished. It requires several stages of cascaded frequency division.

For a frequency allocation of 46.5 Mc the primary center frequency F_1 would be 5.8125 Mc. For the largest permissible frequency excursion of ± 75 kc in the radiated wave, we then have a primary frequency excursion of ± 9.375 kc since it must be one-eighth of 75 kc. As Fig. 34 indicates, the center-frequency stabilization is, for this particular numerical case, based on a piezo reference frequency $F_2 = 5.676269$ kc. How these values are arrived at is described in connection with this figure. A synchronous mechanical drive is arranged to affect the respective trimmer condenser settings of the primary oscillator.

The essential wiring diagram is given in Fig. 75. The primary oscillator uses two tubes 1_a and 1_b. The frequency-determining elements are the inductance L_1 and the condensers C_1 and C_2. The variable portions C_2 are mechanically interlocked with a motor drive which varies the settings of C_2 until the correct center frequency F_1 of the primary oscillator is secured. The correcting motor will, therefore, turn the movable plates of the respective C_2 condensers toward more capacitance setting or less capacitance setting, depending on whether the frequency drift in the value of F_1 is an increase or a decrease. Direct FM is caused by the two reactance tubes 2_a and 2_b which inject reactances into the $C_1 C_2 L_1$ branch. The plates of these reactance tubes are connected in push-pull across the tuning coil L_1. Reactance-tube action takes place, therefore, with double the linearity range with respect to frequency changes. The grids of the reactance tubes 2_a and 2_b are also driven in push-pull by means of a signal voltage due to $e_m \cos \omega t$. The bridged T network in the primary branch of the signal frequency circuit is an a-f accentuator. The tuned network of the oscillator tubes 1_a and 1_b works over a secondary coil L_2 into a phase shifter (series coil and shunt condensers) and applies such h-f voltages of the instantaneous primary carrier frequency to the respective control grids of tubes 2_a and 2_b that the grid voltages are exactly 90 deg out of phase with respect to the voltage E across the tank coil L_1.

The control grids of the reactance tubes are, therefore, affected by both, the primary carrier-frequency voltage and the signal-frequency voltage. The plates of tubes 2_a and 2_b inject generally an impedance across coil L_1, which depends on both the signal frequency and the primary carrier-frequency voltages. It is, therefore, essential that the *h-f voltage* is perfectly constant so that the reactance injections across coil L_1 depend only on the *magnitude* of the *signal*-frequency *voltage*. The phase quadrature caused by this phase shifter produces only a weak AM effect, which can be observed with a headset across the negative feedback coil L_4. A minimum sound will be observed when 90-deg phase shift prevails. The use of a balanced oscillator, as well as a balanced reactance-tube modulator, gives rise to larger primary $\Delta F_1 \cos \omega t$ swings, even though only a small but linear portion of the respective g_m characteristic of respective reactance tubes 2_a and 2_b is being employed.

As was already described in connection with the block diagram of Fig. 34, stabilization of the center frequency is brought about by a mechanical control and is kept in proper step by means of a reference frequency F_2 taken from a piezo source. Using again the same numerical values as for Fig. 34 for a frequency assignment of $F = 46.5$ Mc, the primary center frequency F_1 of the tube oscillator shown in Fig. 75 is one-eighth of this value or 5.8125 Mc. By means of regenerative ring modulators in cascade, the primary frequency F_1 is divided by 1,024, causing the correct reduced center frequency 5.676269 kc. If there exists a slow drift d_1 in the primary center frequency F_1, it will show up as a reduced drift $d_1/1,024$ in the above-mentioned reduced center frequency. The correction motor and its associated networks are so adjusted that the motor drive will stand still when the reduced center frequency is at its exact value of $F_1/1,024$, *i.e.*, $d_1 = 0$. But it will slowly move in one or the other direction when there exists a drift d_1, the direction depending on whether the drift is positive or negative. The motor will keep turning until the trimmer settings C_2 cause the correct primary center frequency $F_1 = 5.8175$ Mc. The mechanical control action is then as follows: The reference piezo source produces the correct reduced center frequency $F_2 = F_1/1,024 = 5.676269$ kc. The output current of the subsequent frequency dividers feeds into two balanced modulators (mixers) using tubes 6_a, 6_b, 7_a, and 7_b. The piezo source supplies current of the correct reduced center frequency in phase quadrature to each balanced modulator. The exciting fields for the correction motor are in space quadrature. Hence, when there is no drift in the center frequency, the beat currents applied to the windings of the correction mechanism are of zero frequency. The motor drive will, therefore, stand still. As a matter of fact the drive will merely vibrate or "buzz" somewhat owing to the equivalent phase flutters of the useful FM in the subharmonic current flowing to the balanced modulators with tubes $6_{a,b}$ and $7_{a,b}$. A corresponding beat frequency will, therefore, be produced and the motor drive starts to rotate in a direction depending on the polarity of the frequency drift d_1 and keeps moving until the proper value of F_1 results.

48. FM Signal Generators.—As has been discussed at several places in this text, many tests on FM networks can be made with simple means, *i.e.*, with high-resistance direct voltmeters, ordinary beat-note indicators, milli- and microammeters, and customary AM signal generators. For the manufacturer of FM sets, better equipment should be used so that all operations of a receiver can be tested thoroughly. A signal FM generator will facilitate a checkup of FM receivers. Such a signal source should cover the carrier-frequency range of FM allocations as well as the intermediate-frequency range. Since such an FM signal generator can be greatly simplified if the center-frequency stabilization is omitted, certain means have to be provided to keep the center frequency fairly constant after the generator is warmed up. A voltage regulator is then used in the power supply, so that the heater, plate, and screen voltages can be considered as though coming from batteries. This is especially a requirement for the reactance tube.

Figure 76 shows a simplified FM generator,[1] which incorporates two frequency triplers; *i.e.*, it is based on ninefold frequency multiplication. If the primary center frequency F_1 is chosen as 4.6 Mc, it will cause an output current corresponding to a frequency allocation of $F = 9 \times 4.6 = 41.4$ Mc. The maximum permissible frequency deviation of $\Delta F = \pm 75$ kc in the FM output voltage requires that primary linear frequency swings of $\Delta F_1 = \frac{75}{9} = \pm 8.333$ kc must be possible with respect to signal-frequency voltages. The band width of the networks before multiplying the instantaneous primary carrier frequency has to be at least $2\,\Delta F_1 = 16,666$ kc wide. Between the first and second tripler tubes, the

[1] Hobbs, M., A Low Power Transmitter for Demonstrating FM Receivers, *Electronics*, January, 1941, p. 20.

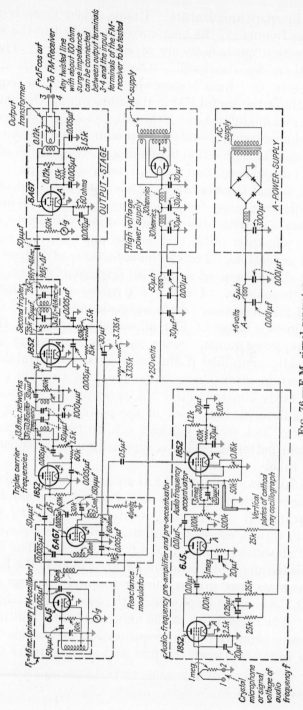

FIG. 76.—F.M. signal generator

networks have to have a band width of at least 6 $\Delta F_1 = 49.998$ kc. After the second tripling occurs, a band width of at least 150 kc is required. For good transfer-network design, the band width should be three times the largest permissible frequency swing and should also have a linear phase characteristic with respect to all pass frequencies. The schematic diagram shown in Fig. 76 is self-explanatory since it is a simplified FM transmitter.

It is stressed that when testing FM receivers with such a signal generator, either pure sinusoidal signal frequency voltages of frequency f should be applied across the terminals where the crystal microphone pickup plugs in or a high-grade crystal pick-up should be used in connection with *direct* sound pickup. This cannot be stressed too strongly since, after all, FM stands for improved a-f fidelity and recordings are just not good enough for testing superior a-f performance.

It will be noted that a single tube is used in the primary oscillator as well as in the modulator. A 6J5 tube, or its equivalent, is employed for the oscillator tube, having a suitable g_m value. A 6AG7 tube, or its equivalent, is suitable as a modulator tube. Such a tube can also be used in the output stage, which feeds into a low-impedance transmission line in order to provide the proper termination toward the input side of FM receivers. Such receivers are usually designed for dipole reception where we have about 100 ohms as a termination. In the tripler stages and for the first and the last tube of the a-f preamplifier 1852 tubes or their equivalent are used. The modulator tube and the 1852's are mounted on cushion sockets and are especially selected from a group of such tubes in order to avoid microphonicness. The output voltage for the indicated termination is between 5 and 10 mv. This is approximately the value experienced in FM receivers in a metropolitan area.

It will be noted that the a-f accentuator is made up of a 20-$\mu\mu$f condenser in parallel with a 5-megohm resistor, and the combination is in series with a 50-000-ohm resistor. This accentuator acts toward the grid branch of the last audio stage of the preamplifier. With only a 20-$\mu\mu$f condenser and a 5-megohm resistor, we shall have a time constant of exactly 100 μsec which is generally accepted as good practice. Having also a 50,000-ohm resistor in series with this predistorting network, we have a means for adjusting the over-all frequency characteristic.

The last 1852 tube of the a-f preamplifier uses a low external plate resistance as is customary in television amplifiers. Such a plate loading will preserve the effectiveness of the audio amplitudes of the higher frequencies, which otherwise would be greatly decreased owing to the capacitance in the modulator grid branch. It will be seen that the 13.8-Mc coupling between the output of the first tripler and the input of the second tripler is obtained by means of a 1,000-$\mu\mu$f condenser joining the two fixed condensers. A certain over-coupling between the two networks also has to be provided in order to obtain the proper band width, which should be somewhat greater than 50 kc. Brass cores in the respective coupling coils are used for tuning to 13.8 Mc for the alignment of this band-pass coupling. Inasmuch as the output branch of the second tripler has a center frequency as high as 41.4 Mc, the inductance effects of the leads are too pronounced to make it advisable to use condenser interstage coupling. Hence, the primary and secondary coils of the interstage transformer are wound on a common insulating core about $\frac{1}{4}$ in. apart so that the needed inductive over-coupling prevails. Tuning is accomplished by 25-$\mu\mu$f trimmer condensers, which are also shunted by resistors of 25,000 ohms in order to flatten out the double hump. An output terminal for applying a-f voltages to the vertical deflection plates of a cathode-ray tube is also provided, so that the wave form can be examined.

CHAPTER IV

RECEIVERS FOR FREQUENCY-MODULATED CURRENTS

In many respects FM receivers are similar to AM super-heterodyne receivers. For instance, the received antenna current is first converted into a suitable intermediate frequency and then several stages of i-f amplification are used. Then a frequency demodulator, instead of an amplitude demodulator, is used and followed by customary high-fidelity a-f amplification. The audio amplifier should be flat from 50 to 15,000 cycles per second within 2 db with respect to the amplitude at 1,000 cycles per second. On account of the many significant side currents, much wider band-pass networks have to be used in all the h-f stages, including the input side of the frequency demodulator. This is, however, no longer a difficult engineering problem, especially for present-day FM allocations. As far as the operation of such a receiver is concerned, it is not any more involved than is the operation of an AM receiver.

49. FM Receivers.—Present-day FM receivers are designed with a sensitivity to respond to voltages as low as 10 to 40 μv. The field intensity contour required by the FCC is 50 μv/m. We note, therefore, that high-gain tubes have to be used, so that sufficient amplitude will be available for amplitude limitation and still leave an i-f carrier level after limitation such that good a-f recovery is possible. Generally, the signal-to-noise ratio of converter tubes is not exactly good in the 40- to 50-Mc band of carrier frequencies. For certain receiver locations it may be desirable to obtain as much gain as possible before frequency conversion into the intermediate frequency takes place. Such increased gains can be obtained by using an antenna gain, as well as by a gain in the radio-frequency stage. Antenna gains as high as about 5 to 10 are possible, as well as a gain of this order of magnitude of h-f stage ahead of the mixer causing the intermediate frequency.

An 1853 tube or its equivalent seems better than an 1852 tube for the h-f amplifier stage, since it can be used with a variable amplification control. Such a control is of benefit when received voltages of more than about 50 μv reach the input side of the FM receiver. Reception of the signal at several positions of the dial may occur unless the h-f gain is reduced. If an 1852, or its equivalent, is used as a converter ($g_c = 3,000$ for a 6,000-ohm loading), with a gain of about 18, good conversion is obtained with peak oscillator voltages of 2 volts or more. For the FM allocations between 42.1 and 49.9 Mc, the grid current is then about 1 μa. A 6SA7 tube, or its equivalent, seems especially good as a mixer tube because, even if no automatic volume control is used, the applied antenna voltage can vary from 1 to 10^5 μv without causing appreciable drifts in the oscillator frequency.

With respect to intermediate frequencies, ordinary i-f transformers, such as are used in AM receivers (460 kc), have been used in FM receivers when quality and image response were of no concern. Intermediate-frequency stages with 1.7 Mc for the intermediate center frequency have also been used. But present-day practice employs mostly i-f center frequencies of 4.3 Mc and sometimes as high as 5.25 Mc. Such higher i-f frequencies move all image-response signals from the FM receptions in the 42.1 to 49.9-Mc band beyond the tuning range. Therefore, the main image frequency interference due to other FM stations is avoided. It is true that oscillator frequencies that occur, say, 4.3 Mc below the center frequency of the tuned-in FM wave, can cause image effects with carriers in the 30- to 40-Mc band. Fortunately, the image ratio for such carriers will hardly cause audible beat-note interference.

The selectivity of a receiver is generally chosen such that it is about 6 db down at ± 75 kc and about 20 db down at ± 100 kc from the center frequency. Generally, two i-f stages precede the limiter stage. For one limiter stage the gain is usually about unity. In some designs an 1853 h-f stage is used, followed, for instance, by a 6SA7 mixer stage, which works into two linear i-f amplifier stages. These i-f amplifier stages use, for instance, 1232 tubes. Then two limiter stages follow employing 6J7 tubes. The output of the last limiter feeds into a 6H6-frequency discriminator and the remaining portion of the receiver is the same as in high-quality AM receivers. Hence, the demodulator feeds into an a-f deaccentuator before a-f amplification sets in. It is important that each coupling stage be shielded by itself. If this is not done, unsymmetrical transmission curves may occur due to feedbacks and consequent regeneration. Regeneration in i-f stages causes nonlinear distortion.

Figure 77 shows block diagrams for two FM receivers. In both designs two limiter stages are provided. This is good engineering practice although many FM receivers are manufactured having but one limiter stage. No attempt has been made to follow up the a-f end in Fig. 77a, since any high-fidelity audio system will do.

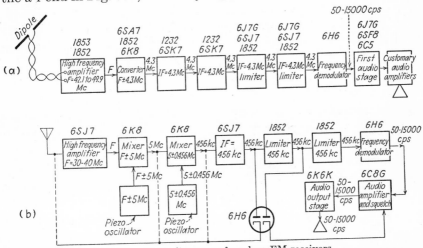

Fig. 77.—Block diagrams of modern FM receivers.

Figure 77b has reference to a police FM receiver and is shown with all tubes designated. In the first diagram several tubes often used are shown, although it is up to the designer of such sets to use his own judgment in selecting appropriate ones. The general remarks made about suitable tube features ought to be sufficient guide for selecting proper tubes. It must be borne in mind that a good tube characteristic is not always the only criterion. The random tube noise due to high gain, microphonicness, and the like, sometimes offsets the features of a somewhat better tube characteristic.

50. Typical Sections in an FM Receiver.—In Chap. II dealing with auxiliary apparatus, many essential portions of FM receivers were described in detail. Discriminators, deaccentuators, and terminations between the frequency demodulator and the a-f amplifier as well as toward the last limiter stage were treated.

Figures 78a and b show typical input tuning units used in commercial receivers. In diagram b it is seen how a three-gang

condenser is arranged and connected in order to line up the
oscillator as well as the other essential variable tuned circuits.   A

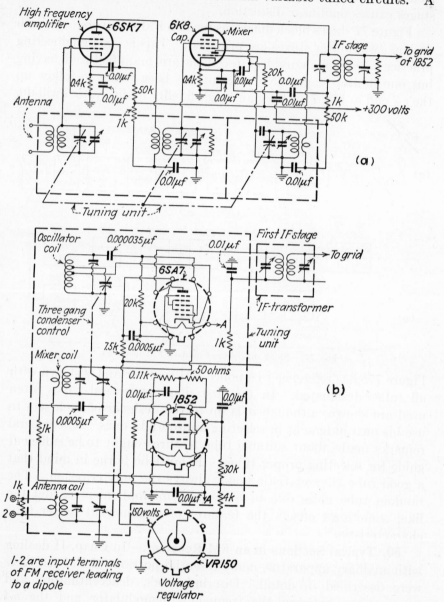

Fig. 78.—Typical tuning units in FM receivers.

regulator tube is also incorporated in order to keep any drifts in the
oscillator frequency to a minimum.

Figure 79*a* shows an 1852 tube or its equivalent acting as a h-f amplifier of the voltage induced by a dipole current. It also shows how the various condensers are ganged up to a common control. Figure 79*b* shows an 1853 tube used as a h-f amplifier and a 6SA7 tube in the converter stage. In such an arrangement we may expect good oscillator stability and can make use of the variable amplification-factor control of the first tube. It will also

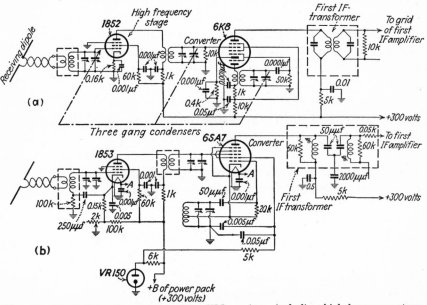

FIG. 79.—Typical input networks of an FM receiver, including high-frequency stage, converter and its outgoing i-f branch.

be noted that more h-f gain can be expected since this tube is neutralized as far as the input conductance is concerned. The neutralization is accomplished by a connection between the grid-return condenser and the cathode of the 1853 tube. Hence, the inductive voltage in the leads of the cathode by-pass condenser neutralizes the voltage across the cathode lead within the tube. It will also be noted that the coupling between the converter output and the first i-f stage, as well as the interstage i-f coupling (the latter not shown in this figure), is by means of a capacitance of about 2,000 $\mu\mu$f common to the 50-$\mu\mu$f condensers. A certain degree of overcoupling between the two networks is also provided, in order to obtain the desired band width, which should be about 225 kc. At ±75 kc from the 4,300-kc center-frequency setting, the selectivity is not much more than 6 db down. At ± 100 kc it is not more than about 20 db down. It should be about 20 db down to avoid adjacent channel interference.

It should be understood that in FM receivers the recovered audio output is a function of the *time rate of change* of the instantaneous value of the carrier frequency. The percentage of time rate of change is larger for the corresponding center frequency in the i-f stages than it is in the FM current flowing in the receiver antenna. This follows from the fact that the frequency swings in the i-f stages are of the same order of magnitudes as are effective in the received antenna current. But the i-f center frequency is only 4.3 Mc; it is somewhere between 42.1 and 49.9 Mc in the antenna FM current.

It is essential that all the interstage couplings, including the one between the last i-f stage—the limiter—and the input network of the frequency discriminator, have transfer characteristics that are *linear with respect to phase shifts*. For nonlinear phase-shift characteristics, even though symmetrical about the center frequency, we would obtain amplitude distortion. Fortunately, it is much easier to design linear transfer networks than to design linear tubes. It may be assumed that for a good engineering design the distortion due to a slight nonlinearity is less than about 1 per cent of the peak value of the recovered a-f signal amplitudes.

With only one limiter stage, which is the stage preceding the frequency demodulator, and with linear transfer characteristics up to the discriminator, the gain is mostly due to the stages preceding the limiter. With such low supply voltages as have to be used for amplitude modulation, the gain in the limiter tube itself is only about one and may be only from two to four for two limiter stages. By using suitable high-gain tubes and a high-efficiency converter for causing intermediate frequency, the over-all gain can be driven to the value needed to produce sufficient a-f recovery.

It is also essential that the time constants in the limiter circuits be relatively fast, say only a few microseconds; they should not exceed 3 μsec. Such speedy actions are required in order to keep the effects due to impulse noise away from the discriminator. When, therefore, two limiter stages, as is desirable, are used in the receiver, then the capacitance coupling toward the first limiter grid is made, say, 50 $\mu\mu$f and the grid resistor from grid to ground is made 50,000 ohms. Then we shall have a time constant of $50 \times 10^{-12} \times 5 \times 10^4 = 2.5$ μsec, which is sufficient to keep impulse noises due to automobile ignition fairly well down so that only a very small portion of them will ever reach the plate branch of the first limiter. It can, therefore, affect the discriminator somewhat if only one limiter stage is employed. But if we use an additional limiter stage with a grid condenser of 50 $\mu\mu$f as in the first limiter, but with a grid-leak resistor only half as large, *i.e.*, equal to 25,000 ohms, then the time constant for the grid input of the second limiter is also only half as large. The resulting value of only 1.25 μsec should, no doubt, cut down the remaining ignition interference to next to nothing.

It is because of such cummulative actions that the desirability of using two stages of amplitude limitation cannot be stressed too much. It is to be hoped that FM receiver engineering will follow good engineering design and not omit just one tube with a few circuit elements whose adjustment is not difficult in order to save economically at the expense of the basic advantage of FM, *i.e.*, quality with less interference.

Figure 80 shows how two limiter i-f stages are connected between the i-f stage which has no amplitude limitation and the 6H6 frequency discriminator. It also shows how the discriminator terminates into an a-f deaccentuator whose output voltage e is applied across a 2-megohm potentiometer, which supplies a suitable a-f driving voltage to a class A amplifier tube. This amplifier tube is the first stage of a-f amplification. All networks following are the same as in customary AM receivers having high-fidelity audio stages, which are flat within 2 db of the 1,000 cycles per second value over the entire audio range from 50 to 15,000 cycles per second. In the wiring diagram, the significant time constants are inscribed at the proper places. Essentially these values of time constants should be used, irrespective of whether the same or other tubes are employed. For instance, the deaccentuator ahead of the first audio amplifier tube must use a time constant of 100 μ sec since such a time constant is employed in the preaccentuator of FM transmitters. The purpose of the deaccentuator in the receiver is, after all, to offset exactly the frequency emphasis toward the upper a-f range introduced in the transmitter. Even though the amplitude a-f characteristic can be varied by

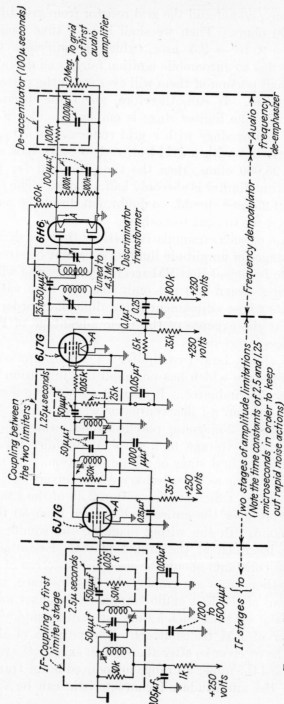

FIG. 80.—Insertion of two limiter stages between the last i-f stage without amplitude limitation and the frequency demodulator.

using a small additional control in the deaccentuator, it does not seem wise to use such additional correction in a *commercial* receiver unless it can be fixed.

51. Characteristic Curves in FM Receivers.—Many of the functions that the different circuit portions have to perform have already been discussed at different places in this text. It is now of importance to apply such functions to actual circuit conditions

In Sec. 50 it was brought out how certain impulse noises can be reduced, as far as their effects in the discriminator output are concerned, by employing grid input networks that cause fast actions, *i.e.*, by using networks that have a small time constant.

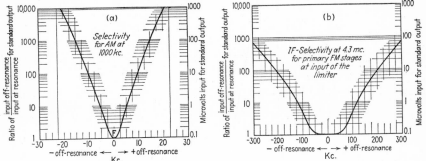

Fig. 81.—Selectivity curves of AM compared with i-f stages used in FM networks.

Generally, circuit actions, if their speed is of interest, are conveniently expressed in terms of time functions such as the time constant (consult Sec. 40). This can then be compared with the desired sinusoidal speed actions as well as with the transient speed of certain desired actions; for instance, the actions in case of television blanking impulses or the perpendicular ascenders of square waves. The time constant can also be compared with undesired actions as ignition and other noise interference.

In ordinary alternating-current applications we know that when a coil with a relatively high natural period feeds, for instance, into a load like the secondary of a h-f output transformer, a good amplitude-frequency characteristic may be expected. The reason is that the natural period of the output coil is high compared with the period of any sinusoidal components of the resulting output current flowing in the coil. This is actually another way of express ing what happens when dealing directly with time constants. Effective time constants must be used when several networks are concerned, since it is not always possible just to accumulate individual time constant effects when there exists appreciable mutual coupling, between the networks, which are reversible.

Figure 81*a* shows a typical selectivity curve. The ratio of the signal input at somewhat off-resonance to the signal input at resonance, referred to normal output, is plotted against the frequency deviation on each side of the true resonance setting. Figure 81*b* gives a typical selectivity characteristic in terms of the input voltage with respect to the detuning. The over-all

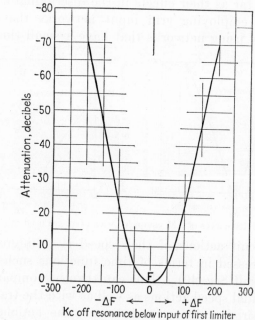

Fig. 82.—Decibel characteristic of the over-all selectivity ahead of the amplitude limiter.

selectivity is what counts, and this can be taken only *before* the first limiter stage since the limiter "clips off" the amplitudes to a constant level. Consequently, constant i-f voltages are impressed on the frequency demodulator. The selectivity characteristic of Fig. 81*b*, therefore, refers to the FM voltage which acts on the first limiter grid. Figure 82 gives the corresponding typical decibel attenuation characteristic for the over-all i-f selectivity observed at the input of the first limiter. Figure 83 shows how the limiter acts when different magnitudes of frequency swings take place. The knees of these deviation characteristics are points above which the flat portions of the characteristics cause constant discriminator input voltages for increasing FM voltages

impressed on the input terminals of the FM receiver. It is the
saturated portion of these characteristics that causes the desired
discriminator action. The saturated input voltages have then
the same value as at the output of the last limiter. It is to be
noted that from about 8 μv upward, the useful FM variations are
effective on the discriminator. Below such input voltages, at the
terminals of an FM receiver, random noise, as indicated by the N
characteristic, becomes more or less prominent.

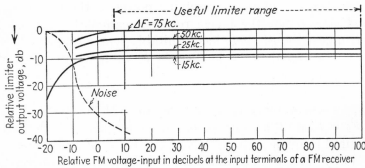

Fig. 83.—Limiter characteristics for different maximum frequency swings.

**52. Image Response in FM Systems in Comparison with Such
Responses in AM Systems.**—From customary superheterodyne
experience we know that in ordinary AM receivers we can classify
five types of interference that result when a local oscillator current
of frequency F_0 mixes with a desired received current of frequency
F_1 to produce an intermediate frequency F_i.

The five types of interference are (1) image interference; (2)
interference on account of harmonics in the oscillator current of
the receiver beating with received currents of undesired frequency;
(3) interference due to received currents that are separated by a
frequency F_i; (4) interference on account of harmonics of the
intermediate frequency produced by the second detector of the
receiver; and (5) interference responses when the difference
frequency is smaller than F_i and such that that the interfering
received current causes a difference frequency equal to $\frac{1}{2}F_i$, $F_i/3$,
etc.

Let us take up first the case of image interference, which
actually has to be considered also in FM receivers. When low
i-f frequencies are used, we know that received currents of carrier
frequencies $F_1 + F_i$ as well as $F_2 - F_i$ will be *accepted* and amplified
in the i-f stages that follow the mixer stage causing the inter-

mediate carrier frequencies. Since it is customary in AM super-heterodynes to have the frequency F_0 of the local oscillator current higher than the frequency F_1 of the desired received current by the frequency difference F_i, the current of frequency F_2 must represent the undesired frequency. Hence, tuning the networks *ahead* of the mixer stage to the frequency F_1 of the desired current, puts, so to speak, the intensity of the image response due to the undesired received current of frequency F_2 into the background. Nevertheless, the immense resolving power of the beat-detection method shows that the image response cannot be ignored altogether, unless the i-f stage has a suitable center frequency. This is due to the fact that the smaller the F_i value with respect to the desired frequency F_1, the stronger will be the background interference due to the undesired received current of frequency F_2. When, as customary, for instance, in AM receivers, $F_0 > F_1$, then $F_2 = F_1 + 2F_i$. For an oscillator frequency F_0 lower than the desired frequency F_1, we have $F_2 = F_1 - 2F_i$. It has already been noted that as the intermediate frequency F_i is increased in value, the effectiveness of the image response is reduced. The amplitude of the desired frequency F_1 is *emphasized* by tuning, and the magnitude of the undesired received current, which is not tuned in, is suppressed all the more the further it is off-resonance, *i.e.*, the larger the $2F_i$ value. The selection of a larger F_i value also reduces the effectiveness of interference due to case 3.

As far as case 4 is concerned, which deals with interference due to harmonics of F_i produced in the second detector and fed back toward the input side of the receiver, this interference applies only to AM receivers. The reason for this is that we deal with frequency demodulators in FM receivers and with amplitude detection only after frequency conversion into amplitude modulation has taken place.

Case 2 means, for instance, that stations of frequencies $2F_0 \pm F_i$ may produce beat currents of intermediate frequency F_i in the mixer, if the local oscillator current of frequency F_0 is distorted. It must be realized, however, that the input network is not tuned to $2F_0 + F_i$ or to $2F_0 - F_i$, but is tuned to the desired frequency F_1. Hence, the chances are against appreciable interference. This happens also to hold true for AM receivers. But it is to be remembered that the beat effect in the amplitude does not concern us in FM receivers since the limiter will eliminate such parasitic AM actions. However, the difference frequency does concern us in FM receivers since any PM effects caused by interfering carriers with the desired carrier causes, in turn, equivalent FM effects, which are proportional to the difference frequency. The larger the difference frequency, the more pronounced will be the undesired equivalent frequency swings.

Case 5 occurs for $F_2 = F_0 \pm \frac{1}{2}F_i$ or for $F_0 \pm \frac{1}{3}F_i$. Then a second harmonic of the beat current produced in the mixer will be readily amplified in the i-f stages and passed on to the frequency demodulator. For proper tuning, *i.e.*, for a good frequency selector ahead of the mixer, this interference will be more or less avoided since the tuning is for $F_1 = F_0 \pm F_i$. As far as the fundamental frequency F_2 of the received interfering current is concerned, this corresponding undesired fundamental current will not be rejected as much in the input networks tuned to the desired frequency F_1 as would an undesired received current which is as much as $2F_i$ off the resonance setting of the networks ahead of the means for frequency conversion to the intermediate frequency F_i. This causes image response. But an undesired current of intermediate frequency $0.5F_i$ can be passed on toward the frequency discriminator only by a second harmonic of frequency $2 \times 0.5F_i = F_i$ if such a harmonic exists with enough amplitude. If such a harmonic prevails, it will be emphasized in the i-f stages since it is of frequency F_i. The chances are that the second harmonic effect in the i-f stages due to a given interfering current is rather less pronounced than the image interference for a properly tuned input system.

Hence, as far as interference in FM receivers is concerned, it is the image interference, *i.e.*, case 1, that needs investigation. We have, therefore, to find out how much an undesired received current of frequency $F_1 \pm 2F_i$ is rejected in a system of networks tuned to frequency F_1. The characteristics of Fig. 84a show the attenuation for detunings from 0 to 800 kc for one, two, and three circuits tuned to the desired current of frequency $F_1 = 600$ kc. These characteristics give a means for finding the image-response ratio since the tuned networks are assumed to be ahead of the mixer that converts the received carrier frequency into an intermediate frequency. These curves apply to carrier frequencies in the standard broadcast range. By image-response ratio is meant the ratio between the carrier voltage applied to the input of the receiver to cause normal output at the image frequency $F_2 = F_1 \pm 2F_i$ and that required to produce normal output at the frequency F_1 to which the receiver is tuned. Hence, the higher the frequency F_i chosen, the more frequency separation exists between the desired frequency F_1, to which the networks are tuned, and the undesired frequency F_2. The image-response ratio is, therefore, *greater for a larger F_i value*. For instance, in customary AM receivers having i-f couplings designed for $F_i = 175$ kc, the desired response to frequency F_1 can be made 1,000 times the

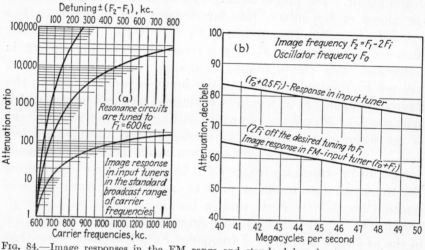

FIG. 84.—Image responses in the FM range and standard broadcast range of carrier frequencies.

value of the undesired response to frequency F_2 at the upper end of the standard broadcast range, *i.e.*, around 1,600 kc. The desired response can be made about 10,000 times the undesired response at the lower broadcast carrier frequency values, *i.e.*, near 540 kc. With i-f couplings designed for $F_i = 460$ kc the image response is still further suppressed, but higher F_i values emphasize some of the other interferences as far as AM receivers are concerned. This is brought out above. The image-response ratio for $F_i = 460$ kc can be made as much as 20,000 to 1 using two circuits tuned to F_1 ahead of the conversion into intermediate frequency. This ratio has reference to the range of 540 to 1,600 kc. When two such tuned networks are used ahead of the mixer in the 10- to 20-megacycle range of carrier frequencies, a response ratio between 100 to 1 and 200 to 1 is obtained.

Since efficient rejection of the undesired currents of respective image frequencies $F_2 = F_1 \pm 2F_i$ depends on good selectivity, which can be secured only by good shielding, the question may arise how we can obtain good selectivity with networks that have to be designed for wide-band FM. As was previously mentioned, the networks should be designed for a band width more than the highest permissible peak-to-peak frequency swing of 150 kc, since this width would give the correct required band width only for large $\beta = \Delta F/f$ values where $\Delta F = 75$ kc. It is best to allow for a band width which is $3 \Delta F$ or 225 kc wide so that full permissible FM can be accommodated for all signal frequencies f. But present-day carrier-frequency allocations are in the 42.1- to 49.9-Mc frequency band, ignoring the frequency assignments used for FM relay work. Taking the lower limit of center-frequency allocation, we have to meet the most severe requirement with respect to selectivity. The percentage of band width to the center frequency for FM receivers is then $225 \times 100/42{,}100 = 0.535$ per cent. For input networks in AM receivers working in the standard broadcast range at the most favorable end of this range, we have for high-fidelity transmission a band width of $2 \times 15 = 30$ kc and a carrier frequency of 1,500 kc. The percentage of band width, therefore, becomes $30 \times 100/1{,}500$ or as high as 2 per cent. Hence, the percentage condition for present-day FM allocations is relatively smaller than for AM systems in the present-day standard broadcast allocations. Conditions are even more favorable in FM receivers used for relay work.

The important cases that interest us in FM receivers are the image-response rejections in the tuned input network of the receiver ahead of the mixer stage, as well as the rejection of received currents that cause a fundamental intermediate frequency of $0.5F_i$ instead of F_i. The corresponding decibel attenuations for these cases are as shown in Fig. 84b.

As in AM superheterodynes, the proper choice of the intermediate frequency F_i is of importance in FM superheterodynes. When, therefore, in the standard broadcast range of AM stations we select 175 kc for F_i, the second harmonic, which could be caused by distortion, falls outside the assigned carrier-frequency range. The third harmonic, $3F_i$, also falls outside of this range. The fourth harmonic, which is $4 \times 175 = 700$ kc, as well as still higher harmonics, may be assumed to have insufficient amplitude to cause much interference although they fall within the range. For 460-kc intermediate stages, however, the very pronounced second harmonic of frequency 920 kc falls into the standard broadcast range, as also falls the third harmonic, and interference may be expected.

The two preferred intermediate frequencies for FM systems are $F_i = 4.3$ Mc and 5.25 Mc, the first frequency being the one generally used. Choosing the oscillator frequency F_0 below the frequency F_1 of the desired FM current, *all* image responses for *all* center-frequency assignments then fall *outside* the tuning range of the FM receiver. The image responses due to the carrier-frequency assignments in the 30.5- to 39.5-Mc range are only theoretically possible as can be readily understood from Fig. 84*b*.

53. All the Networks in an FM Receiver.—Inasmuch as the field intensity contours for commercial FM require at least 50 μv/m electric field strength, normally good a-f recovery can be expected with the network indicated in Fig. 85 where only one stage of h-f amplification takes place before conversion into intermediate frequency is effected. The network of Fig. 85 is a composite of circuit sections already described in detail. Voltage regulation is provided so that the frequency of the local oscillator is not appreciably affected by fluctuations in the line voltage. If more than one stage of h-f amplification is used, the image rejection is still more pronounced. Neutralized input stages should be employed. In many FM sets doubly tuned transformers are being used between the i-f stages, although capacitance coupling or both capacitance and transformer coupling can be used.

54. Alignment of FM Receivers.—If an FM signal generator is available, the receiver can not only be aligned more conveniently, but also can be tested in every respect. If no FM signal generator is at hand, a customary type of signal generator can be used. It should work up to 50 Mc on the fundamental frequency, although the upper range needed for carrier-frequency tests from 42 to 50 Mc can also be covered with second harmonics produced from fundamentals between 21 and 25 Mc. Since the band width of the networks of the FM receiver should be as much as 225 kc, the signal generator should have a good frequency spread around a frequency of 4.3 Mc, which is usually the center frequency of the i-f stages. This will permit, then, an experimental amplitude-frequency curve to be taken at the output side with respect to

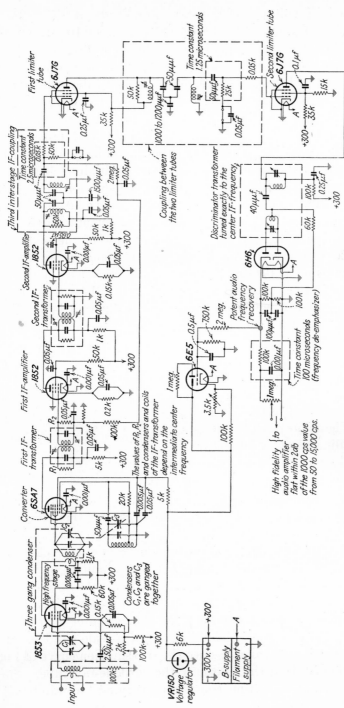

Fig. 85.—Complete FM receiver with two stages of amplitude limitation.

impressed i-f voltages of constant amplitude at the input side of the i-f amplifiers. As a matter of fact, a good frequency spread in the signal generator should exist from about 1.6 Mc up to about 5.4 Mc so that i-f stages with center frequencies different from 4.3 Mc can be tested also. A good vacuum-tube voltmeter is of use in such tests. For some readings one set of deflection plates of a cathode-ray oscillograph can be used as a tube voltmeter. The length of the linear trace is proportional to the applied voltage. The amplifier of the cathode-ray tube should be used only when a calibration for the frequencies employed is obtained at first. For measuring carrier-frequency voltages, diode voltmeters are a convenient means. If a center-scale direct-current microammeter is at hand, like the Weston student galvanometer having about 600 μa full-scale deflections toward each side of the scale center, this meter can be converted into a high-resistance direct voltmeter by connecting a 1-megohm resistor in series with it. Such a voltmeter is then a ready means for testing the output voltages of a discriminator when input voltages of different i-f frequencies are impressed. A customary type of 0-1 direct-current milliam-meter is likewise of great use. Even with such simple equipment an FM receiver can be aligned in every respect.

The essential receiver tests consist of the following determinations.

1. Alignment of the h-f networks.
2. Alignment of the i-f stages.
3. Adjustment of the limiter.
4. Alignment of the frequency demodulator.
5. Customary tests on the a-f section.

Generally, when testing several amplifier stages that have like operating functions, such as successive i-f stages, there is a *temptation* to adjust immediately for an "over-all" transmission curve like that shown in Fig. 86. Such a curve might be obtained at the output of the last i-f stage which is not limited, or across the input side of the first limiter stage. It can also be obtained at the input side of the last limiter when the impressed signal voltage causes limiter action below the knee of the limiter characteristic. Such a temptation is especially strong if a wide-band frequency signal generator is available since the transmission curve of Fig. 86 can be observed on the screen of the cathode-ray tube. Such a poor procedure of testing consists in varying "at random" the different adjustments in all the stages until the over-all transmission curve "appears" to be satisfactory. The resultant apparently good-looking transmission curve is then only too often due to a compromise. This means that generally a poor alignment in one stage is compensated by overemphasized and shifted alignment in other stages. Surely this cannot lead to good quality. The reason for this is that one stage may be peaked unsymmetrically, another stage may have a center peak, and the other stages

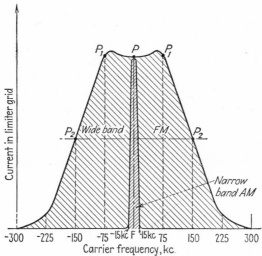

Fig. 86.—Over-all resonance curves as experienced at the input of the limiter.

may have two response peaks. This has reference to all i-f stages. Hence, no stage by itself satisfies the condition required for linear networks with respect to *amplitude and phase*.

Normally, we have only two i-f stages ahead of two limiter stages. Suppose the first one is peaked near the center frequency and falls off "badly" on each side of it. This stage cannot pass on all the significant side currents or pass the i-f center-frequency current component with proper amplitude relationship with respect to the amplitude of all the important side currents. This stage also will not satisfy the correct phase relationship of the significant currents to be passed. To make the over-all characteristic appear correct, *each stage by itself* must have a tendency to satisfy the phase as well as the amplitude linearity with respect to all instantaneous intermediate frequencies that are possible. This is clear if we realize that if the first i-f stage by itself does not pass on all the significant spectrum currents as required by the

FM of the incoming electromagnetic wave, then the output voltage passed on to the next i-f stage can no longer be the correct FM voltage. Hence, on account of the poor alignment of the first i-f stage, a distorted FM voltage will be impressed on the control grid of the second i-f amplifier. Such an alignment should decidedly be avoided. It is not apt to be made if no wide-swing signal source is available since then we have to take readings step by step and stage by stage, which is the correct procedure. No matter what method is used, *i.e.*, customary signal source or wideband signal source, the correct alignment should always be made by aligning at first the i-f stage ahead of the last limiter, then the i-f stage ahead of the stage just aligned, etc.

As far as the h-f stage or stages ahead of the mixer stage, which converts into i-f frequencies, are concerned, ordinary single peaking is practiced. At the frequency allocations used for FM systems, coil and tube damping provide the required broadness of the resonance curve. The input coil of the FM receiver is conveniently connected to a dipole, each rod being about 5 ft or somewhat shorter in length, and a twisted-pair leadin used. If the receiver location is close to the transmitter, one end of the input coil may be connected to an aerial of about 10 ft in length while the other terminal is connected to ground and to the chassis of the receiver. The dipole antenna not only is more efficient, but avoids also more ignition noise and other undesirable pickups. It should, therefore, be used. A suitable resistance of about 1,000 ohms across the input terminals of the FM set may improve the matching when several FM stations are to be received.

In the alignment of the h-f stage, we have to bear in mind that we are dealing with an antenna gain, a h-f amplifier gain, and a subsequent converter gain as far as the voltage impressed on the first i-f stage is concerned. When testing the FM receiver, the tuned-in receiver is adjusted for maximum response, *i.e.*, for maximum gain. It is also necessary to obtain a setting of the oscillator trimmer such that proper tracking exists for all FM stations to be received. The process is as follows: The signal generator is connected to the input terminals of the receiver as shown in Fig. 87 and set to the range that covers the FM carriers of frequencies 42.1 to 49.9 Mc. The limiter input current and the induced antenna voltage that is applied to the FM receiver have to bear a definite relation to each other, in order to avoid undue

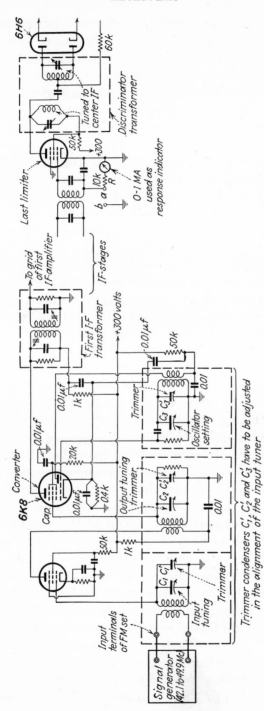

FIG. 87.—Shows how grid return of last limiter tube can be used in alignment tests.

noise interference.   Hence, it is this current that has to be measured.   The corresponding voltage reading can, of course, be used
instead of the limiter current if desired.   The milliammeter is,
therefore, inserted in the grid return of the limiter as indicated in
Fig. 87.   The magnitude of the meter reading gives the response
with respect to the carrier-frequency voltage impressed on the
FM set.   An ordinary signal generator will do and without any
modulation since we deal with an FM receiver which is based on
constant carrier level.   The frequency of the signal generator is
then set to a frequency value near to 49 Mc, *i.e.*, near to the h-f
end of the FM band.   The calibration of the signal generator
should be known.   The setting of the tuning dial driving the
three-gang condensers C_1, C_2, and C_3 is varied until the milliammeter registers a maximum value.   If the dial reading on the
receiver also indicates 49 Mc then the trimmer of the oscillator is
adjusted to its correct setting.   However, if, for instance, the
maximum response on the milliammeter occurs at a 48.2-Mc
setting, then we have to turn the knob of the FM receiver until
maximum response gives a dial setting of exactly 49 Mc.   Here-
after, the trimmer condenser C_3' of the oscillator is varied until
maximum response is noted again on the grid meter of the last
limiter.   Next, vary the trimmers C_1' and C_2' until a still better
limiter current response is obtained.   It is *important* that the
voltage applied by the signal generator be *just sufficient* to indicate
decided maximum effects in the milliammeter when the best
adjustment occurs.   It is necessary, therefore, that the signal
voltage be decreased for the latter trimmer adjustments.   The
next step is to check the tracking.   This test requires that the
frequency of the signal generator be set to such frequencies
as 48, 47, 46 in succession down to about 43 Mc.   In each case, the
dial of the FM receiver under test is set for maximum response as
noted by the grid-current meter of the first limiter tube.   Assuming equal input voltages, for proper tracking the milliammeter
indications should be essentially equal in each case.   If this is not
so, a compromise has to be made with respect to the trimmer
settings.   How to do this is well known from the AM technique.

Inasmuch as it is possible to use the oscillator frequency F_0 on
either side of the tuning frequency F_1 of the desired received
current, we can obtain a tracking for a condition when F_0 is either
smaller or larger than F_1 and in each case by an amount equal

to the center intermediate frequency F_i which is generally 4.3 Mc. No possibility will arise of aligning the receiver on the wrong side, since in FM systems with i-f values as large as 4.3 Mc or even 5.25 Mc the image frequency is far removed.   It was brought out in Sec. 52 that for F_0 below F_1, the image frequency will be $2F_i$ below the desired frequency F_1.   For F_0 above F_1 it will be $2F_i$ above F_1.   Hence, if the tracking cannot be improved by resetting the trimmers C_1' and C_2' it may be that the receiver was designed for the oscillator frequency on the other side of F_1.   It should be noted that the signal voltage can also be applied to the signal grid which feeds the mixer tube.   Since, in such an application of the test voltage the tuned antenna and h-f branch are not used, the maximum responses in the grid meter of the first limiter tube would be the same whether the oscillator frequency F_0 is larger or smaller than F_1.

In the alignment of i-f stages, the signal generator is set to a signal frequency equal to the center frequency, which is, for instance, 4.3 Mc.   The limiter of the receiver performs its useful function for signals of intensities beyond the knee of the limiter characteristic.   Only for the horizontal or saturation portion of the characteristic does complete limitation occur.   The characteristics shown in Fig. 81 are over-all selectivity curves as experienced at the input side of the last limiter.   Figure 86 shows over-all resonance curves as experienced at the input side of the last limiter.   It should again be noted that the voltage of the signal generator should be just sufficient to show *decided* milliammeter responses.   If too much voltage were applied, the second limiter would work beyond the knee of the limiter characteristic.   In Fig. 86, point P corresponds to the center frequency, points P_1 to i-f frequencies which are ± 75 kc off the center frequency, and points P_2 to i-f carrier frequencies which are ± 100 kc off the center frequency.   A good over-all transmission characteristic is, as already mentioned, about 6 db down at ± 75 kc and about 20 db down at ± 100 kc.   This latter requirement applies especially for FM receivers that have to be used in locations subject to adjacent channel interference.   Characteristics of this type are the result of at least six properly tuned i-f circuits.

The knee of the limiter characteristic (Figs. 83 and 88) is the threshold value upward from which complete limiter action is expected.   This limiter characteristic has an important influence not only on the design of the preceding i-f stages, but also on the desirable characteristics of the frequency demodulator that follows the limiter. Suppose that it requires 20 μv at the input side of the FM receiver at the center frequency to bring about complete limitation, *i.e.*, to produce saturation output voltage at the output of the limiter. This intermediate frequency is also applied to the input of the frequency discriminator. Suppose that the FM in the i-f stages has an instantaneous carrier frequency which is 70 kc off the center frequency. On account of the over-all selectivity of the i-f stages, the voltage applied to the input side of the limiter is only about one-third the voltage value at the center frequency. At this moment the limiter operation is on the left side of the knee of the limiter characteristic and three times as much signal voltage, or 60 μv, would have to be impressed at the input side of the FM receiver, in order to secure complete limitation. Hence, we must expect a certain amount of distortion. Suppose that the i-f stages preceding the limiter are changed, for instance, by reducing some of the gain in order to obtain better flatness than was assumed in the above numerical example. Then it will be clear that less distortion is apt to take place. Hence, it is essential that the transmission curve of i-f amplifiers be approximately flat, at least toward the 70-kc off positions, and should be as indicated in Fig. 86 or as in the over-all selectivity curves of Fig. 81.

If a wide-swing-signal FM generator is available, it is set to the center frequency of 4.3 Mc and the vertical deflection plates of a cathode-ray oscillograph connected between terminals *a* and *b* of Fig. 87, in order to observe the shape of the transmission curve. This curve should look like the characteristic shown in Fig. 86. However, the symmetrical curve should not be obtained just by adjusting by "cut and try" most of the i-f settings. It should be obtained by starting with the last i-f stage ahead of the last limiter and securing first for this stage a fairly good flat characteristic response. Then the i-f voltage, which is again frequency modulated, should be applied to the input of the i-f stage preceding the stage just lined up, and the settings of this stage adjusted, and so on. Next, a compromise setting is finally made for all i-f stages until a good-looking response curve is obtained. The compromise settings should be still close to the settings obtained for the single stage adjustment.

The alignment can, however, also be accomplished with an ordinary signal generator which is not modulated at all. Then we use again the milliammeter deflection in the grid return of the last limiter stage, shown in Fig. 87. If the resistor R is not of very high value, but is in the neighborhood of 10,000 ohms, as usually the case, then the indicated 0-1 milliammeter will serve well for the response deflections. If high grid-return resistors are used in an FM receiver, then a microammeter has to be employed. The alignment of the i-f stages then consists in adjusting the intermediate frequency transformers one at a time, for maximum deflection of the grid-return meter, *starting* with the i-f transformer next to the limiter and proceeding backward to the mixer stage.

In connection with the alignment of commercial FM receivers, it is also necessary to know the requirements of the manufacturer. The reason for this is that the condition for the best over-all transmission curve can be improved by good engineering design. It depends on how the individual selectivity characteristic is produced in each stage. We often have transformer coupling between i-f tubes. In other cases either condenser coupling is employed or both kinds of couplings are used. For all such couplings the circuit decrement is kept large in order to broaden the resonance curve and overcoupling is employed for emphasizing the band width. The designer of an FM receiver does this with customary electric circuit theory. But he will often find when the stages are actually tested in a laboratory that the flatness can be improved if certain circuit parameters, such as degree of interstage coupling or parallel resistance value with tuning condensers, are somewhat changed from the calculated magnitudes. For this reason some manufacturers may request a certain alignment. Usually the experimenter then resorts to two expedients. In one expedient the over-all transmission curve has two peaks as is, for instance, shown in Fig. 86. The other alignment calls for a single peak in the over-all transmission curve.

For a single-peak transmission characteristic the signal generator is set to the center frequency of 4.3 Mc, for instance. In case of 5.25 Mc i-f stages, the unmodulated signal frequency is set to 5.25 Mc. We start again with the alignment of the i-f transformer which feeds the grid of the limiter. It is understood that in case of two limiter stages the response meter is conveniently inserted in the grid return of the *last* limiter tube. We have then a limiter gain of from 2 to 5 for the two stages and the signal frequency voltage applied has to be made smaller than for one limiter stage only. This is important to remember since we must not "flood" the limiter with too much input voltage in order to avoid saturation readings that could not yield maximum response deflections as needed for this test. The grid-return meter must show maximum responses in these tests. The secondary as well as the primary settings of the last i-f stage preceding the limiter are adjusted for maximum response on the grid-current meter. This can be done by applying i-f voltages of the center frequency between the grid and ground of the stage that is aligned. This will require somewhat more voltage; but the voltage should be kept as low as possible so that only decided responses occur in the grid-return meter. Then the stage ahead of the i-f stage just aligned is adjusted in the same way. This will require somewhat less i-f voltage from the signal generator. As we proceed with this test we come to the stage with the converter. For the case of a 6SA7 tube, the i-f signal is fed into terminal 8; for a 6K8 mixer tube, it is fed into the grid cap. It should be noted that the h-f tuning coil is connected between grid and ground. We would, therefore, require altogether too much signal voltage for causing sufficient response on account of the low reactance offered to i-f currents. For this reason we have to unsolder the connection from the h-f coil and connect a high resistance anywhere between 25,000 to 100,000 ohms between the signal grid and the chassis. This resistor, which is used only during the final i-f alignment, acts also as a bias. In this alignment the i-f voltage is applied between signal grid and chassis. After the first stage has also been aligned, it is good practice to make *minor* adjustments in all the settings in order to improve the over-all characteristic. This is done by first applying an i-f voltage of the correct center frequency and noting the limiter current reading. Then an i-f voltage that is, say, ± 40 kc off is applied and it is noted whether symmetry occurs in the reduced maximum responses for such carrier frequencies. Then the procedure is repeated for intermediate carrier frequencies which are ± 75 kc off the center frequency. For a good over-all alignment, symmetry about the center frequency should prevail and the grid-current readings should not be reduced to more than about one-tenth of the center-frequency value for frequencies that are ± 75 kc off center. Since no meter measures correct relative readings for currents with a ratio of 1/10, a double-scale meter should be used or a single-scale meter with a removable shunt.

The double-peak over-all characteristic is aligned as follows: If the alignment is not too much off at first, the i-f voltage of the signal generator is applied to the grid of the mixer. By slowly sweeping the intermediate frequency on each side of the center frequency, the maximum responses of the limiter current are found. This will lead approximately to the intermediate frequencies at which peaking takes place. The peaks are usually equally spaced with respect to the center frequency. Unequal peaks prevail if the alignment is somewhat off. In case the responses are not too unequal and occur at intermediate frequencies that are still symmetrical with respect to the center frequency, it is necessary to make adjustments either for only the lower peak frequency or the upper peak frequency. Using the lower peak frequency, we start again with the alignment of the i-f stage next to the limiter. After the entire i-f system has been aligned, stage by stage, we apply again a voltage of the correct center frequency and note the grid current response. Then a voltage with a carrier frequency that is 75 kc above the inter-mediate center frequency is applied and the response noted. Next, a voltage with a frequency that is 75 kc below the center frequency is applied. The grid-current response should be the same that was obtained when the frequency was 75 kc above the center frequency.

Sometimes the i-f alignment is so poor that it is difficult to determine what are the correct peaking frequencies. It is then best to set the signal generator at an intermediate frequency which is about 50 kc below the center frequency and then to line up, stage by stage, for maximum responses at this off frequency. Also here we begin with the i-f stage next to the limiter and proceed toward the mixer. To do this, the respective trimmer condensers have to be set first toward maximum capacitance setting and then reduced until the grid-current meter gives maximum response, first when the secondary and then when the primary of the i-f stage is tuned to a frequency of $(F_i - 50 \text{ kc})$. After such an alignment of all stages, signals of intermediate frequencies $F_i -$ 75 kc, F_i, and $F_i + 75$ kc are applied in turn and the resulting transmission curve should look symmetrical. It should also show equal peaking at ± 50 kc off the intermediate center frequency F_i. If this is not the case, it is a sign that we assumed the incorrect peaking frequency. The entire process is then repeated with a somewhat higher off frequency and a new over-all transmission curve obtained. If this curve comes out still more unsymmetrical, then the alignment is repeated with an off frequency of somewhat less than the 50-kc off frequency. The process is repeated until equal symmetrical peaks with respect to the center frequency F_i are obtained. If the correct off frequency for double peaking is guessed in the first place, the process

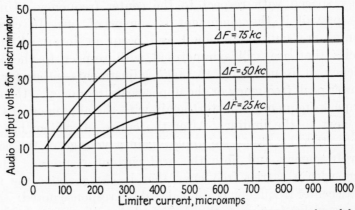

FIG. 88.—Audio-frequency recovery at the output of the frequency demodulator for different degrees of FM.

is just as quick as for single peaking since the alignment is based on obtaining response readings only for the lower peak frequency or only for the upper peak frequency. Generally, the manufacturer will provide information as to which are the correct peaking frequencies so that the method of repeated alignment can be simplified.

With respect to the alignment of the frequency demodulator, refer to the description of the alignment of the frequency discriminator on page 208. When the i-f stages, as well as the discriminator, are properly aligned, in case of a single-peak operation the grid-current meter of the last limiter tube should show a maximum response when a voltage of the intermediate center frequency F_i is applied (Fig. 87). The output voltage of the discriminator must vanish since center-frequency balance prevails. Now if the i-f stages are excited by a voltage which is, for instance, 75 kc off the center frequency in one direction, then the grid-current reading should indicate less response, and a direct voltmeter across the output of the discriminator should now show a considerable reading. For an instantaneous intermediate frequency that is 75 kc off in the other direction, the output voltage should be of opposite polarity and of the same magnitude as for the 75-kc off-frequency deviation in the original direction.

With respect to the determination of the limiter action, refer to page 209. It is also of importance to take curves for which the recovered a-f voltage is plotted against the limiter grid current for different frequency swings as in Fig. 88. The a-f voltage is measured across the cathodes of the 6H6 discriminator tube and the length of the linear trace of a cathode-ray oscillograph may be used as a measure of this voltage. The vertical deflection plates of the cathode-ray tube are then connected through a condenser to the respective cathodes of the 6H6 rectifier.

Inasmuch as an FM receiver represents a high-fidelity transmission system, it should not be overlooked in the tests that the a-f response through all stages of a-f amplification should be flat within 2 db with respect to the 1,000 cycles per second value over the entire range from 50 to 15,000 cycles per second. When this audio-response curve is taken, it is to be borne in mind that the audio voltages from a beat oscillator should not be applied directly following the discriminator since the frequency deaccentuator is connected between the output of the discriminator and the first a-f stage. Hence, the a-f voltage of the beat-frequency oscillator must be applied *after* the deaccentuator.

CHAPTER V

TRANSMITTER AND RECEIVER AERIALS

Inasmuch as the carrier frequencies assigned to FM stations are in the upper megacycle range, antenna arrays can be used without going into undue dimensions. Such arrays can be made to have antenna field gains in definite directions with a circular horizontal pattern. Such a pattern is desirable since the largest service area can be covered with it.

55. Radiation of Waves in the Carrier Frequency Spectrum of FM Waves.—As was described in connection with wave propagation in the FM range of carrier currents, transmission primarily along the "path of sight" takes place. It is true, however, that electromagnetic waves are partly refracted near ground, and are, so to speak, bent somewhat around the earth's surface. Consequently, distances that are a small percentage longer than the line-of-sight limit can be covered, but the distance gained is not enough to play an important part. It is also true that, on account of reflections from mountains and other large objects, reception may be possible in the electromagnetic shadow region of the direct wave propagation direction. Nevertheless, it does not seem wise to include in the service area some of the apparent shadow regions. In other words, a transmitter aerial should be located at a relatively high elevation with respect to the service area, which is essentially below it. A circular radiation pattern should be approached practically as much as possible. This can be accomplished theoretically with vertical radiators and also with horizontal radiators if they are properly arranged as well as phased. By phasing are meant radiation field excitations with respect to time angles as well as to space angles.

56. Input Impedance and Mutual Impedance of Dipoles.—A dipole such as is indicated in Fig. 89 is conveniently used as a receiving antenna. Generally, it is believed that for true half-wave-length dipoles the impedance looking into the dipole gap is equal to the radiation resistance of about 75 ohms. By true half-wave dipoles is meant that the total length of the conductors

278

is exactly equal to half the wave length of the electromagnetic wave length in empty space. Hence, an ordinary twisted lamp cord can be used as a feeder since its characteristic impedance is in this neighborhood. If a good commercial twisted leadin is employed, the decibel loss in the feeder will be considerably smaller and, therefore, more FM voltage will affect the input of the receiver. Unlike television reception, where a broad impedance across the dipole input is desirable, on account of the 6-Mc band width of the received video modulation, even for wide-band FM, we have only a relatively small band width with respect to the magnitude of all the carrier frequencies. This statement, of

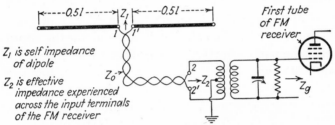

Fig. 89.—Dipole feed with a balancing ground connection.

course, has reference only to the case of a dipole that is especially dimensioned with respect to a certain center-frequency allocation. Usually a compromise has to be made with respect to the length of the dipole. Often two 5-ft colinear rods are employed as a receiver aerial. It is of interest that then a twisted feeder line makes a suitable impedance match with respect to terminals 1-1', as well as with respect to the effective input impedance at terminals 2-2'.

Generally, a linear conductor of length l does not show a pure resistance, even if excited in a theoretical half-wave distribution. This is true whether a single antenna rod of length l equal to 0.5λ is used with a shunt feed termination, or whether two rods each 0.25λ long are lined up colinear and the series feeder is connected across the center gap. In each case λ denotes the wave length in free space, *i.e.*, it is dependent on the true velocity of light c with respect to the frequency F of the exciting current. A true resistance termination of about 75 ohms can be expected when the two rods are each about $0.95 \times \frac{1}{4}\lambda$ long with respect to the carrier frequency F of the exciting current. It is, therefore, necessary to use dipoles that are *about 5 per cent shorter* than required by the wave-length distribution in empty space. If this is not done, we shall generally have an input impedance that has a reactive component, besides the active radiation resistance component.

There are two ways of obtaining a physical feeling of why this is the case. One is based on the fact that there is a difference between the "unhindered" wave-length distribution in free space and the "apparent" or phase distribution along the dipole halves. In empty space an electromagnetic wave moves with the velocity of light c and, hence, passes through a complete wave length λ during the duration $1/F$ of a h-f cycle of the antenna current that causes the electromagnetic wave. Along a conductor the group velocity c'' of propagation is somewhat smaller than that of light and the apparent wave-length distribution along the conductor is, therefore, somewhat shorter. According to experience, for FM frequency allocations the wave-length distribution along the conductor is about 5 per cent shorter than the distribution in empty space. The other way of obtaining a physical concept of why the actual length l of a dipole has to be somewhat shorter than the true half of the operating wave length is that for a length $l = 0.5\lambda$, we actually have an input *impedance* across terminals 1-1' of value $Z_1 = \sqrt{R_1^2 + X_1^2}$, where $R_1 = 73.4$ ohms. As will be shown, the reactive component X_1 is an inductive reactance. Hence, by shortening somewhat the length l, a condition can be found for which a pure resistance termination results. For this condition we have then also a somewhat different R_1 value.

Generally, a linear conductor of any length l must have a driving impedance anywhere along the conductor, otherwise a current flow could not be possible and could not form certain distributions along the conductor. By the driving impedance at a point is meant, the potential at a certain point of the conductor divided by the current flowing through the cross section of the conductor at that point. For colinear half dipoles, as indicated in Fig. 89, it is convenient to use the impedance at the gap point, *i.e.*, at terminals 1-1'. If the dipole acts as a transmitter antenna, the feeder will impress a voltage E_1 across the input terminals 1-1' and will send currents toward each open end of the respective dipole rods. At the respective open ends the effective current must be zero; it has a value I_1 at the driving points 1 and 1'. This would be the maximum value of the current distribution if the two rods were each excited in the exact quarter-wave-length distribution. The ratio E_1/I_1 is then the driving impedance Z_1 at the points 1 and 1', which must be equal to the characteristic impedance of the feeder for maximum energy transfer. When the dipole acts as a receiver antenna, the same thing occurs at the current loop and the impedance Z_1 may be taken as the ratio of the induced voltage E_1 at the dipole gap 1-1' to the current value I_1 at the gap points 1 and 1'. The impedance at the gap of the dipole may be called the self-impedance of the dipole. It can be computed from

$$Z_1 = 30\{[0.5772 + 2.303 \log_{10}(2pl) - Ci(2pl)] + j[Si(2pl)]\}$$
$$= R_1 + jX_1 \quad \text{ohms} \quad (145)$$

where $p = 2\pi/\lambda$ and for $q = 2p$, where ql is twice the electrical length of the dipole.

$$
\left.
\begin{array}{l}
\text{for } -17 \leq q \leq 17
\left\{
\begin{array}{l}
Ci(q) = 0.5772 + 0.576 \log_{10}(q)^4 \\
\qquad\qquad - \dfrac{1}{2}\dfrac{q^2}{2!} + \dfrac{1}{4}\dfrac{q^4}{4!} - \cdots \\[2ex]
Si(q) = q - \dfrac{1}{3}\dfrac{q^3}{3!} + \dfrac{1}{5}\dfrac{q^5}{5!} - \cdots
\end{array}
\right. \\[6ex]
\text{for } q > 17
\left\{
\begin{array}{l}
Ci(q) = \dfrac{\sin q}{q}\left(1! - \dfrac{2!}{q^2} + \dfrac{4!}{q^4} - \cdots\right) - \\
\qquad\quad - \dfrac{\cos q}{q}\left(\dfrac{1!}{q} - \dfrac{3!}{q^3} + \dfrac{5!}{q^5} - \cdots\right) \\[2ex]
Si(q) = 1.57 - \dfrac{\cos q}{q}\left(1! - \dfrac{2!}{q^2} + \dfrac{4!}{q^4} - \cdots\right) \\
\qquad\qquad - \dfrac{\sin q}{q}\left(\dfrac{1!}{q} - \dfrac{3!}{q^3} + \dfrac{5!}{q^5} - \cdots\right)
\end{array}
\right. \\[6ex]
1! = 1; 2! = 1 \times 2; 3! = 1 \times 2 \times 3; \\
\qquad 4! = 1 \times 2 \times 3 \times 4; 5! = 1 \times 2 \times 3 \times 4 \times 5
\end{array}
\right\} \quad (146)
$$

where 0.5772 is the well-known Euler constant. The factor 0.576 happens to be almost equal to this constant, but is actually the outcome of 2.303/4. The terms $Si(q)$ and $Ci(q)$ are the integral sinus and integral cosinus defined by

$$Si(q) = \int_0^q \frac{\sin \alpha}{\alpha}\, d\alpha = 1.57 - \int_q^\infty \frac{\sin \alpha}{\alpha}\, d\alpha$$
$$Ci(q) = - \int_q^\infty \frac{\cos \alpha}{\alpha}\, d\alpha$$

There is no difficulty at all in applying these expressions to engineering computations. Figure 90 shows how these functions behave. For values $q = 2p = 4\pi/\lambda$ of the conductor, which cause, when multiplied with l, points P_1, P_2, and P_3 on the Ci curve, the effective resistance at the mid-point gap of the conductor is

$$R_1 = 30 \left[0.5772 + 2.303 \log_{10} \left(\frac{4\pi l}{\lambda} \right) \right] \quad \text{ohms} \quad (147)$$

since the integral-cosine value vanishes. When a dipole is excited at its fundamental or any higher mode, we may expect in FM

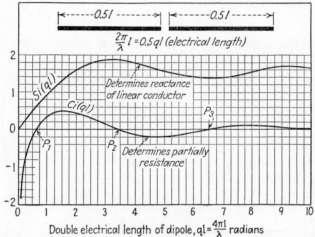

FIG. 90.—Integralsinus (Si) and integralcosinus (Ci) functions for computing the self-impedance of linear conductors.

systems high radiation efficiency and may assume that R_1 represents essentially the radiation resistance. This means that the square of the effective loop current I_1 flowing at the mid-point of the dipole of length l times the R_1 value then represents essentially the radiated power.

For point P_1 in Fig. 90 we have an electrical length of the dipole of $0.5ql = 0.5 \times 0.617 = 0.3085$ radian. This is equivalent to $0.3085 \times 57.3 = 17.7$ electrical space degrees. This would correspond to a dipole of very short electrical length as far as the operating wave length λ in empty space is concerned. This is evident when we realize that the fundamental mode or half-wave-length distribution desired, corresponds to an electrical length of the dipole of 180 electrical degrees. Point P_3 of Fig. 90 corresponds to $6.45/2 = 3.225$ radians. For such a condition the dipole has an electrical length of 184.7 deg. If we take the case of an electrical length of exactly 180 electrical degrees, we have $pl = 6.28l/\lambda = 6.28 \times 0.5\lambda/\lambda$ or 3.14 radians. According to Eq. (145) we find then for the resistance, by using the more accurate Ci table in the Appendix, the expression

$$R_1 = 30[0.5772 + 2.303 \log_{10} (6.28) - Ci(6.28)]$$
$$= 30(0.5772 + 2.303 \times 0.798 + 0.026)$$
$$= 30 \times 2.4432 = 73.4 \quad \text{ohms} \quad (148)$$

which checks very well with the well-known radiation resistance value of a half-wave radiator.

The well-known value is, however, derived by means of the radiation effects that exist at a very large distance (many wave lengths away) from the dipole. This is the reason why such a derivation will not include the reactance component, which is wattless. But Eq. (145) is based on what happens immediately surrounding the dipole surface and yields also the reactance value

$$X_1 = 30Si(2pl) = 30Si(6.28) = 30 \times 1.43 = 42.9 \quad \text{ohms} \quad (149)$$

At the center of the dipole we have then an impedance Z_1 acting which is

$$Z_1 = 73.4 + j42.9 = \sqrt{73.4^2 + 42.9^2} = 85 \quad \text{ohms} \quad (150)$$

with a phase angle of $\tan^{-1} (42.9/73.4) = 30.3$ deg. This result shows that the termination has to be made with respect to an *impedance* value of 85 ohms, instead of with respect to the radiation resistance of 73.4 ohms.

This is the general solution. It depends apparently only on the length l of the dipole. In practice we have to use hard-drawn copper tubing or some other suitable material of suitable outside diameter for the dipole. The magnitude of the diameter has to be chosen with regard to two requirements. One considers the physical strength required to keep the dipole in shape against wind pressure and gravitation action. It also keeps the dipole in the desired orientation for maximum electromagnetic field pickup. The other requirement is that the self-impedance of the dipole, where the feeder connects to it, should remain essentially constant. As far as the percentage of frequency deviation width of the induced FM current in the dipole is concerned, there is no serious difficulty. But we have to realize that a receiver dipole has to pick up FM waves for the entire frequency range from about 40 to 50 Mc. Under such conditions it is impossible to expect pure resistance terminations at the center of the dipole. Hence, a compromise has to be made.

Quite often manufacturers suggest the use of dipoles that have an over-all length of 10 ft. Such a dipole would be $l = 0.3048 \times 10 = 3.048$ m long. The dipole then consists of two 1.524-m tubings if series feed is employed. The two tubes of respective equal lengths l_1 are colinear, as shown in Fig. 91. For the *ideal* case, where the velocity of propagation from input points 1 and 1' toward the respective open ends is equal to 3×10^8 m/sec, $l = 2l_1$ would correspond to a half-wave-length distribution for the exciting current of frequency $3 \times 10^8 \times 10^{-6}/2l = 150/3.048 = 49.5$ Mc. This value happens to coincide exactly with a carrier-frequency assignment in the FM range. For such an ideal

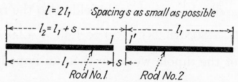

Fig. 91.—Two colinear conductors which are either excited as a dipole or as each rod separately.

excitation a pure resistance would be the value of the impedance Z_1. But if, as experience and theory teach, the group velocity c'' of propagation is smaller by about 5 per cent, then the phase velocity $c' = c^2/c'' = 9 \times 10^{16}/c''$ must be correspondingly larger. We have then $c'' = 0.95c$ and $c' = 3 \times 10^8/0.95 = 3.16 \times 10^8$ m/sec. Hence, for a length $l = 3.048$ m we have actually a frequency value of $c'/(2l)$; when expressed in megacycles,

$$3.16 \times 10^8 \times \frac{10^{-6}}{(2 \times 3.048)} = 51.9 \text{ Mc.}$$

The frequency discrepancy between 51.9 and 49.5 Mc for the ideal case can be explained only by the fact that a reactance also exists. It will be found then that for *ideal* dipole excitation the pure resistance effect is only about 68 ohms instead of $R_1 = 73.4$ ohms as in the *actual* case.

A dipole, whether excited in the fundamental mode $\lambda/2$ or not, does not behave any differently than a closed network, except that when excited in the fundamental mode, the resistive component is essentially the radiation resistance.   Generally, we can, therefore, ascribe an effective Q value to a dipole just as is done for any closed network.   The Q value is the ratio of the reactance of the dipole to its ohmic resistance.   It gives a means for predicting the voltage gain taken off near the mid-point of the dipole.   In case of a single conductor which is excited at the half-wave distribution, we have to make a suitable shunt termination, as is shown in Fig. 109, while series termination as in Fig. 91 exists for a dipole.   Since the dipole exhibits both distributed inductance and distributed capacitance as well as distribution of effective resistance, we must have an impedance at terminals 1-1' of Fig. 91 that can exhibit positive or negative reactance effects depending on the frequency of the exciting dipole current.   Using larger diameter dipoles, the change in the impedance Z_1 with a change in the instantaneous carrier frequency F_t of an FM current is smaller than if smaller diameter dipoles are used.   Hence, the receiving dipoles should not use wires of small diameter.

A formula for colinear straight conductors, as indicated in Fig. 91, has been derived by P. S. Carter.[1]   We have then no longer the ordinary dipole case with a self-impedance Z_1 as in Eq. (145) where $Z_1 = -(1/I_1) \int_0^{l_1} \varepsilon_1 \sin(py)\, dy$, but the relation $Z_m = -(1/I_1) \int_0^{l_1} \varepsilon_m \sin(py)\, dy$ where dy is a line element of each conductor of length l_1.   The quantity ε_1 is the electric field component parallel to l_1 in case of Eq. (145) and due to I_1 in this conductor.   If we now assume that in Fig. 91 the electric field component ε_m, which is parallel to radiator rod 2, is caused by a current I_1 in rod 1, we deal with a *mutual* impedance Z_m, which is likewise complex.   We have then $l_2 > l_1$.   For the abbreviations

---

[1] Carter, P. S., Circuit Relations in Radiating Systems and Applications to Antenna Problems, *Proc. IRE,* **20**, 1004, 1932.   Other useful references where the Poynting vector is integrated over the surface of the antenna wire instead of over a spherical surface whose radius is large compared with the wave length: A. A. Pistolkors, The Radiation Resistance of Beam Antennas, *Proc. IRE,* **17**, 562, 1929; R. Bechmann, Calculation of Electric and Magnetic Field Strengths of Any Oscillating Straight Conductors, *Proc. IRE,* **19**, 461, 1931; J. Labus, Computation of Antenna Impedance, *Hochfrequenz und Elektroakustik,* January, 1933, p. 17; G. H. Brown, Directional Antennas, *Proc. IRE,* **25**, 78, 1937; S. Goldman, *Electronics,* May, 1940, p. 20.

$$\left.\begin{aligned} A &= -2Ci(2pl_2) + Ci(2ps) + Ci[2p(l+s)] \\ &\qquad - 2.303 \log_{10}\left[\frac{(l+s)s}{l_2^2}\right] \\ B &= 2Si(2pl_2) - Si(2ps) - Si[2p(l+s)] \\ D &= 2Ci(2pl_2) - Ci(2ps) - Ci[2p(l+s)] \\ &\qquad - 2.303 \log_{10}\left[\frac{(l+s)s}{l_2^2}\right] \\ p &= \frac{2\pi}{\lambda} \end{aligned}\right\} \quad (151)$$

we have for the mutual impedance Z_m, between terminals 1-1′ of Fig. 91, the relation

$$Z_m = -15A \cos (pl_2) + 15B \sin (pl_2) - j15B \cos (pl_2) + j15D \sin (pl_2) \text{ ohms} \quad (152)$$

This expression can also be written as

$$Z_m = 15[B \sin (pl_2) - A \cos (pl_2)] + j15[D \sin (pl_2) - B \cos (pl_2)] = R_m \pm jX_m \text{ ohms} \quad (152a)$$

with a phase angle of $\tan^{-1} (X_m/R_m)$ and a scalar value $\sqrt{R_m^2 + X_m^2}$. The application of Eq. (152*a*) is not any more difficult than the application of Eq. (145). The various lengths such as l_1, l_2, l, and the spacing s must be expressed in the same units as the wave length. We have then a means of computing the mutual impedance Z_m as long as there exists a finite spacing s. When two conductors of equal length l_1 are not colinear, as in Fig. 91, but run parallel and at a distance d apart, as shown in Fig. 92, we have for the mutual impedance the relation

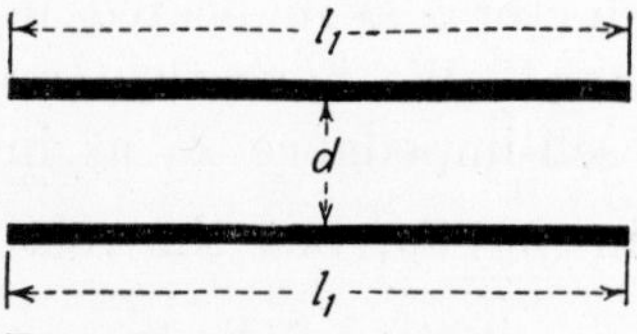

FIG. 92.—Two conductors in parallel relative position.

$$\begin{aligned} Z_m &= 30[2Ei(-jq_1) - Ei(-jq_2) - Ei(-jq_3)] \\ &= R_m \pm jX_m \end{aligned} \quad (153)$$

where

$$\left.\begin{aligned} &q_1 = pd;\ q_2 = p(\sqrt{l_1^2 + d^2} + l_1);\ q_3 = p(\sqrt{l_1^2 + d^2} - l_1) \\ &p = \frac{2\pi}{\lambda};\ \text{and } Ei(-jq) = Ci(q) - jSi(q) \end{aligned}\right\} \quad (154)$$

Generally, the $Ei(x)$ function can be computed from the series

$$Ei(x) = \begin{cases} 0.5772 + 0.576x^4 + x + \dfrac{1}{2}\dfrac{x^2}{2!} + \dfrac{1}{3}\dfrac{x^3}{3!} + \cdots \\ \qquad\qquad\qquad \text{for } -17 \leqq x \leqq 17 \\[2ex] \dfrac{\epsilon^x}{x}\left(1 + \dfrac{1!}{x} + \dfrac{2!}{x^2} + \dfrac{3!}{x^3} + \dfrac{4!}{x^4} + \cdots\right) \\ \qquad\qquad\qquad \text{for } x > 17 \end{cases} \qquad (155)$$

We obtain again, therefore, a complex value for the mutual impedance Z_m since according to Eq. (154) the respective Ei

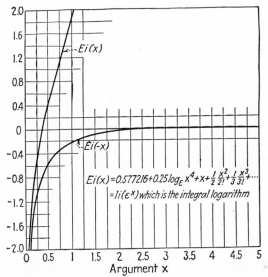

Fig. 93.—The Ei functions which play a part in the computation of dipole resistance and reactance.

functions can be expressed in Ci and Si functions where jSi appears with respect to Ci. We can also directly compute the impedance from the Ei series given in Eq. (155). Figure 93 gives an idea of how the Ei functions behave with respect to different arguments.

In FM applications, especially when dealing with receivers, the simple dipole plays an important part. The curves in Fig. 94 show what occurs when, for instance, two 5-ft rods of ½-in. diameter are colinear so that a series antenna feed is possible. By series antenna feed is meant that the effective impedance of the feeder acts in series with the self-impedance Z_1 of the dipole. According to Eq. (145) we have then generally an input impedance $Z_1 = R_1 \pm jX_1$. It is understood that I_1 is the current value at the distribution point 1 or at the distribution point 1' caused by a potential E_1.   If, for instance, the dipole is driven, *i.e.*, if it is used as a transmitter antenna, then E_1 drives a current I_1 at point 1 as well as at point 1′ over an impedance Z_1.   The plus sign of the j term in the expression for Z_1 holds for overexcited dipoles and the negative sign of the reactance term holds for under-excited dipoles.   The dipole reactance X_1 vanishes altogether for true resonance, which occurs with the assumed over-all length l of 10 ft at a carrier frequency of 49.5 Mc according to calculations already given.

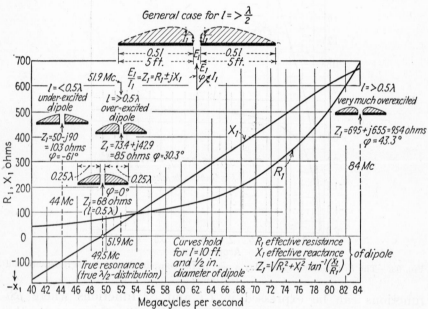

FIG. 94.—Effective resistance and reactance of a dipole.

For carrier frequencies higher than 49.5 Mc, the dipole acts like an inductive reactance X_1 in addition to the effective resistance R_1.   According to calculations given previously the *apparent* half-wave-length distribution occurs, for the dimensions given in Fig. 94, at a frequency of 51.9 Mc.   The impedance Z_1 is as given in Eq. (150) and as also indicated in Fig. 94.   The voltage E_1 at the terminals 1-1′ where the leadin is connected to the dipole is then no longer in phase with the current value either at 1 or at 1′, but makes an angle with it of 30.3 deg.   Hence, more than a quarter-wave-length distribution must occur on the respective conductors of 5 ft each.   This is even more the case at an operating carrier frequency of 84 Mc since the dipole is still more overexcited. It is only for a dipole self-impedance, which is a pure resistance, as for the 49.5 Mc case considered above, that two quarter-wave-length distributions take place on the respective rods that constitute the 10-ft dipole. For exciting carrier frequencies lower than 49.5 Mc, the dipole becomes underexcited; *i.e.*, it behaves like an ohmic resistance R_1 and a *capacitance* reactance X_1. The self-impedance is then $Z_1 = R_1 - jX_1$. For this reason less than half-wave-length distribution then takes place for the full 10-ft length of the dipole. We find, then, that at 44 Mc we have a dipole impedance $Z_1 = 103$ ohms compared with a minimum impedance, for the optimum frequency, of 68 ohms, which is purely resistive.

It is, therefore, an easy matter to compute in the same manner, by means of these R_1 and X_1 curves, the impedance values $\sqrt{R_1^2 + X_1^2}$ for all the carrier frequencies in the FM range from about 40 to 50 Mc, in order to learn the order of magnitude required for the matching impedance of the feeder. If the diameter of the rod were larger than $\frac{1}{2}$ in., the impedance change would take place slower, which is desirable, especially after the true resonance frequency of 49.5 Mc is exceeded. More data of this kind show that the same change of Z_1 with the carrier frequency F occurs for 1-in. as for $\frac{1}{2}$-in. diameter rods, as shown in Fig. 94, for frequencies *below* the resonance frequency; *i.e.*, for frequencies between 40 and about 50 Mc. Hence, nothing would be gained by increasing the diameter of the rods. Fortunately, it is this range that concerns us in FM work. Therefore, for FM receiver dipoles, hard-drawn copper tubing of about $\frac{5}{16}$-in. diameter should work very well.

57. FM Voltage Effective at the Input Terminals of an FM Receiver in Terms of the Electric Field Intensity.—Inasmuch as the electric field intensity ε, which affects a receiver antenna, is usually expressed in terms of microvolts per meter, it will induce more voltage at the antenna output terminals for longer effective lengths of the antenna. The term of effective *length* instead of effective *height* seems more appropriate in case of FM aerials, since, for instance, the receiver antenna has to pick up essentially a horizontally polarized electromagnetic wave due to the customary turnstile wave emission. The effective length l_e of the dipole indicated in Fig. 89 is then kl; *i.e.*, it is smaller than the true length l. The factor k may be called the *form factor of the dipole excitation*. This factor depends on both the current distribution along the dipole and on the orientation of the dipole with respect to the polarization of the electric field intensity ε of the arriving electromagnetic wave.

The sensitivity pattern of the dipole is well known and is the figure-eight pattern, showing that broadside reception gives maximum antenna effects. When the length of the dipole points along the propagation direction of arriving waves, theoretically no voltage can be induced in the dipole. The factor k has a value of 0.636 when the dipole is excited in the true fundamental mode, *i.e.*, in the half-wave-length distribution, and is oriented broadside to the direction of propagation of the arriving waves. For a dipole of length $l = 10$ ft, we have a physical length of 3.048 m and an effective length $l_e = 0.636 \times 3.048 = 1.94$ m, for the broadside orientation of the dipole. Hence, if the arriving field intensity of the FM wave has just the marginal value required by the FCC, namely $\varepsilon = 50 \, \mu v/m$, the induced voltage across the dipole gap would be $E_1 = l_e \varepsilon = 1.94 \times 50 = 97 \, \mu v$. This value would hold for the optimum condition, requiring besides perfect feeder termination at the center of the dipole. It would occur for a frequency of 49.5 Mc of the induced dipole current.

Such an ideal condition usually does not exist since the arriving electromagnetic wave is generally elliptically polarized. Consequently a dipole efficiency cannot be such that k is as high as 63.6 per cent of the actual dipole length. It is also to be understood that the actual dipole length l is a compromise between all the instantaneous carrier frequencies of all the FM allocations. In other words, we have to use a receiver dipole essentially for a frequency range from about 40 to about 50 Mc. Therefore, for most of the instantaneous carrier frequencies of FM waves, we have a dipole self-impedance Z_1 that is complex; *i.e.*, it is not purely resistive, and much smaller induced voltages than calculated for the optimum case will result.

Nevertheless, with proper leadin termination and coupling toward the grid of the first tube of the FM receiver, we may expect to obtain a good overall voltage gain between the field intensity ε of the arriving electromagnetic wave and the effective grid voltage affecting the first tube of the FM receiver. This is, of course, only a voltage gain, since in reality the insertion loss due to any feeder is more than the inherent feeder loss due to its own attenuation. This will be discussed in more detail later on.

If E_1 is the induced dipole voltage and I_1 the current value either at terminal 1 or at terminal 1' of Fig. 89, we have for the self-impedance of the dipole the relation $Z_1 = E_1/I_1$. Choosing the surge impedance Z_0 of the feeder equal to the dipole impedance Z_1, then also the same current $I_1 = E_1/Z_0$ will flow into the matched feeder. If k_1 denotes a factor equal to or smaller than unity, to account for any feeder attenuation, then the current k_1I_1 will pass into the small input coil connected across the input terminals 2-2' of the FM receiver. This assumes that the input impedance of the FM receiver is also equal to Z_0 ohms, *i.e.*, also equal to Z_1 ohms of the dipole. Hence, the feeder is terminated at each end in equal image impedances.

For a voltage step-up ratio N of the input transformer, the voltage E_g impressed on the control grid of the first tube has a value of $E_g = NZ_0I_1$. For any effective length $l_e = kl$ of the dipole, the dipole extracts the power $klI_1\mathcal{E}$ from the arriving electromagnetic wave. In reality the self-impedance Z_1 of the dipole is in series with the surge impedance Z_0 of the leadin and if perfect matching between Z_1 and Z_0 is assumed, the extracted power must be equal to $(Z_1 + Z_0)I_1^2$. The current I_1 flowing into the leadin is, therefore,

$$I_1 = \frac{kl\mathcal{E}}{Z_1 + Z_0} = \frac{l_e\mathcal{E}}{Z_1 + Z_0} \qquad (155a)$$

If no attenuation took place in the leadin, this same current would flow into the input terminals 2-2' of the FM receiver whose input network is indicated in Fig. 89. For a certain amount of leadin attenuation we have then a current k_1I_1 flowing in the input coil, where k_1 is normally smaller than unity. The voltage effective on the control grid of the first tube can be computed from

$$E_g = k_3lN\mathcal{E}\frac{Z_0}{Z_0 + Z_1} \qquad (156)$$

where E_g is in microvolts if $\mathcal{E}$ is expressed in microvolts per meter and the constant $k_3 = kk_1$. The expression is conveniently written in this form since in FM work we deal with instantaneous carrier frequencies about the center frequency which is also the allocation frequency for a particular FM station.

This expression holds for any matching and, therefore, also for the mismatches as experienced with a fixed dipole dimension. For matching, *i.e.*, $Z_0 = Z_1 = Z_2$, the above formula simplifies to $E_g = 0.5l_ek_1N\varepsilon$ μv. For good leadins k_1 is close to unity if the length of the leadin is not more than about one wave length long. Hence, the product l_eN is mostly responsible for the voltage advantage on the control grid of the first tube with respect to the voltage induced across the dipole gap. We have noted already in the preceding numerical example that the product $0.5l_e$ is almost unity for pure resonance excitation of the dipole. Hence, the real voltage gain depends on the gain N of the input transformer action, as well as on suitable terminations toward the dipole and toward the input side of the FM receiver. Calling Z_g the impedance to ground of the control grid of the first tube, optimum voltage will be applied to the grid when the transformer gain $N = \sqrt{Z_g/Z_0}$. For the ideal matching case this gain becomes $N = \sqrt{Z_g/Z_1}$. We note, therefore, that a low-impedance dipole is desirable since this causes the highest voltage gain N in the input transformer. This is also evident from the fact that the transferred antenna power is proportional to the square of the current. This current is all the larger, the smaller the self-impedance Z_1 of the dipole. Figuring with impedance values not exceeding much more than about 100 ohms, an appreciable voltage advantage on the control grid of the first tube is possible.

58. Effect of the Q Value of Linear Conductors on the Self-impedance.—The discussion advanced in Secs. 56 and 57 shows that as far as the diameter of linear conductors is concerned, it affects somewhat the effective current distribution along the conductor. This is a well-known fact in dealing with transmission lines. A dipole is nothing else but an open-ended transmission line, which, instead of being a parallel-wire system, is made up of two wires extending in opposite directions. It is true that the capacitance effects per elementary section of the dipole, *i.e.*, per unit length, are considerably smaller between respective elementary sections near the open end of the respective dipole rods than for such sections near the leadin. For the open-ended parallel-wire system, the unit capacitance has the same value everywhere along the conductors. As far as the resultant effect is concerned, we actually deal with *effective* lengths that refer to equal potential distributions if we think of capacitance effects per unit length. We deal with equal current distributions for the effective length for the concept of inductance and resistance effects per unit length.

With respect to *actual* distributions, the Q value of the conductor plays a part, whether we deal with Lecher wires or with dipole conductor arrangements. The larger the Q value of a conductor, the more impedance variation will take place when the frequency of the conductor current changes, since the reactance component is large compared with the resistance component. We have to realize this, since in FM waves the carrier frequency undergoes changes. For a good matching approximation, we require as small an impedance variation as possible. Hence, the smaller the Q value of the conductor employed, the better the matching that occurs. Since small-diameter conductors have less capacitance effects than inductance effects per elementary section of the conductor, small-diameter conductors must be the poorer size for dipoles and for any other lines where impedance variations of the conductor are of concern.

A dipole is nothing but a modification of an open-ended transmission line. This can be understood from the fact that the impedance looking into an open-ended transmission line is $Z_1 = Z_0 \coth nl$, where l is the actual length from dipole input gap toward the open end of each rod. The quantity nl is the generalized electrical length, and Z_0 is the surge impedance $\sqrt{L/C}$ of the colinear line if L and C are the inductance and capacitance per elementary section. We then have $n = \alpha + \beta$, where $\alpha = 0.5R/Z_0$ is the attenuation constant and $\beta = 6.28/\lambda = 6.28F \sqrt{CL}$ is the phase constant per elementary section. The symbol β here should not be confused with the modulation index. The quantity R denotes the resistance per elementary section. It is an easy matter to show that for h-f excitation we have for the input impedance

$$Z_1 = \sqrt{\frac{L_t}{C_t}} \frac{0.5R_t \sqrt{C_t/L_t} - j\beta l \cos \beta l}{p + \sin^2 \beta l} = R_1 - jX_1 \quad (157)$$

if $p = 0.25C_t R_t^2/L_t$ and the total line capacitance, inductance, and resistance are $C_t = lC$, $L_t = lL$, and $R_t = lR$, respectively. We then have

$$R_1 \cong \frac{0.5R_t}{\sin^2 (\Omega \sqrt{C_t L_t})}; \qquad X_1 \cong -jZ_0 \cot (\Omega \sqrt{C_t L_t}) \quad (158)$$

where $\Omega = 6.28F$ and the approximations hold except near frequencies of $2F$, $4F$, etc.

59. Dipoles for FM Reception.—As far as transmitter aerials are concerned, we are mostly concerned that the station serve as large a populated area as possible with field intensities that are strong enough to outweigh interference at the location of reception. For this reason, the FCC requires a higher field intensity in cities than in rural districts.

The reception of receiver aerials can be improved if aerials having a gain with a tendency to avoid interference are used. Hence, the receiver-antenna design must be based on directivity, as well as on the ability to reject interference. Even though customary antennas as employed in AM systems in the standard broadcast range may be satisfactory in many locations, they can never avoid interference picked up on the open antenna wire itself, and especially so with respect to the single feed line connecting to the antenna terminal of a set. A dipole having a matched double-line feeder will improve the reception greatly. Even for mismatches a twisted feeder and the like will hardly pick up interference, since it is inherently self-balanced as far as feeder pickups are concerned. We can emphasize this balance if the feeder is connected as in Fig. 89.

That a customary antenna wire has a longer physical length does not mean at all that its electrical length is such as to make it a good converter from electric field intensity ε to voltage as experienced at the input terminals of a receiver. We have to realize that for all the FM allocations (not including the relay bands), the entire center frequency band is only about 16 per cent wide. The highest center-frequency assignment is only 8 per cent above the mean center frequency assignment. The lowest center frequency is the same amount below the mean center-frequency assignment. It is, therefore, possible to find a dipole length l that will give fairly good antenna gain for all the FM assignments. Since the dipole has, in addition, the well-known directivity feature and also has comparatively small physical dimensions in the FM range of frequencies, it can be turned into a position for maximum reception of a desired station. The lines of electric force are then parallel to the dipole elongation. It can also be turned to a position in space that weakens appreciably an undesired signal with respect to the desired signal. With present-day FM transmission, a dipole that can be rotated around a vertical axis so as to keep the colinear dipole always horizontal will probably be very satisfactory for most cases. However, it may happen that a dipole in an inclined direction toward ground and at the same time rotated about a vertical axis may give even better reception effects.

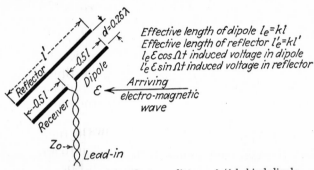

Effective length of dipole $l_e = kl$
Effective length of reflector $l'_e = kl'$
$l_e \varepsilon \cos \Omega t$ induced voltage in dipole
$l'_e \varepsilon \sin \Omega t$ induced voltage in reflector

Arriving
electro-magnetic
wave

Fig. 95.—Dipole with reflector a distance λ/4 behind dipole.

60. Dipoles with a Reflector.—The directivity toward a certain direction can be greatly increased if a reflector is used behind the receiver dipole. For maximum effect, the reflector should face the desired arriving electromagnetic wave broadside. We have then to deal with mutual effects due to the mutual impedance Z_m, which is operative between dipole and reflector. The location of the reflector at a distance of 0.25λ behind the receiving dipole, as indicated in Fig. 95, is then based on the fact that it takes a certain time for the arriving wave to pass through this distance d. Since a space distance d which is one-quarter of a wave length long corresponds to a phase delay in the arriving field intensity ε of 90 time degrees, for an effective length l_e of the receiving dipole, a voltage $kl'\varepsilon \sin \Omega t$ must be induced in a reflector of effective length $l'_e = kl'$, when $kl\varepsilon \cos \Omega t$ is the induced dipole voltage. In practice it will be found that better results are obtained if the actual reflector length l' is made somewhat larger than the desired dipole length l.

Corresponding currents I and I' will exist in the dipole and the in reflector rod. The reflector current I' must induce in the near-by receiver dipole a corresponding voltage E_1, just as the dipole current I must induce a corresponding voltage E_2 in the reflector. The mutual impedance Z_m between the two conductors is then $Z_m = E_1/I' = E_2/I$. This is true because the mutual action of the dipole current on the corresponding induced reflector voltage must be exactly the same as the mutual action of the reflector current on the corresponding induced voltage in the receiver dipole. Besides mutual impedance effect we have to deal with the effects of the self-impedances Z and Z' of the dipole and of the reflector. Realizing that the surge impedance Z_0 of the twisted leadin acts in reality in series with the self-impedance Z of the dipole to which it is connected, the induced dipole voltage $kl\varepsilon \cos \Omega t$, due to the arriving wave, must balance the voltage drop $(Z + Z_0)I$ as well as the mutual voltage drop $Z_m I'$. We have, therefore,

$$(Z + Z_0)I + Z_m I' = kl\varepsilon \cos \Omega t \qquad (159)$$

In the same way the relation

$$Z'I' + Z_m I = kl'\varepsilon \sin \Omega t \qquad (160)$$

must satisfy the voltage balance in the reflector. For any distance d in wave lengths other than $d = 0.25\lambda$, the time-delay angle of 90 deg must be changed accordingly. The retardation and spacing assumed in this solution give, at least theoretically, the best reflector action.

Inasmuch as we are not utilizing *directly* the reflector current I' but the dipole current I, which actually flows into a matched feeder line, we have to eliminate the current I' from Eqs. (159) and (160). Doing this, we find for the current passing from the receiver dipole toward the FM receiver, in comparison with the value when no reflector is present, the relations

$$
I = \frac{\text{driving voltage}}{\text{impedance}} =
\begin{cases}
\dfrac{\varepsilon[kl \cos \Omega t - kl' (Z_m/Z') \sin \Omega t]}{Z + Z_0 - (Z_m{}^2/Z')} & \text{with reflector} \\[3mm]
\dfrac{kl\varepsilon \cos \Omega t}{Z + Z_0} & \text{no reflector}
\end{cases}
\qquad (161)
$$

For any suitable distance d between the receiving dipole and the reflector, we have

$$
I = \underbrace{\frac{l_e\varepsilon \cos \Omega t}{Z + Z_0 - (Z_m^2/Z')}}_{\substack{\text{dipole current that} \\ \text{would exist with-} \\ \text{out reflector}}} - \underbrace{\frac{(Z_m/Z')l_e\varepsilon \cos (\Omega t - \theta)}{Z + Z_0 - (Z_m^2/Z')}}_{\substack{\text{change of dipole current} \\ \text{due to the reflector action}}}
$$

$$
\theta = 360 \frac{d}{\lambda} \quad \text{deg}
$$

$$(162)$$

The comparison formulas of (161) show that the effect of the reflector is twofold. The presence of the reflector changes the dipole voltage which drives the current I flowing into the leadin, as well as the impedance that tends to hinder such a current flow. The upper formula of Eq. (161) holds for a spacing d equal to one-quarter of the free-space operating wave length λ; Eq. (162) holds for distances d to the reflector larger or smaller than 0.25λ. The angle θ tells how much corresponding phase delay takes place.

Let us first examine the case for $d = 0.25\lambda$ and assume that true fundamental resonance excitations occur in both the reflector and the dipole. Hence, a true half-wave distribution occurs in each antenna and the current flowing into the leadin must be equal to the loop value of the current distribution along the dipole. Let us further assume that these resonance currents are not caused by an arriving wave, but inherently by the dipole itself and inherently by the reflector itself. In other words, assume that there is no external agency that is the cause of these respective resonance currents except the mutual actions between the dipole and the reflector. We have, therefore, so-called "self-generating antennas." Hence, each antenna will transmit an electromagnetic wave of exactly the same wave length λ. Now let us also assume that the dipole current is lagging the reflector current by 90 time degrees. By the time the electromagnetic field radiated from the reflector reaches the dipole, the induced current in the dipole produced by the field of the reflector antenna must be *exactly* in phase with the inherent resonance current of the dipole. Hence, it will cause an increased current flow in the dipole and, consequently, an increased radiation effect due to the larger dipole current.

Now let us find out what happens to the reflector, which also was assumed to be a self-generating antenna. The inherent resonance current of the dipole radiates an electromagnetic wave, which, after moving through a distance of 0.25λ, induces a resonance current in the reflector antenna. Since the inherent dipole current already lagged the inherent reflector current by 90 time degrees, the induced current in the reflector must be in phase opposition with respect to the inherent reflector current and, therefore, tends to cancel the inherent reflector current. The reflector, therefore, behaves like an obstacle for anything behind it, but like a field accentuator toward the dipole and farther out. The consequence is that the resultant electromagnetic field against the arrow of the ε field, which would be due to an arriving FM wave in our case, would tend to keep this field from reaching the reflector antenna.

Now suppose that the resonance current of the dipole is leading the reflector current by 90 time degrees and is no longer inherent but is due to the arriving FM wave, just as the reflector resonance current is due to the arriving ε field. Matters are then just reversed since the ε field is now the cause. An increased dipole current must again result when the field comes from the right as is indicated in Fig. 95. A decreased dipole current would occur when the arriving ε field strikes first the reflector; *i.e.*, when it arrives from the left. This is also brought out in Eqs. (161) and (162). But it is more difficult to realize what actually happens since the reflector has an effect on both the driving voltage and the agency that impedes the flow of current into the feeder.

Let us again take the case for $d = 0.25\lambda$, for which the upper expression of Eq. (161) holds. Both the driving voltage and the impedance in this expression are no longer $l_e\varepsilon \cos \Omega t$ and $Z + Z_0$, as in absence of the reflector, but are changed by the voltage $(l'_e Z_m \sin \Omega t)\varepsilon/Z'$ and by an impedance Z_m^2/Z', respectively. The impedance change Z_m^2/Z' can be pronounced only if the reflector is rather close to the dipole. Therefore, this impedance change, although existent, must be relatively small compared with the change taking place in the driving voltage due to the reflector. This voltage change can be written for a spacing $d = 0.25\lambda$ as $[-kl'Z_m\varepsilon \cos (\Omega t - 90)]/Z'$, where l' is the actual length of the reflector rod. From the explanation given above, the time angle of 90 deg would be positive instead of negative if the arriving electromagnetic field ε strikes first the reflector; *i.e.*, if it arrives from the left instead of the right side, as is indicated in Fig. 95. For the direction of arrival shown in Fig. 95, this voltage change is additive to the voltage $kl\varepsilon \cos \Omega t$ that would exist only in absence of the reflector. Hence, the corresponding current I flowing to the leadin of the dipole must be larger than if the reflector were not present.

We have also the ratio Z_m/Z' as a factor in the change of the driving voltage when a reflector is present. It is a ratio of the two impedances, where the self-impedance Z' of the reflector has a phase angle which changes quite rapidly with change of the carrier frequency F_t of the arriving electromagnetic wave. This is

due to the fact that for a good reflector action, the actual length
of the dipole should be approximately equal to half the value
of the operating wave length λ.   For such a condition, if exactly
met, Z' would be a pure resistance and
equal to about 68 ohms.   Hence, when
the carrier frequency is changed for fixed
dipole and reflector dimensions and a
fixed relative orientation of the reflector
with respect to the dipole, then the phase
of Z' changes rapidly.   There will also
be a phase change in Z_m which emphasizes this effect and there must also be a
change in the value of θ of Eq. (162) when
F changes.   All these changes work in
the same direction; *i.e.*, they all bring

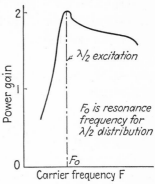

Fig. 96.—Dipole power gain.

about a voltage subtraction instead of a voltage addition in the
driving voltage of the dipole if we either increase or decrease the
carrier frequency F by only a few megacycles.   Figure 96 indicates
what happens.

Inasmuch as the length l' has much to do with the change in
phase of the self-impedance Z' of the reflector and also in the
change of phase in the mutual impedance Z_m, we have a ready
means for experimentally adjusting the length l' of the reflector
to secure the best reflector action when we desire to use a reflector
for quite a wide band of center frequencies.   The best spacing d
should also be determined experimentally, if the reflector is to be
used in connection with the reception of several FM stations.
Because with a dipole and reflector array, the dimensions are still
comparatively small, provision can and should be made to rotate
the entire array about a vertical axis.

It is stressed that the actual experiment is the only criterion on
what will actually take place, but the formulas and arguments
presented here will surely facilitate the experimentation.

61. Feeders Used in FM Systems.—The dipole self-impedance
acts in series with the self-impedance of a leadin, *i.e.*, with the
impedance looking into the leadin terminals when the leadin is
connected at the other end to an FM receiver.   The less
power lost due to the insertion of the leadin, the more effective will be the voltage applied to the input terminals of the FM
receiver.

The fundamental feeder system consists, as shown in Fig. 97, of two parallel go-and-return wires. External field actions on such a feeder system are usually small and can be greatly reduced if, for instance, the outgoing potent conductor is shielded by the return conductor. This is done in a concentric feeder. Since in each case we have line constants, such as resistance, capacitance, and inductance, all uniformly distributed, the feeder must offer a certain wave resistance which is also known as surge impedance

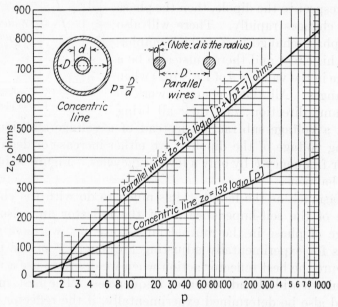

FIG. 97.—Surge impedance of parallel and concentric feeders.

Z_0. This impedance acts essentially like an ohmic resistance at carrier frequencies such as are used in the FM range. It will be noted from the characteristics shown in Fig. 97 that the concentric line gives much lower impedances than does the parallel-wire feeder. A low-feeder impedance will extract more power from an arriving electromagnetic field ε, since then antennas with low self-impedances can be used. The transposed double line, and especially its modification in the form of a twisted leadin, is much used in connection with FM reception since the latter also has a low characteristic impedance Z_0 which is in the neighborhood of 100 ohms. For a ratio of $D/d = 3.6$ the concentric line feeder exhibits minimum self-attenuation. By self-attenuation is meant inherent attenuation due to the feeder itself. It is, therefore, characteristic of the physical dimensions as well as of the electrical properties of the feeder and also depends on the frequency of the current. The self-attenuation has nothing to do with the attenuation due to mismatches. According to Fig. 97 such an optimum diameter ratio of 3.6 causes a characteristic impedance $Z_0 = 77$, ohms. This is very fortunate since this is about a dipole match.

Inasmuch as the receiving antenna extracts more power from an arriving electromagnetic wave the lower its self-impedance is, we note that the concentric line and the much cheaper twisted-wire feeder are admirably suited for feeding an FM receiver from a dipole.

Since the surge impedance is the impedance that an outgoing or an incoming wavelike electrical disturbance experiences, it denotes at any point of a conductor, for a unidirectional wave propagation along the conductor, the potential at that point divided by the current that flows though the cross section at the point. Hence, it is essential that we deal only with a power propagation *in one direction*. This direction of power flow should be from the dipole terminals toward the input network of an FM receiver. A unidirectional power flow can occur *only* under two conditions. One condition requires a very long electrical length of the feeder, for which the arriving power at the far end would be so small that any reflections at that end would hardly play a part. For such a condition the impedance looking into the feeder will be exactly equal to the surge impedance Z_0. The resistance component of Z_0, which is essentially equal to the impedance Z_0 itself, may be regarded as the radiation resistance of the *guided* outgoing wave propagation. Such an infinite line condition could not be useful in FM systems since essentially no power would arrive at the load end.

It is the second condition that guarantees only an efficient unidirectional power transfer from dipole to the FM receiver. It requires that the load impedance caused by the effective input impedance of the FM receiver be equal to the surge impedance Z_0 of the leadin. By equality is meant that the modulus as well as the phase of Z_0 must be equal to the modulus as well as the phase of the input impedance of the FM receiver. For such a condition the power is extracted from the leadin by the FM set at the same rate as it arrives since no reflections are possible at the input terminals of the receiver. This is, therefore, the requirement that must be satisfied as closely as practically possible at the input terminals of the FM set. The impedance Z_0 of the leadin acts in series with the dipole self-impedance Z_1. For maximum power transfer in the most ideal case (where the excitation of the dipole occurs in the true half-wave-length distribution), Z_0 must be purely resistive and equal to 68 ohms. Such an ideal condition can hardly be expected in commercial installations and the self-impedance Z_1 of the dipole is usually complex; *i.e.*, it has a resistance component R_1 in quadrature with a reactance component X_1.

The transition loss, when the power extracted by the dipole from the arriving electromagnetic wave passes from the dipole gap into the feeder of the FM set, is smallest when the resistance component of the dipole impedance is equal to the resistance component of the surge impedance Z_0 of the feeder and the sum of the reactances of both impedances Z_1 and Z_0 is zero. Hence, to match a dipole impedance effect in order to secure an ideal power transfer P, we must use for the input a feeder that has also a similar impedance. The surge impedance Z_0 of the feeder must then have the same resistance value as the radiation resistance of the dipole and an equal but *opposite* reactance value. In order to produce also a maximum power flow from the other end of the feeder into the input side of the FM receiver, the receiver input impedance should also be *conjugate* with the value of Z_0. This means, the input impedance of the FM receiver should be exactly like the self-impedance Z_1 of the dipole. Such terminations are then not a true match since the respective phase angles are plus and minus, and must, therefore, cause some reflection effects. These reflection effects happen to be negative losses or reflection gains. Since in FM receivers we use generally one and the same dipole for receptions of different stations, such conditions can be met only by a compromise.

Hence, when the dipole impedance is $Z_1 = R_1 \pm jX_1$ and the surge impedance of the feeder is $Z_0 = R_0 \pm jX_0$, where the plus and minus signs denote that for certain carrier frequencies we deal only with positive or only with negative reactance components, we have generally different resistance values as well as different reactance values. Then we do not have the ideal conjugate impedance Z_0 acting in series with Z_1 as far as the current flow into the feeder is concerned. Hence, the power P_0 passing into the feeder from the dipole must be less than the amount of power P that would pass into the feeder if the impedances were conjugate and the *transition loss* will be $10 \log_{10} (P_0/P)$ decibels. This results in the formula

$$\text{Transition loss} = 20 \log_{10} (\sqrt{R_1^2 + X_1^2} + \sqrt{R_0^2 + X_0^2}) - 10 \log_{10} (4R_1R_0) \quad \text{db} \quad (163)$$

But Z_0 is essentially resistive, *i.e.*, equal to R_0, and we have essentially a transition loss of $10[2 \log_{10} (Z_1 + R_0) - \log_{10} (4R_1R_0)]$ decibels.

It should be understood that ideal conjugate impedances establish *only* maximum power transfer across the termination terminals, and do not result in maximum current. Nevertheless, maximum power transfer is the best condition since, after all, it is the power that counts as long as the reflections caused by the phase mismatch do not cause appreciable distortion.

Designating the real component of the impedance ratio at a junction as U and the imaginary component as V, we arrive at the following derivations. Suppose a feeder of surge impedance R_0 is to be matched for maximum power transfer with a dipole impedance $Z_1 = R_1 + jX_1$. We have the substitutions $U = R_1/R_0$ and $V = X_1/R_0$ with a phase angle of $\theta = \tan^{-1} (X_1/R_1)$. If two impedances $Z_1 = R_1 + jX_1$ and $Z_2 = R_2 + jX_2$ are terminated into each other, the total reactance becomes $X = X_1 + X_2$, and $U = R_2/R_1$ and $V = X/R_1$. Maximum power transfer would then occur when U is equal to unity and V vanishes. For any other respective impedance termination, less power will pass across the termination terminals in the ratio of $4U/[(1 + U)^2 + V^2] = p$. We can compute the transition loss with respect to maximum power transfer from the relation

$$\text{Transition loss} = 10 \log_{10} (p) \quad (164)$$

H. A. Wheeler has given a graphical method[1] where the decibel losses are represented by circles. Equal abscissa and ordinate scales are used, with the U values plotted as ordinates and the V values plotted along the abscissa axis. Each circle is drawn about U as the center with a radius equal to V_{max}.

Ideal matching without reflections across the common terminals occurs only when the respective impedances have equal

[1] *Electronics*, January, 1936, p. 26.

phase angles as well as equal moduli; for conjugate impedances at the common terminals, maximum power transfer occurs. We have then the comparisons

$$\left.\begin{array}{l} R + jX \longleftrightarrow R - jX \qquad \text{for maximum power transfer} \\ R + jX \longleftrightarrow R + jX \\ R - jX \longleftrightarrow R - jX \end{array} \quad \text{for no reflections} \right\} \quad (165)$$

The increased power in case of conjugate impedance terminations may also be thought of as being due to a definite *reflection gain* on account of a suitable mismatch. For the condition of matched impedances, for which no reflections can take place at the joints, we have a resultant phase angle since the reactances do not cancel. The power transfer must be accordingly less than maximum possible power transfer by an amount

$$20 \log_{10} [\sqrt{R^2 + X^2}) - \log_{10} (R)] \quad \text{db.}$$

We have now a picture of what will cause maximum power transfer and what conditions will have to be met at the dipole terminals, as well as at the input terminals of the FM receiver, to avoid reflections at such joints. In actual FM systems the feeder, for instance, a twisted-wire feeder of surge impedance Z_0, as shown in Fig. 98, is connected to the dipole terminal 1-1' at one end and to the input terminals 2-2' of the FM receiver at the other end. The insertion of the feeder must cause some loss of power, even if we have a voltage advantage at the grid of the first tube with respect to the voltage E_1 across the dipole terminals 1-1'. We have already learned that at best we have to make a compromise in order to keep reflections down to a minimum and to secure good but not maximum possible power transfer. That our feeder has a surge impedance Z_0 does not mean at all that it will have exactly such an impedance value when we look into the terminals 2-2' of the feeder or into its terminals 1-1'. This is exactly true only when respective terminations Z_1 and Z_2 are image impedances with respect to the surge impedance Z_0. Hence, we must expect some reflection losses and, therefore, must also take into account an additional loss due to this unsymmetry, besides considering the fact that a loss due to interaction occurs. If I_2 is the current flowing into the input coil of the FM receiver when the dipole is connected by means of the feeder to terminals 2-2', and I_2' is the current when the dipole terminals 1-1' are directly connected to the receiver terminals 2-2', then the insertion loss will be $20 \log_{10} (I_2/I_2')$ db. Inasmuch as E_1 is the driving voltage, we have for the direct connection $I_2' = E_1/(Z_1 + Z_2)$. Since the FM receiver loads the feeder with an impedance Z_2, which is not exactly equal to the surge impedance Z_0 of the feeder, we must experience, when looking into terminals 1-1' of the feeder, an impedance not equal to Z_0 but equal to a value $Z_1' = Z_{op}'(Z_s'' + Z_2)/(Z_{op}'' + Z_2)$.

The impedances Z_{op}', Z_{op}'', and Z_s'' will be defined now. They are based on the fact that any four-pole network, of which the

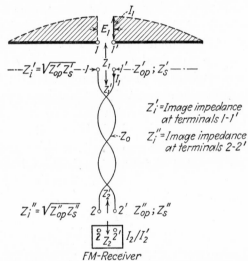

FIG. 98.—Matching feeder between dipole and FM receiver.

feeder shown in Fig. 98 is an example, can be treated generally, no matter what is between the input terminals 1-1' and the output terminals 2-2' of the four pole. As a matter of fact, the general electrical constants of the four-pole network can be found experimentally from only four straightforward measurements. The experimental method consists of measuring the input impedance Z_{op}' across 1-1' when the other end, *i.e.*, terminals 2-2', is open. The second measurement determines the input impedance value Z_s' when the output terminals 2-2' are shorted. The geometrical mean of these two measured impedances, *i.e.*, the value of $\sqrt{Z_{op}'Z_s'}$, determines then the image impedance Z_i', which has to act in effect across the input terminals 1-1' in order to avoid reflections. This impedance must, therefore, have not only the same magnitude as the surge impedance Z_0 of the feeder, but also the same phase with respect to magnitude and polarity. If a generator is exciting the feeder, then the generator must have an internal impedance Z'_i if matching is to exist without reflections.   In Fig. 98 the generator is the dipole and, therefore, the self-impedance of the dipole has to be equal to Z'_i for match.   In the same way, the third measurement yields the input impedance Z''_{op} when looking into the output terminals 2-2' of the feeder with the input terminals 1-1' kept open.   The fourth measurement determines the impedance of Z''_s at terminals 2-2' when the terminals 1-1' are short-circuited. Also this geometric mean $\sqrt{Z''_{op}Z''_s}$ yields a nonreflecting image impedance Z''_i for terminals 2-2'.   For a nonreflecting condition, the input impedance of the FM receiver has to have, therefore, a value $Z_2 = Z''_i = Z_0$, which can be met only approximately, as at the other end of the feeder.

We are now in a position to determine what the magnitude as well as the phase of the current I_2 flowing into the FM receiver will be.   This must be a current value which is different from the value I'_2 which exists if the dipole is directly connected to the input terminals of the FM receiver.   The driving voltage is the dipole voltage E_1.   At the input terminals 1-1' of the feeder, with the FM set connected to the output terminals 2-2', we experience generally an input impedance of Z'_1, the solution for which in terms of known values has already been given.   Hence, the driving voltage E_1 has to overcome this impedance as well as the impedance Z_2 experienced at the input terminals of the FM receiver.   If the feeder were free from all internal energy absorption, the current flowing to the receiver would be simply $E_1/(Z'_1 + Z_2)$.

Since a certain amount of inherent attenuation takes place in the feeder, the input current I_1 flowing into the feeder will be attenuated to a value I'_1.   The attenuation can be measured by sending a known input current into the feeder of a known length and noting the current value at the end of this length, or at the end of any suitable length, when the feeder is terminated into its surge impedance Z_0.   The attenuation found is then expressed in terms of the actual length used in the dipole feeder.   For the ratio $p = I'_1/I_1$ we have then for the value of current flowing into the FM receiver, the relation

$$I_2 = p\,\frac{E_1}{Z_1 + Z_2} \qquad (166)$$

This formula looks simple and adapts itself to a simple experimental method that determines either I_1', I_1 and E_1, and I_2 from computations or by direct measurement of I_2. This has to be done either with larger currents in order to yield measurable values or by means of corresponding voltage readings upon amplification. Accurate results are then difficult to obtain.

It seems, therefore, to be simpler to use a more involved expression for the I_2 value of Eq. (166), which yields a somewhat slower but more reliable experimental method with subsequent computations. The more involved expression is used to advantage with recurrent networks and employs quantities that were defined above. Forming the ratio of the received current I_2, when the feeder is used, to the received current when the receiver is directly connected to the dipole terminals, and expressing the ratio in decibels, we find for the *insertion loss* $\mathcal{L}$ due to the feeder

$$\mathcal{L} = 20 \log_{10} \left[\frac{(Z_2 + Z_1) \sqrt{Z_{op}''(Z_{op}' - Z_s')}}{Z_1 Z_2 + Z_{op}' Z_2 + Z'' Z_1 + Z_{op}' Z_s'} \right] \quad \text{db} \quad (167)$$

We note that in this expression the impedances due to the dipole and the input impedance of the FM receiver for a given carrier frequency appear, as well as the respective input impedances for the far end of the feeder both opened or short-circuited. It is, therefore, possible to plot curves for different carrier frequencies with respect to decibel loss. It is also noted that some of the products of impedances in the denominator show that interactions are also taking place when reflections occur at the respective insertion terminals of the feeder.

The foregoing expression is not difficult to evaluate, even though from an analytic point of view it is better to write Eq. (167) in summation terms where each term expresses a significant loss portion of the entire insertion loss $\mathcal{L}$. Doing this, we have the conventional form

$$\mathcal{L} = 20[\log_{10}(a) + \log_{10}(b) + \log_{10}(c) + \log_{10}(d) + \log_{10}(e)]$$
$$\text{db} \quad (168)$$

where

$$a = \frac{0.5(Z_1 + Z_2)}{\sqrt{Z_1 Z_2}}; \qquad b = \frac{2\sqrt{Z_i' Z_1}}{Z_1 + Z_i'}; \qquad c = \frac{2\sqrt{Z_i'' Z_2}}{Z_2 + Z_i''}$$

$$d = \frac{1}{1 - gmq}; \qquad g = \frac{Z_i'' - Z_2}{Z_i'' + Z_2}; \qquad m = \frac{Z_i' - Z_1}{Z_i' + Z_1}; \qquad q = \epsilon^{-2\tau};$$

$$\tau = \tanh^{-1}\sqrt{\frac{Z_s'}{Z_{op}'}} = \tan^{-1}\sqrt{\frac{Z_s''}{Z_{op}''}}; \qquad e = \epsilon^{-\tau}$$

$$(169)$$

The expression of Eq. (168) is then based on the form

$$\mathcal{L} = 20 \log_{10} (abcde) \quad \text{db}$$

for the insertion loss $\mathcal{L}$. In these expressions τ is known as the image transfer constant. The first loss term in Eq. (168) is 20 $\log_{10} (a)$. The value of a given in Eq. (169) shows that this term accounts for the difference between the power delivered with an ideal matching network between the dipole and the FM receiver and that delivered with a direct connection from dipole terminals to the FM receiver. This loss, therefore, vanishes when $a = 1$; i.e., when the self-impedance Z_1 of the dipole is equal to the effective input impedance Z_2 of the FM receiver. The second and third loss terms with arguments b and c, respectively, are the reflection losses at the joints 1-1' and 2-2'. They vanish when the self-impedance Z_1 of the dipole is the same as the surge impedance Z_0 of the feeder with respect to both the modulus and the phase angle, and the input impedance Z_2 of the receiver is equal in magnitude to Z_0, as well as having the same phase as Z_0. The loss due to the interaction is represented by the term 20 $\log_{10} (d)$ and vanishes also for the conditions just mentioned. Since such ideal requirements can only be approximated, we must expect a small interaction loss as well as reflection and symmetry losses, the latter being accounted for by the a term. According to Eq. (169), we have $e = \epsilon^{-\tau}$ where τ is generally complex for a twisted pair feeder but with an essentially resistive component. The loss term 20 $\log_{10} (e)$ accounts for the inherent attenuation loss in the feeder as well as for a small phase delay.

With respect to reflection losses, it must be borne in mind that the phase of the resultant impedance has to be taken into account and, therefore, a *reflection gain* is also *possible*. Such a gain has already been pointed out in connection with Eq. (165) where the additional power transfer between conjugate impedances is due to phase angles that are positive for one impedance and negative for the other.

62. Formulas and Computations for Feeders and Matching Sections.—Several methods for the determination of line constants, such as the surge impedance, the attenuation, and the like have been described in two other publications[1] in detail. For this

---

[1] "High-frequency Measurements," pp. 383–403, McGraw-Hill Book Company, Inc., New York. "Phenomena in High-frequency Systems," pp. 406–453, McGraw-Hill Book Company, Inc., New York.

reason only methods and formulas that apply to cases useful in the FM range of frequencies are given here.

As far as the surge impedance Z_0 is concerned, it is essentially the ratio $Z_0 = \sqrt{L/C}$ where L and C are the inductance and capacitance per unit length of a feeder. When L and C are expressed in henrys and farads, the surge impedance Z_0 is in ohms. Since for certain feeders such as twisted leadins, the C and L values may change if the unit length is taken too short, it is better to use a unit length of at least a few hundred feet. This will lead then to average values of the respective line or feeder constants and will take into account irregularities in the feeder. When a feeder of at least 500 ft. in length is connected to a 1,000-cycle bridge with the far end open, the total feeder capacitance is large enough so that it can be measured. If the feeder is shorted at the far end, a determination of its total inductance is possible. The surge impedance is then computed from $Z_0 = \sqrt{L/C}$ and gives in approximation the value for it. The values L and C then hold for the chosen length, say 500 ft.

When the chosen length l of the feeder is expressed in meters and divided by $\sqrt{CL}$ we obtain the group velocity c'' of wave propagation in meters per second. It is understood that C and L are again in farads and henrys. The group velocity c'' is somewhat less than the velocity c of wave propagation in empty space. If the foregoing value for c'' in meters per second is multiplied by 6.214×10^{-4}, we obtain the corresponding velocity in miles per second. Since[1] the group velocity c'' is the velocity with which *energy* is being moved along the feeder, it must also be equal to $c'' = l/t$ where t denotes the time in seconds for the power to travel over a length l of the feeder. Hence, the substitution of $Z_0 = \sqrt{L/C}$ and $c'' = l/\sqrt{CL}$ yields $t = L/Z_0$ sec, where the total measured inductance L is in henrys and the surge impedance Z_0 of the feeder is in ohms. Inasmuch as the angular velocity $\Omega = 6.28F$, owing to the frequency F of the feeder current, is equal to the angular distance (phase angle described) divided by the corresponding time, we have for the phase angle, which is also known as the phase delay δ of a feeder of length l, the formulas

$$\delta = \begin{cases} 6.28tF & \text{radians} \\ 360tF & \text{deg} \end{cases} \qquad (170)$$

[1] Phenomena in High-frequency Systems, pp. 378–380.

if t is again in seconds and the frequency F in cycles per second.

At this point it should be understood that when we are dealing with an aperiodic feeder there can be only inherent attenuation, since the feeder input behaves like an ohmic resistance. When feeder transformers, *i.e.*, quarter-wave-length sections, are employed, we have a certain amount of both feeder attenuation and wave distribution, since $\delta = 90$ deg. The effective time delay δ then gives a means for finding out how much shorter than the free-space quarter-wave-length distribution, the actual length l of the matching feeder has to be in order to produce a true quarter-wave distribution. Suppose we have a carrier frequency $F = 50$ Mc, and let us at first assume that the group velocity c'' at which the energy is being propagated along the matching section of length l is the same as the velocity $c = 3 \times 10^8$ m/sec which holds in empty space. Then the length has to be

$$l = \frac{0.25 \times 3 \times 10^8}{50 \times 10^6} = 1.5 \text{ m}$$

which is $3.281 \times 1.5 = 4.925$ ft. Since it takes $t = 1.5/(3 \times 10^8)$ $= 5 \times 10^{-9}$ sec for the wave energy to move along the feeder length of 1.5 m, the time delay is equal to

$$\delta = 360 \times 5 \times 10^{-9} + 50 \times 10^6 = 90$$

electrical degrees, which in this restricted case happens to be equal also to 90 space degrees as far as the actual length l of the matching feeder is concerned. Hence, this numerical result confirms the fact that with a group velocity c'' equal to the velocity c in empty space, the length l of an impedance-matching feeder is actually one-quarter of the operating wave length λ in free space.

Such a feeder section is shown in Fig. 99a. The surge impedance Z_0 of the quarter-wave-length section is so chosen that the surge impedance is the geometrical mean of the impedances to be matched. When looking into the 1-1' terminals with Z_2 connected across 2-2', the input impedance is Z_0^2/Z_2, just as the impedance looking into the 2-2' terminals with Z_1 connected across 1-1' is Z_0^2/Z_1. For a half-wave-length section as shown in Fig. 99b we have a one-to-one impedance transformation. For the quarter-wave-length section we have also the relations $Z_1 = pZ_0$ and $Z_2 = Z_0/p$ for the current ratio $p = I_2/I_1$. Whether such a matching section is made up of parallel wires, a concentric line, or some other suitable practical design, depends on the impedances to be matched. On account of the relation $\sqrt{Z_1 Z_2} = Z_0$, the surge impedance Z_0 has to be chosen according to the magnitude of $Z_1 Z_2$.

Now, let us assume that we have the actual condition, for which a measurement shows that the group velocity c'' is somewhat smaller than the velocity c in empty space. Assume that

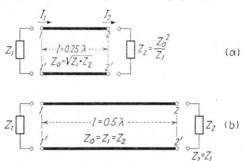

Fig. 99.—Quarter- and half-wave length matching lines.

the energy transfer occurs with a velocity that is 5 per cent less than the value for c. We have then $c'' = 0.95 \times 3 \times 10^8 = 2.85 \times 10^8$ m/sec and require only a length of

$$l = \frac{0.25 \times 2.85 \times 10^8}{50 \times 10^6} = 1.425 \text{ m}$$

or 4.67 ft. The section has, therefore, to be chosen also 5 per cent shorter than would be the case for $c'' = c$. Since now the energy is transmitted along a length of only 1.425 meters, it requires $1.425/(2.85 \times 10^8) = 0.005 \mu$ sec for the energy to be transmitted along this length. According to Eq. (170) the phase delay is then $\delta = 360 \times 0.005 \times 10^{-6} \times 50 \times 10^6 = 90$ deg as should be the case for a true quarter-wave length. If the length l had been figured out with a velocity of 3×10^8 m/sec, we would have obtained the former value of 1.5 m which would cause a longer wave-length distribution. Hence, it would require a longer time interval $t = 1.5/(2.85 \times 10^8) = 5.264 \times 10^{-9}$ sec and, therefore, cause a larger phase delay

$$\delta = 360 \times 5.264 \times 10^{-9} \times 50 \times 10^6 = 94.9 \text{ deg.}$$

Since 90-deg phase delay corresponds to a true quarter-wavelength distribution, we have now a $0.25 \times 94.9\lambda/90 = 0.2635\lambda$ distribution, which is larger than is needed for impedance matching and cannot result in proper termination impedance regulation.

This brings us now to the concept of the phase velocity c' when energy is being propagated through a medium that is not empty space. When the medium is not empty space, a certain *guiding action* occurs as far as the path or the phase speed, respectively, of a wavelike disturbance is concerned. If the guiding action is due to an atmosphere of electrons, or generally due to an atmosphere of both electrons and positive ions, as in the ionized layer of the upper atmosphere, then electromagnetic waves will no longer progress *freely*. The electromagnetic waves will undergo successive refractions so that a linear path of propagation changes into a curved path of propagation. The ionized medium then, so to speak, "guides" the wave motion along a curve. The path is then a longer distance. In feeder lines, antennas, and as a matter of fact along any conductors, the guiding is accomplished by the conductor. We have then in each case a group velocity c'' with which energy is being propagated. The group velocity c'' can *never* exceed the velocity c in empty space, but the phase velocity c', which accounts for the actual phase distribution, exceeds values of 3×10^8 m/sec, as was brought out on page 284, since we have the relation

$$c = \sqrt{c'c''} \tag{171}$$

What just happened in the computation of the impedance matching section will, therefore, enlighten us as to what is actually meant by the phase velocity c' and why it can be larger than the velocity c of light, which is, so to speak, the upper limit.

In the first place, the phase velocity is not the speed with which the energy flow propagates. In the second place, we found from the computation that if we design a matching feeder based on the velocity of light, we cannot expect that the section is actually a "teeter totter"; *i.e.*, it will automatically lower the input impedance on one side when the load termination impedance on the other side of the feeder increases, and vice versa. In other words, the automatic impedance regulation cannot occur correctly. But we found that if we use a somewhat shorter feeder section, proper impedance regulation will take place. The phase distribution was computed from the phase delay formula (170). Hence, a wavelength distribution occurs at an apparent *faster* rate than is due to the exciting-frequency cycle. Since the distribution is actually a phase distribution, we may assume that it corresponds to an apparent frequency that is somewhat higher than the operating frequency. The value of the apparent frequency is found from the phase velocity c', which for a group velocity c'', as in above computations of $c'' = 2.85 \times 10^8$ m/sec, becomes $c' = c^2/c'' = 9 \times 10^{16}/2.85 \times 10^8 = 3.16 \times 10^8$ m/sec. This velocity value can be imagined as causing a frequency of phase distribution that is no longer equal to the operating frequency of 50 Mc but is changed in the ratio of c'/c. Hence, we find this apparent frequency, which determines the current as well as the corresponding voltage distribution along the feeder section, as

$$\frac{3.16 \times 50 \times 10^6}{3} = 52.6 \text{ Mc.}$$

Inserting this value in Eq. (170) yields

$$\delta = 360 \times 5 \times 10^{-9} \times 52.6 \times 10^6 = 94.9 \text{ deg}$$

as was found before. Hence, when "guided" wave energy propagation takes place, the energy is being transferred somewhat slower, but the corresponding current as well as the voltage distribution occurs according to the phase velocity c'. This is equivalent to saying that the conductor has to be shortened by the same percentage as the group velocity c'' is slower than $c = 3 \times 10^8$ m/sec in order to produce a natural mode of feeder excitation.

From the computations with Eq. (170), we note that we can conveniently determine directly the time t required for passing the power along a feeder with quarter-wave-length excitation of the feeder. Since the feeder is generally homogeneous along its entire length, any suitable length can be used for making experimental determinations. As a matter of fact even if irregularities as in twisted-wire leadins exist, it is best to make determinations with a length of several hundred feet or at least with the actual length l used in the final installation of the feeder. If possible, the tests should be made within the operating range of frequencies for which the feeder will be used, since line losses may be different with frequencies remote from the intended operating frequency. This may cause a somewhat different group velocity c''. The test then consists of using a suitable length of the feeder and exciting it in the true quarter-wave-length distribution and noting the value of the exciting carrier frequency F.

Generally, the resonance frequency of a closed circuit* is $F = 1/2\pi \sqrt{CL}$ if C denotes the capacitance in farads and L the inductance in henrys for F in cycles per second. The total capacitance and total inductance of a feeder become greater, the longer the feeder. Their values are, therefore, less for a quarter-wave-length feeder than they would be for a feeder that is, for instance, excited in the half-wave-length distribution. According to foregoing calculations, as well as the general definition of the quarter-wave-length line, the electrical space distribution along its length l is 90 deg or 0.5π radian. Hence, the frequency F which causes quarter-wave-length resonance requires only the time of a quarter of a cycle, *i.e.*, only a frequency $F_0 = 0.5\pi F = 1/4 \sqrt{CL}$. Since the group velocity is $c'' = 1/\sqrt{CL}$, the operating wave length must be $\lambda_0 = c/F_0$ for a quarter-wave-length excitation. Hence, $c'' = l/\sqrt{CL} = 4lF_0 = 4cl/\lambda_0$ yields the formula

$$c'' = \frac{12 \times 10^8}{\lambda_0} l \quad \text{m/sec} \tag{172}$$

if l and λ_0 are in the same dimensions, for instance in meters or in feet. With the explanations already given, it is now evident that λ_0 cannot be equal to $4l$, where l is the physical length of the feeder in meters, since the slower group velocity c'' causes a faster phase or distribution velocity c' than the velocity c in empty space. Hence, the phase distribution, which means also the current and voltage distributions along the feeder, occur faster and a shorter feeder length l will bring about the quarter-wave-length resonance condition. It is, therefore, only necessary to choose at first a length l of the feeder or of any other line approximately equal to the quarter-wave-length λ_0 and to vary the corresponding frequency of the exciting current until maximum response occurs. The length l of the feeder is then measured in meters and the true operating wave length λ_0 in meters computed from the observed frequency F_0 in cycles per second by means of the relation $\lambda_0 = 3 \times 10^8/F_0$ meters.

The use of *measured* values of C and L for a certain feeder length, rather than the theoretical values per unit length, gives the advantage that the actual operating condition is taken into account. This is all the more advisable when cheaper feeder lines are in the final installation, where the line constants may differ somewhat along the feeder. With such measurements over a length of several hundred feet, we can then always find the corresponding C and L values for any desired length since proportionality with the length exists, at least as far as the average values are concerned.

The attenuation constant α of a feeder is just as important as its surge impedance Z_0. This constant accounts for a somewhat smaller output current and a somewhat smaller corresponding output voltage of the feeder, even when perfectly terminated at each end. For any feeder of surge impedance Z_0 terminated into an impedance Z_2, we experience, when looking into the open terminals of the feeder, an impedance

$$Z_1 = Z_0 \frac{Z_2 + Z_0 \tanh nl}{Z_0 + Z_2 \tanh nl} \tag{173}$$

where nl is the generalized electrical length of the feeder, which includes both the total attenuation αl as well as the total phase retardation $360l/\lambda$ where λ denotes the operating wave length. The above formula is the outcome of the relations

$$\left. \begin{aligned} E_1 &= E_2 \cosh nl + Z_0 I_2 \sinh nl \\ I_1 &= I_2 \cosh nl + \frac{E_2}{Z_0} \sinh nl \end{aligned} \right\} \tag{174}$$

for the input voltage E_1 and input current I_1 with respect to the output voltage E_2 across the load impedance Z_2 and the current I_2 flowing through Z_2. For $Z_2 = 0$ in Eq. (173), we find the input impedance when the load end is short-circuited. For the load removed, $Z_2 = \infty$, Eq. (173) gives an indeterminate solution. But the basic equations of (174) give a solution for $Z_1 = E_1/I_1$ since for such a condition the terms with I_2 must vanish. We then have

$$Z_1 = \left\{ \begin{aligned} &Z_0 \cotanh nl \quad \text{open-ended} \\ &Z_0 \tanh nl \quad \text{short-circuited} \end{aligned} \right\} \tag{175}$$

Since the propagation constant $n = \alpha + j360/\lambda$ is complex, we can separate the real term, which accounts for the attenuation loss, and find

$$\alpha = 0.5 \left(\frac{R}{Z_0} + GZ_0 \right) \cong 0.5 \frac{R}{Z_0} \quad \text{nepers per unit length} \tag{176}$$

where R denotes the feeder resistance per unit length. If, as in most efficient feeders, the conductance G per unit length, which acts across a section of the feeder, is essentially negligible, then the approximation holds.

At this point it is of importance to realize what is actually meant by an attenuation constant. Equation (176) shows that the attenuation constant α represents a negative exponent to the base $\epsilon = 2.7182818$. It must have such a base since it is expressed in nepers. The exponent must have a negative value since dissipative line constants like resistance R and conductance G use up energy. They cause, therefore, a gradual decrease in the energy as energy is being passed on along the feeder. It is also important to note that the attenuation constant α *decreases* with an increase in surge impedance Z_0 since normally the conductance effect across the feeder is small in comparison to the resistance effect. Hence, a matched feeder of physical length l generally must have an output current amplitude I_2, which is equal to $I_1 \epsilon^{-\alpha l}$, if I_1 is the amplitude of the current passing into the feeder and α is its attenuation constant per unit length. The current ratio I_1/I_2 is conveniently expressed in decibels and we have for the decibel loss in a feeder of a length l the relations $20 \log_{10}(I_1/I_2)$ $= 20 \ \log_{10} \ (\epsilon^{\alpha l}) = 20\alpha l \ \log_{10} \ (2.7183) = 20 \times 0.4343\alpha l$. The feeder loss due to attenuation is then

$$\text{db} = \begin{cases} 0.4343 \left(\dfrac{R}{Z_0} + GZ_0 \right) l & \text{for twisted feeder} \\[3ex] 0.4343 \dfrac{R}{Z_0} l & \begin{array}{l}\text{for a good concentric and} \\ \text{parallel-wire system}\end{array} \end{cases} \tag{177}$$

since only for twisted wires and concentric lines, which use a dissipative dielectric between the conductors, can the conductance G play an appreciable part. If there is any doubt about the value of G, the upper relation should be used.

Suppose we are dealing with feeder lines that have a physical length l, which is an integral number N of the quarter-wave-length excitation. Then $l = N\lambda/4$ has to be inserted in Eqs. (173), (174), and (175). We have to distinguish between odd and even integer values of N. For odd values as $N = 1, 3, 5$, etc., we obtain $\lambda/4, 3\lambda/4, 5\lambda/4$, etc., feeder lengths; for even integers as $N = 2$, 4, 6, etc., we have a feeder length l equal to a half wave length, a full wave length, and three-halves wave length, etc. If we write down from the first equations of (174) the driving impedance, which is the voltage E_1 impressed across the feeder *input* divided by the current I_2 leaving the feeder *output*, we have

$$Z_d = \frac{E_1}{I_2} = Z_2 \cosh nl + Z_0 \sinh nl \tag{178}$$

For a negligible α value in comparison with $j360/\lambda$ in $n = \alpha + j360/\lambda$, we find $n \cong j360/\lambda$ and

$$\frac{E_1}{I_2} = Z_2 \cosh \left(j\frac{360}{\lambda} l\right) + Z_0 \sinh \left(j\frac{360}{\lambda} l\right)$$

$$= Z_2 \cos \left(\frac{360}{\lambda} l\right) + jZ_0 \sin \frac{360}{\lambda} l) \tag{179}$$

For $N = 1$, which is by far the most usual case, we have $l = \lambda/4$ and

$$\frac{E_1}{I_2} = jZ_0 \tag{180}$$

This result expresses that the load current I_2 has a *constant* relation to the driving voltage E_1 at the input side of the feeder, since the surge impedance Z_0 is fixed. Hence, if the load impedance Z_2 should change for some reason, for instance, should decrease, then the quarter-wave-length feeder would inherently increase its input impedance by the same amount in order to compensate for the change in the load impedance. For $N = 2$ we obtain an argument of 180 deg in Eq. (179). If we compare the result with the one obtained in Eq. (180), we find for the driving impedance of a feeder

$$Z_d = \left\{ \begin{array}{ll} jZ_0 & \text{an impedance-matching action} \\ & \text{so that } Z_0 = \sqrt{Z_1 Z_2} \\ \\ -Z_2 & \text{an impedance matching of one-to-one} \\ & \text{since } Z_1 = -Z_2 \end{array} \right\} \tag{181}$$

For upper equation $l = \lambda/4$; for lower equation $l = \lambda/2$.

These important features of quarter-wave-length and half-wave-length feeders can also be realized if we neglect α in Eq. (174) and make the comparison

$$\frac{E_1}{I_1} = \left\{ \begin{array}{ll} \dfrac{I_2}{E_2} & \text{shows that } Z_1 = \dfrac{Z_0{}^2}{Z_2} \text{ "teeter totter"} \\ & \text{impedance action} \\ \\ -\dfrac{E_2}{I_2} & \text{shows that } Z_1 = -Z_2 \text{ one-to-one impedance} \\ & \text{transformation} \end{array} \right\} \tag{182}$$

For upper equation $l = \lambda/4$; for lower equation $l = \lambda/2$.

Also it should be realized in these relations, that by quarter- and half-wave-length distributions we do not mean that the physical length l is exactly equal to one-quarter wave length or to one-half wave length of the operating wave length $\lambda = c/F$, but is equal to a somewhat shorter length l, which causes feeder resonance response effects for the exciting frequency F. This has been brought out in detail already in Sec. 62. For the correct length l corresponding to the half-wave-length distribution, the feeder, if short-circuited at the far end, would show maximum current response for the current passing into the feeder when constant input voltage E_1 is impressed on the feeder. Maximum response current would also be noted when terminated into a low-resistance current meter at the end of the line. Since the low resistance should be zero ohms, the first method of determining maximum response is more reliable. For a length l that causes quarter-wave-length distribution for a current of exciting frequency F, maximum current will flow into the feeder when the load end of the feeder is open. Since the actual length l in each case is always somewhat shorter than 0.25λ and 0.5λ, respectively, for a frequency F in Mc, it is only necessary to cut off a piece which is $0.25 \times 3.281/F = 246/F$ ft long for the quarter-wave-length line and $492/F$ ft long for the half-wave-length feeder. This would yield a feeder length of 4.94 ft for a preliminary quarter-wave length feeder in case of a 50-Mc exciter current. Then the line is gradually shortened until maximum current response occurs for the applied voltage of 50-Mc frequency.

A matched feeder line acts aperiodic and essentially like an ohmic resistance of Z_0 ohms. But a feeder line that is an integer multiple of the quarter-wave length has an input impedance of

$$
Z_1 =
\begin{cases}
Z_0 \tanh\,(0.25\alpha\lambda N) & \text{for} \begin{cases} N = 1, 3, 5, \text{ etc. (end of feeder open)} \\ N = 2, 4, 6, \text{ etc. (end short-circuited)} \end{cases} \\[2em]
Z_0 \coth\,(0.25\alpha\lambda N) & \text{for} \begin{cases} N = 1, 3, 5, \text{ etc. (end short-circuited)} \\ N = 2, 4, 6, \text{ etc. (end open-circuited)} \end{cases}
\end{cases}
\tag{183}
$$

For upper equation Z_1 is a low impedance; for lower equation Z_1 is a high impedance.

Hence, the *input impedance* is due only to the *attenuation* α when modes of feeder resonance prevail. This is similar to the case of closed circuits where, for instance, for voltage resonance the maximum current flow is not infinite, but is only a large finite value on account of the circuit losses due to the total effective resistance. A feeder in the quarter, three-quarter, five-quarter, etc., wavelength distribution ($N = 1, 3, 5$, etc.) with the load end open, behaves, as far as the input current is concerned, like voltage resonance. As a matter of fact, it is equivalent to it if lumped constants were used. The value of the maximum response current is, therefore, limited only by the attenuation α as Eq. (183) shows.

With ordinary closed circuits, current resonance is also known as the condition of maximum rejection to a current flowing to a parallel combination of a condenser C in multiple with a coil of inductance L and resistance R. Also here only a limited rejection occurs since the multiple combination does not exhibit an infinite impedance at current resonance, but still has a finite ohmic resistance $(6.28F)^2L^2/R = L/CR$ ohms. The case of current resonance occurs, for instance, with *even* multiples of quarter-wave-length lines, *i.e.*, half-wave-length, full-wave-length, etc., lines that are open at the load end. It also occurs with odd multiples of quarter-wave-length lines which are short-circuited at the load end.

Hence, by means of the relations given in Eq. (183) we have an experimental method of finding the attenuation α since it is only necessary to determine the input impedance Z_1, which is an *ohmic resistance* for such conditions. Suppose we take the case of a quarter-wave-length distribution along a feeder, *i.e.*, $N = 1$. For such a distribution, the argument of the hyperbolic functions is $0.25\alpha\lambda$ and corresponds normally to a small hyperbolic angle. Hence, tanh $(0.25\alpha\lambda)$ is approximately equal to the argument $0.25\alpha\lambda$ itself. Since for small argument values of $0.25\alpha\lambda$, the tanh function gives a small value and the corresponding cotanh function a large value, the upper impedance value in Eq. (183) must be small compared with the impedance value of the lower expression. This should be borne in mind when making the input impedance measurements, otherwise it may happen that a meter will be "burned out." For a feeder length $l = 0.25\lambda$, we have then an input impedance

$$Z_1 = \begin{cases} \begin{aligned} Z_0(0.25\alpha\lambda) \\ = \underbrace{0.125R\lambda\left(1 + \frac{GZ_0^2}{R}\right)}_{\text{a low impedance}} \quad \text{load end open} \\[2em] \frac{4Z_0}{\alpha\lambda} = \underbrace{\frac{8Z_0^2}{R\lambda\left(1 + \dfrac{GZ_0^2}{R}\right)}}_{\substack{\text{a higher impedance} \\ \text{of a few hundred ohms}}} \quad \text{load end short-circuited} \end{aligned} \end{cases} \tag{184}$$

For a negligible conductance G in Eq. (176), we obtain the approximations

$$Z_1 \cong \begin{cases} 0.125R\lambda & \text{end open} \\[1em] \dfrac{8Z_0^2}{R\lambda} & \text{end short-circuited} \end{cases} \tag{185}$$

Equations (184) and (185) are important since the input impedance Z_1 can be directly determined by the resistance-substitution method as will be shown in Sec. 63. We have, therefore, a means for determining the value of α at the operating wave length λ which corresponds to the actual feeder frequency $F = c/\lambda$ which is used in the feeder installation. The upper equation of (185) shows that for the quarter-wave-length $l = 0.25\lambda$, the input impedance $Z_1 = (0.5R)0.25\lambda = 0.5lR$. Hence, the effective h-f resistance is *only* 50 per cent of the true resistance value lR of the feeder of length $l = 0.25\lambda$.

Such a determination should be made for the range of the instantaneous operating frequency F of the FM current since the value of α increases with the magnitude of the carrier frequency F. At this point it should be realized that the attenuation α is by no means constant when the carrier frequency F is increased or decreased. Also it is not directly proportional with F as is often assumed, but is proportional to F^m, where the exponent m has a value anywhere between 0.5 and unity. We have, for instance, $\alpha = 0.05$ neper at $F = 0.8$ Mc and $\alpha = 0.18$ neper at $F = 6$ Mc for a length of $l = 100$ ft. Since the decibel loss is 8.686α, the decibel loss per wave length decreases with an increase of F.

For a feeder terminated into a resistance equal to the value of the feeder surge impedance Z_0, the current flowing along the feeder is gradually attenuated, owing to α, toward the load end.

Whatever energy arrives at the load end is completely absorbed in the load resistance. The voltage E_2 across the matched load resistance, which is equal to Z_0 ohms, becomes

$$E_2 = \frac{E_1}{\text{antilog}_{10}\,(\text{db}/20)} \tag{186}$$

where E_1 is the input voltage across the feeder and the decibel loss is due to α.

Inasmuch as in the upper formula of Eq. (183) the factor 0.25λ stands for the physical length l of the open-ended quarter-wave-length feeder and $N = 1$ for a quarter-wave-length excitation, the attenuation loss per unit length is

$$8.686\alpha = 8.686 \tanh^{-1}\left(\frac{Z_1}{Z_0}\right) \quad \text{db}$$

$$\cong 8.686\,\frac{Z_1}{Z_0} \quad \text{db} \tag{187}$$

The unit length is then in the same dimension as λ; *i.e.*, when λ is expressed in feet, Eq. (187) holds for a feeder length of 1 ft.

The theoretical formulas for the h-f resistance R and the surge impedance Z_0 of a concentric line feeder are

$$\left. \begin{aligned} R &= 2\sqrt{\rho\mu F}\left(\frac{1}{D} + \frac{1}{d}\right)10^{-9} \quad \text{ohms/cm} \\ Z_0 &= 138 \log_{10}\frac{D}{d} \quad \text{ohms} \end{aligned} \right\} \tag{188}$$

where D = inner diameter of outer conductor, cm.
d = outer diameter of inner conductor, cm.
ρ = specific resistance, em-cgs units (about **1,700** for copper).
μ = magnetic permeability ($=1$ for copper).
F = frequency, cycles per second.

This leads, on account of the approximation $\alpha = R/2Z_0$, to the theoretical formula for the attenuation per centimeter length

$$\alpha = 725 \times 10^{-14}\,\frac{\sqrt{\rho\mu F}\,[1/D + 1/d]}{\log_{10}\,(D/d)} \quad \text{nepers/cm} \tag{189}$$

where the portion GZ_0 in Eq. (176), due to the cross conductivity G, is neglected. The decibel loss is then 8.686α for each centimeter of length.   These expressions hold for a length of 1 ft if α is multi-plied by 12×2.54, *i.e.*, by a factor of 30.5.

Figure 100 shows how the attenuation constant α per 100 ft changes with the frequency F.   We note that we have to figure with losses from 2 to 3 db per 100 ft.   Ordinary twisted lamp cord, depending on the condition of the cord, *i.e.*, whether dry or affected by humidity, shows an attenuation per 100 ft of from

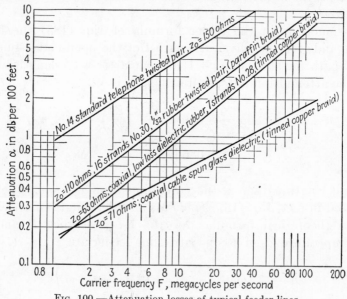

Fig. 100.—Attenuation losses of typical feeder lines.

about 3.5 to 10 db and surge impedances from about 80 to 140 ohms.

Since for a ratio $D/d = 3.6$ the attenuation α in Eq. (189) becomes a minimum value, the decibel loss for concentric copper lines for such an optimum condition ($D = 3.6d$), which should also be met, can also be expressed by

$$\frac{db}{1{,}000 \text{ ft}} = \frac{0.256 \sqrt{F}}{D} \tag{190}$$

if the frequency F is in megacycles per second.

63. Feeder Tests.—For engineering design the two important characteristic feeder constants are its surge impedance Z_0 and its attenuation constant α.   The latter accounts for the inherent feeder losses even though the feeder behaves in an aperiodic manner; *i.e.*, when it is terminated at each end in impedances that are equal to the surge impedance Z_0 with respect to modulus as well as phase.

On pages 309, 314 a method is given where, by means of ordinary a-f measurements of the total feeder capacitance and inductance, Z_0 is computed from the square-root value of the ratio of the inductance in henrys to the capacitance in farads. Methods that make the determination in the actual frequency range, for which the feeder is to be used, are more reliable than methods using audio frequencies. There are then several procedures. One is based on the fact that a feeder that is terminated in a load impedance Z_2, which is equal to the feeder surge impedance Z_0, has an input

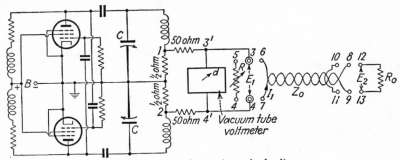

FIG. 101.—Setup for testing a feeder line.

impedance Z_1 also equal to Z_0. This can be readily understood from Eq. (173) if we replace Z_2 by Z_0. We can then use a h-f source, as shown in Fig. 101, which is, for instance, a push-pull oscillator and has a two-gang condenser C-C for varying the frequency from about 30 to 60 Mc/sec. The test current is taken off from output terminals 1-2 and is due to a small voltage drop across a 1-ohm resistor. The two output wires from these terminals lead over two suitable and equal resistances to terminals 3-4 of a double-pole double-throw switch. For tests of dipole feeders each of the two equal resistances is about 50 ohms. If the terminals 3-4 are closed on the input terminals 6-7 of the feeder with the feeder output terminals 8-9 connected to a nonreactive resistor R_0, then a vacuum-tube voltmeter connected across terminals 3'-4' will indicate a certain deflection d which is a measure of the voltage E_1 across the input terminals of the feeder under test. This voltmeter deflection is also a measure of the input impedance $Z_1 = E_1/I_1$ of the feeder. This input impedance can be found by connecting a standard resistance R across terminals 3-4 instead of the test feeder, and changing the magnitude of R until the same deflection d obtains. Then $Z_1 = Z$ ohms.

Since we are dealing here with very high frequencies, customary decade resistors cannot be used. One-quarter-watt carbon resistors hold approximately their direct-current values up to very high frequencies. Thin pieces of constantan or manganin wire, if of short length and suspended inside glass tubes, are still better. But it seems easier to adjust carbon resistors by grinding off some of the thickness until a suitable resistance value obtains. Precision measurements in this range of frequencies are just impossible, even though a balance can be met just as readily as at lower frequencies. Fortunately, when in a measurement the true resistance component is, so to speak, "masked" by unavoidable reactance effects, which sometimes can be avoided by tuning, this will also be the case for the actual installation and we shall meet the actual condition.

The measurement of the input impedance of dipole feeders at a certain frequency requires an adjustment range of the standard resistance R from 20 to about 200 ohms. It is, therefore, easy to express the tube voltmeter deflections d in terms of the standard resistance R. All that is necessary is to pick out, say, a 10-ohm resistor and note the corresponding deflection d. Then, the corresponding deflections for 20-, 30-, up to 200-ohm resistors are found. In each case only one resistor is used. It does not matter whether the resistor is exactly a decade value, since the measured bridge value with direct-current supply is just as good for obtaining a calibration curve of voltmeter deflection d with respect to R values.

As far as the terminating resistance R_0 is concerned, resistors of the type just mentioned also have to be used. If a square-wave generator is available, the determination can be carried out very quickly since we can use the fact that for proper R_0 termination the arriving power at R_0 will be completely absorbed in the termination resistor R_0. The square-wave generator is set to its highest output frequency and its output terminals connected through a 2,000-ohm resistor in series with a 100-ohm resistor. The wave shape across the 100-ohm resistor is noted. It should be rectangular, or at least nearly so. The vertical deflection plates of a cathode-ray oscillograph are, therefore, connected across the 100-ohm resistor. The rectangular-wave shape means that we have also about 20 higher harmonics present in proper phase and amplitude relation with respect to a fundamental sinusoidal current.   Hence, a network connected to the 100-ohm resistor has to be able to transmit at least currents of a width of 20 Mc if the fundamental frequency of the square wave generated is 1 Mc/sec and it is expected that at the output of the network we will still have a square wave.   The latter condition requires besides that the network must also have a linear phase shift with respect to the frequencies used.   We have, therefore, a very severe test and can find whether a network is actually aperiodic in action.

We connect, therefore, the feeder input also across the 100-ohm resistor while the output end of the feeder is closed over $R_0 = Z_0$ ohms. If R_0 is exactly equal to the surge impedance of the feeder, then the wave shape noted on the cathode-ray tube is the same whether the line is connected to the 100-ohm resistor or not.   If the R_0 loading is not correct, then reflections will take place at the load end and will return some of the energy toward the 100-ohm resistor.   This will, in turn, distort the rectangular-wave

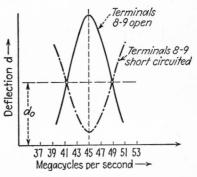

Fig. 102.—Determination of surge impedance Z_0 by means of the common deflection d_0.

shape when the feeder is connected to the input of the feeder under test.   It is, therefore, only necessary to change the loading R_0 until the wave shape remains square.   The value of R_0 is then equal to Z_0.

When the method shown in Fig. 101 is employed, we have a system that is based on the relation $Z_0 = \sqrt{Z_{op}Z_s}$.   The impedance Z_{op} is then measured at the input side of the feeder when the load terminals 8-9 are open and the input impedance across terminals 6-7 is found when the terminals 8-9 are short-circuited. It is, therefore, necessary to obtain in Fig. 101 only the different tube voltmeter deflections d for several exciter frequencies F when terminals 8-9 are open and terminals 6-7 are on terminals 3-4.   In the same way, for different frequencies the voltmeter deflections d are noted when the terminals 8-9 are short-circuited. The corresponding curves are then plotted as in Fig. 102 and by means of the intersections of these curves the deflection d_0 obtained. Since for intersections, we must have the same input impedances for both the open and short-circuited load end condition of the feeder under test, the deflection d_0 is directly a measure for the surge impedance Z_0 of the feeder. Then $Z_{op} = Z_s$ and is equal to Z_0 because $Z_0 = \sqrt{Z_{op}Z_s}$.

The line loss can then be measured by terminating the feeder with the correct resistance loading $R_0 = Z_0$ and measuring the input and output voltages E_1 and E_2. The decibel loss is then computed from the expression $20 \log_{10} (E_2/E_1)$.

Figure 103 depicts another arrangement for measuring the inherent feeder loss due to attenuation α. An ordinary signal

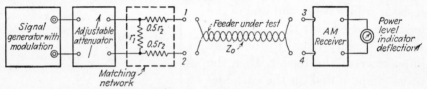

Matching
network

Fig. 103.—Determination of feeder attenuation.

generator that is modulated in amplitude is connected to an attenuator having a known variable attenuation. The output terminals have an ohmic resistor r_1 bridged across them, and the output wires each lead through $0.5r_2$ resistors to terminals 1-2. At first terminals 1-2 are directly connected to the input terminals 3-4 of an AM receiver and the attenuator setting so chosen that the power level indicator of the receiver gives a suitable deflection d. Next, the feeder is inserted between terminals 1-2 and 3-4 and the attenuation decreased by an amount α until the same deflection d obtains. The value of 8.686α then yields the decibel loss of the feeder used in the test. It will be noted that by the r_1, r_2 network the attenuator and the feeder under test can be matched, since r_1 terminates the output of the attenuator and $r_1 + r_2$ terminates the input of the feeder under test.

If the first formula of Eqs. (174) is written down for a feeder having the load end open, then there can be no current flow I_2 at this end. Hence, $E_1 = E_2 \cosh nl$ gives a relation that contains both the applied terminal voltage E_1 at the input end of the feeder to be tested and the voltage E_2 at the open load end. When the physical length l of the feeder is made equal to that required for quarter-wave-length resonance, we have

$$E_1 = E_2 \cosh (0.25n\lambda) \tag{191}$$

According to Eq. (175), for an open-ended quarter wave-length feeder, the input impedance is $Z_1 = Z_0$ cotanh $(0.25n\lambda) = Z_0$ tanh $(0.25\alpha\lambda)$. The proof of this result is as follows: Since the propagation constant $n = \alpha + j\delta$ for a phase delay $\delta = 6.28l/\lambda$, we find, for a unit feeder length $l = 1$, that

$$Z_1 = Z_0 \text{ cotanh } (n) = Z_0 \frac{\cosh (\alpha + j\delta)}{\sinh (\alpha + j\delta)}$$
$$= Z_0 \frac{\cosh \alpha \cosh j\delta + \sinh \alpha \sinh j\delta}{\sinh \alpha \cosh j\delta + \cosh \alpha \sinh j\delta}$$
$$= Z_0 \frac{\cosh \alpha \cos \delta + \sinh \alpha \cdot j \sin \delta}{\sinh \alpha \cos \delta + \cosh \alpha \cdot j \sin \delta}$$

Hence, for a feeder length l instead of unity, we have to use αl and δl instead of α and δ in these formulas. For a quarter-wave-length excitation $l = 0.25\lambda$ and $\delta = 360 \times 0.25\lambda/\lambda = 90$ deg. The input feeder impedance, for an open-ended feeder of length $l = 0.25\lambda$, becomes

$$Z_1 = Z_0 \text{ cotanh } (0.25\alpha\lambda + j0.5\pi) = Z_0 \frac{0 + \sinh (0.25\alpha\lambda)}{0 + \cosh (0.25\alpha\lambda)}$$
$$= Z_0 \tanh (0.25\alpha\lambda) \quad (192)$$

Hence, the hyperbolic *cotangent* function with the generalized line angle of $0.25n\lambda$ changes for the open-ended quarter-wave-length excitation into a hyperbolic *tangent* function, which contains only the pure hyperbolic line angle $0.25\alpha\lambda$ for the total feeder length $l = 0.25\lambda$. This result expresses the fact that only the attenuation effect remains. This result is also the reason why in Eqs. (183) the tanh function appears in the upper equation instead of the customary cotanh function.

In a similar way it is now evident why in Eq. (191) we have cosh $(0.25n\lambda) = \sinh (0.25\alpha\lambda)$ and we obtain another important formula as far as experimental methods are concerned. It is

$$E_1 = E_2 \sinh (0.25\alpha\lambda) \quad (193)$$

Hence, a feeder line with the load end open and excited in the fundamental mode $(l = 0.25\lambda)$ has an input voltage E_1 which is equal to the resonance voltage E_2 measured at the open-load terminals times the hyperbolic sine function. But the ratio of the resonance voltage E_2 acting at the open end of the feeder to the driving input voltage E_1 is, since only attenuation remains in the sinh term, also equal to the reactance voltage divided by the voltage consumed in the effective resistance of the quarter-wave-length feeder. Hence, E_2/E_1 must also be the Q *value of the quarter-wave-length feeder.* From two voltage measurements, one at the input and the other at the open output end of the feeder, we have the formulas for the attenuation α and the decibel loss per unit length

$$\left.\begin{array}{c} \alpha = \dfrac{E_1}{lE_2} \quad \text{nepers} \\[2mm] \text{Decibel loss} = 8.686\alpha \end{array}\right\} \qquad (194)$$

since the argument of the hyperbolic sine function is normally smaller than about 0.35 hyperbolic radian. Here l denotes the length of the resonant feeder. It does not matter whether it is in feet or in meters since in each case it is the same length as found by the experiment.

The experiment consists in noting the maximum response in the current I_1 flowing into the feeder and measuring the input voltage E_1, the output voltage E_2, and the length l. The experiment is somewhat awkward when we postulate exactly the frequency F at which resonance is to take place, since we had to shorten the feeder gradually until maximum resonance occurs. It is then possible that we shall shorten the length too much and have to start over again. It is, therefore, advisable to use a length that is approximately equal to the quarter-wave-length distribution. Then we measure the length l and change the frequency F of the exciting current until the open-end voltage E_2 passes through a decided maximum. Next, the voltage E_1 is measured. The frequency of the test will then not be very far off.

Equation (192) gives another method for finding the attenuation constant α per unit length. It is based on the determination of the surge impedance Z_0 and the input impedance Z_1 of the open-ended quarter-wave-length feeder. The subsequent computations are made with the formulas

$$\left.\begin{array}{c} \alpha = \dfrac{Z_1}{lZ_0} \quad \text{nepers} \\[2mm] \text{Decibel loss} = 8.686\alpha \end{array}\right\} \qquad (195)$$

where the attenuation and the decibel loss are again per unit length and l is the actual length of the feeder when excited in the fundamental quarter-wave-length mode. Also here the hyperbolic tangent function is replaced by its argument since the error is small for arguments smaller than about 0.35 hyperbolic radian. If much larger arguments occur, then, the accurate formulas for both methods are

$$\alpha = \begin{cases} \dfrac{1}{l}\, \sinh^{-1}\left(\dfrac{E_1}{E_2}\right) \\[2ex] \dfrac{1}{l}\, \tanh^{-1}\left(\dfrac{Z_1}{Z_0}\right) \end{cases} \quad \text{nepers} \qquad (196)$$

with the corresponding decibel loss being 8.686 times larger than the value of α.

In connection with Eq. (195) it is noted that we require reliable methods for determining impedances. We deal with very high frequencies in such measurements. The surge impedance Z_0 can be determined by the input impedance that exists when a feeder is terminated into a load which is equal to the surge impedance. We require a procedure, therefore, that determines the input impedance of the feeder. That such a feeder loaded into the correct value of Z_0 produces an input impedance Z_0 we can see from Eq. (173) by putting $Z_2 = Z_0$. If the feeder is open at the load end and is excited in the fundamental quarter-wave-length mode, then the upper formulas of Eqs. (184) and (185) hold. The measured input impedance Z_1 then gives either a means for computing the attenuation α, as well as the corresponding decibel loss, by using Eqs. (195), or the effective high-frequency resistance R_e by using the upper expression of Eq. (185). In this formula, $0.125\lambda R = 0.5 l R$ since $l = 0.25\lambda$. If this formula is expressed in terms of the unit length of a feeder, we have for the high-frequency resistance per unit length, in terms of the measured input impedance Z_1,

$$R = \begin{cases} \dfrac{2Z_1}{l} & \text{for values of } 0.5 l R/Z_0 < 0.35 \text{ and con-} \\ & \text{ductance } G \text{ effect of feeder neglected} \\[2ex] \dfrac{2Z_0}{l}\, \tanh^{-1}\left(\dfrac{Z_1}{Z_0}\right) & \text{for any value of } 0.5 l R/Z_0 \\ & \text{and } G \text{ effect neglected} \end{cases} \qquad (197)$$

To neglect the conductance effect $0.5 G Z_0$ in comparison to $0.5 R/Z_0$ in the α expression of Eq. (176) seems a justified approximation for concentric lines and parallel wires but not for twisted feeders. If the input impedance Z_1 of the open-ended feeder of length l is measured, we have only to divide the double value of Z_1 by the actual length l, which causes fundamental feeder resonance. The quantity Z_1 is then, besides, a resistance, and any suitable method that determines high-frequency resistance can be used for its determination.

At this point it is of interest to realize that the measurement is based on a feeder when it is excited in its "gravest" or fundamental resonance condition. Like all line constants, such as C, L, and R of a feeder, the total corresponding values for any length l are equal to lR, lC, and lL only when[1] *constant* potential as well as current distributions prevail along the feeder in the operating condition for which the feeder is being used in the installation. The constant potential distribution refers to the total capacitance lC of a feeder of length l. It would also refer to the total conductance value lG. The constant current distribution requirement refers to both the total resistance lR as well as to the total inductance lL of a feeder.

Fortunately, this holds true in very good approximation for feeders that are aperiodic, *i.e.*, terminated into impedances that are identical in all respects with the surge impedance of the feeder. The slight exponential taper due to the inherent feeder attenuation can be overlooked as far as the total line constants are concerned. But when feeders are used as an impedance-matching transformer, as the quarter-wave-length feeder, then the total h-f resistance is not lR and the total feeder inductance is also not lL, but only $0.5lR$ and $0.5lL$, where R and L are the h-f values per unit length, assuming fixed distributions. For the quarter-wave-length feeder, the total effective capacitance is also only $0.81lC$; *i.e.*, it is only 81 per cent of the total capacitance of an aperiodic feeder of exactly the same length. It should be clearly understood that it is the total capacitance, the total inductance, as well as the total resistance of a certain feeder length that count and not the value per unit length. This is true because the total effective h-f values account for the average velocity of energy propagation as well as for the frequency for which fundamental quarter-wave-

---

[1] For other details consult, "Phenomena in High-frequency Systems," pp. 427–439, with special reference to Fig. 242 and Tables XXI, XXII, and XXIII.

length resonance occurs. Hence, they also determine the physical length l which is required.

Returning to Eqs. (197), the physical length l in these formulas is the outcome of an actual operating condition. It is the length that gives maximum input current flowing into the open-ended feeder at the desired exciting frequency for which the test has to be made. Therefore, it does not matter whether we express this length in feet, centimeters, or meters, because in each case it is the same length obtained experimentally.

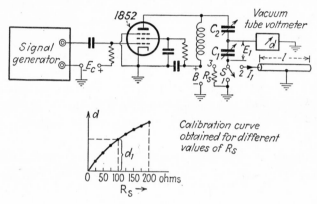

FIG. 104.—Useful circuit for testing feeder lines by the resistance-substitution method.

The experimental determination depends on measuring the effective input impedance Z, which is, for the quarter-wave-length excitations, a pure resistance. Figure 104 shows the arrangement where an 1852 tube, or its equivalent, is driven by an unmodulated voltage of the desired frequency. Inasmuch as a pure sinusoidal test current is essential, the inductance-to-capacitance ratio of the plate tank must be chosen low. The driving voltage E_1, which causes the feeder current I_1 at the input of the feeder to be tested, is taken off across the terminals of the variable condenser C_1, and the tuning of the tank to the desired frequency is accomplished by both condensers C_1 and C_2. Hence, when C_1 is set at its minimum value, the following comparison determination is made essentially in a series circuit. It is, therefore, very suitable for the determination of a low input resistance of the feeder. This would correspond to Z_1 determinations as given by the upper expression of Eq. (183). The lower expression for Z_1 calls for input resistances up to several hundred ohms and a larger value of C_1 is then desirable.

The procedure is a resistance substitution method and is also based on the method of equal deflection. Hence, the characteristic of the tube voltmeter can have any form as long as it gives a good spread with respect to ohms of the standard resistance and with respect to the corresponding deflections d. The determination is made as follows: The switch S is first closed on 1 and the respective settings of C_1 and C_2 are changed until the tube voltmeter indicates maximum response deflection for the applied grid voltage of the desired frequency. Such a maximum deflection indicates that the plate tank is tuned. Next, the switch is closed on 2 and the length l of the feeder is changed until it is excited in the quarter-wave-length resonance, which happens when maximum tube voltmeter response again occurs without resetting either of the two variable condensers. When we, therefore, connect S on 1 or on 2, in each case the tuning should not be changed. But the maximum response deflection d_1 with the switch S on 2 is less than the maximum response with the switch on 1. This is due to the fact that the input resistance $Z_1 = R_1$ of the quarter-wave-length feeder is now inserted in the plate tank. Next, the switch is closed on 3 and, at first, a pure resistance standard R_s of about 10 ohms is connected, which causes a certain deflection d on the tube voltmeter. If a small resetting of any of the tuning condensers is required to produce a still larger deflection, this would be a sign that the standard resistor has an additional capacitance effect. It is the maximum deflection that counts and is used in the calibration curve of Fig. 104. Normally, $\frac{1}{2}$-watt carbon resistors, short pieces of hard-drawing pencil leads, or short pieces of constantan wire will do for R_s. The direct-current measurement is used for the value of R_s. The calibration curve is then obtained by using several different standard resistors in succession. The curve then gives for the deflection d_0 obtained when the switch is on 2, the input resistance R_1 of the quarter-wave-length feeder.

It is now of interest to learn how a fixed dipole behaves for the entire FM band of instantaneous carrier frequencies from about 40 to 50 Mc. The output of an oscillator is connected as shown in Fig. 105 to two short rods a and a' which induce currents in the actual receiving dipole b and b' employing the actual length of the feeder used in the installation. The test should be made well above the ground and with vertical polarization, *i.e.*, with the dipoles vertical. The oscillator should have an output voltage E_0 which is essentially constant over the frequency range of 40 to 50 Mc, and with a good frequency spread. No modulation is required. The FM receiver is set to the lowest station frequency noted on the dial. A tube voltmeter is connected across the output terminals of the last i-f tube preceding the first limiter stage. The frequency of the oscillator is then varied until the tube voltmeter shows maximum response, and the deflection is noted.

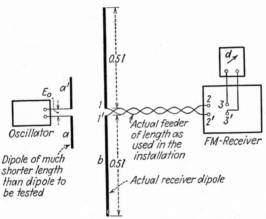

Fig. 105.—Testing the overall sensitivity from dipole to set.

Instead of a tube voltmeter, the vertical deflection plates of a cathode-ray tube can be used. The length of the linear trace is then a measure of the received voltage. Next, the tuning dial of the FM receiver is set to another station allocation. The setting does not have to be accurate. The received output voltage is then noted as before. With this procedure it is, therefore, possible to plot the output deflections against the carrier frequencies. We have then a picture of the *over-all* sensitivity with respect to all FM waves. The deflection curve can be flattened out by using a suitable resistor across the dipole terminals 1-1'. It can also be improved by finding a suitable length of the dipole rods, which is a good compromise for all FM stations. In addition it can be improved by using a resistor of about a 1,000 ohms across the input terminals of the FM receiver.

It should be understood that all methods and formulas given in this and in Sec. 63 apply also to any antenna elements if their corresponding line constants are used.

64. Linear Conductors Used as Radiators.—As far as the radiation pattern of conductors excited in the 0.5λ, λ, 1.5λ, etc., distributions are concerned, reference is made to Fig. 106. It is seen that only the 0.5λ distribution has a decided directivity since all other distributions have several radiation lobes. When a

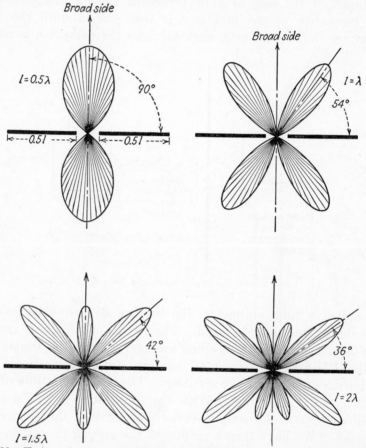

Fig. 106.—Horizontal radiation pattern of horizontal dipoles of total length *l* in terms of different wave-length distributions.

concentric line is mounted perpendicular to ground and so dimensioned that it has a characteristic impedance $Z_0 = 37$ ohms, it can be used for feeding without any reflections a quarter-wave-length radiator as shown in Fig. 107. This condition then causes the indicated distributions. As long as the diameter of the inside conductor extension is a small fraction of the radiator length *l*, the radiation resistance at the input point 1 is essentially independent of the diameter. Since the radiation resistance at any point of a radiator is the ratio of the power passing through that point of the radiator to the square of the current at the point, the radiation resistance must decrease for consecutive points from 1 toward 2. Since we have a quarter-wave-length distribution along the radiator 1-2, the ratio E_1/I_1 can be due only to a resistance drop; for all other ratios like E/I we have also additional reactive drops, besides the fact that the radiation resistance at such other points along the radiator has different values.

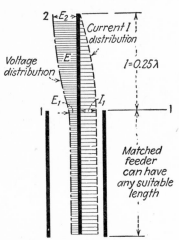

Fig. 107.—Concentric feeder using its axial conductor extension of length l as a quarter-wave-length antenna.

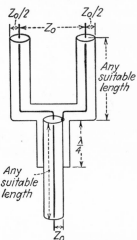

Fig. 108.—Matching two lines of half the surge impedance against a line of surge impedance Z_o.

If a vertical radiator that is a quarter-wave-length long stands perpendicularly over a conductive surface, the surge impedance Z_0 is larger for places on the radiator farther remote from the conductive reference surface. In Fig. 107 this reference surface is a conductive plane (not shown), which connects to the outside conductor of the concentric line that supplies the radiation power. Such an increase of the surge impedance Z_0 of the radiator can be avoided by changing the cross section of the radiator to appropriate larger values toward the open end of the radiator. It should be understood that it is not the cross section that brings about the equalization in all the Z_0 values along the radiator, but the outside surface of the radiator. Generally, it is the *surface* of the radiator.

Since feeder lines act like their surge impedance Z_0 when properly matched, a quarter-wave-length section of surge imped-

ance Z_0 can be used for matching two feeder characteristic impedances Z_0' and Z_0'' by choosing

$$Z_0 = \sqrt{Z_0'Z_0''} \qquad\qquad (198)$$

After all, lines act like their lumped equivalent values and we can,
therefore, connect lines in series or in multiple and apply ordinary
laws holding for lumped circuit constants.   When two feeders act
with their respective surge impedances Z_0' and Z_0'' in series, the
result is an impedance $Z_0' + Z_0''$; for a parallel connection of the
two feeders, we have the resultant impedance $Z_0'Z_0''/(Z_0' + Z_0'')$.
Figure 108 shows how this is done in actual designs.   Figure 109

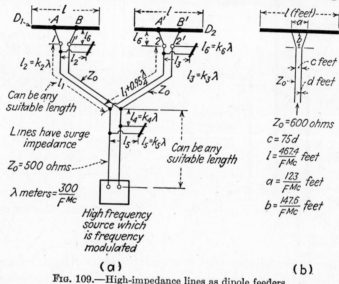

Fig. 109.—High-impedance lines as dipole feeders.

shows how relative phases as well as amplitudes of currents
exciting the dipoles D_1 and D_2 can be obtained from a *single*
common h-f source.   This case has a direct application when
dipoles, as in turnstiles, have to be fed in time phase quadrature.
With respect to Fig. 109a, the constant k_5 is 0.95×0.25, so that
quarter-wave-length excitation takes place on this stub.   The
length l_1 can be any suitable length, as far as the phases are concerned.   Nevertheless, the shortest feasible length should be
used in order to keep the feeder losses to a minimum value.   If
the other length is $l_1 + 0.95 \times 0.25\lambda$, then the dipole D_2 will be
excited with a current that is lagging 90 deg behind the current
that excites the dipole D_1.   The constant 0.95 holds very well in

the FM range of carrier frequencies for normal conductor dimensions. It assumes that the group velocity c'' of power transfer occurs 5 per cent slower than in empty space. Stubs of lengths l_2 and l_3 are used for bringing about the proper matching with the respective input impedances across terminals 1-1′ and 2-2′. The sketch in Fig. 109b shows how a half-wave radiator rod is excited with a parallel feed if a 600-ohm parallel line feeder is employed. The formulas given hold likewise for frequencies well in the FM range of carrier frequencies.

The Q value of a line is the ratio of its total effective reactance at the operating frequency to its total effective resistance. Hence, the smaller the Q value, the less the feeder will be affected by frequency deviations from the center frequency. In other words, the electromagnetic storage ability of the feeder should be comparatively small if the feeder is to be used over quite a wide band of carrier frequencies as in FM systems. On page 328 we have shown how the Q value of a feeder can be computed from actual experimental data. It is a hyperbolic sine function for quarter-wave-length feeders, and depends *only* on the attenuation α of the feeder. Hence, when impedance transformations are to be made between the terminating points on an aerial and the source of an FM transmitter, or the input terminals of an FM receiver in case of reception, several quarter-wave-length feeders should be cascaded rather than making the impedance transformation in one step with only one quarter-wave-length feeder. Such cascading causes a lower over-all Q value since the resultant reflection loss is actually smaller than the emphasized reflection loss for only one large step impedance transformation. The most ideal case would be an infinite number of quarter-wave impedance transformations.

This brings us then to an exponential surge impedance taper $Z_0 \epsilon^{-p}$ where $p = 360l/\lambda$ deg. This can be done with a Lecher wire system, which instead of using parallelism has a suitable spread along the length l of the feeder. Such an exponential wire system could lead only to a limited lower termination of about 150 ohms (see Fig. 97, curve for parallel wires), from a practical point of view. Also from a practical point of view it would be difficult to keep such a mathematical spread in an actual outdoor installation. An exponential surge impedance variation along a feeder could also be obtained by having a suitable expansion of the concentric outside cylinder of a concentric line. According to the corresponding curve of Fig. 97, very low terminations can then be matched efficiently.

It must be stressed again that we are chiefly interested in low-impedance terminations in present-day FM systems since more power can be extracted from an arriving electromagnetic field. With present-day FM antenna arrays it is likewise more or less a low-impedance termination that is required. The low-impedance feeder has, in reception, the added advantage that it will keep out more interference, just as in feeders used in the audible range of frequencies, "hum" is kept out more with 50-ohm lines than with 1,000-ohm lines.

An ideal impedance transformation could also be obtained by using two flat strips which are equally spaced but which change their areas along the length direction in order to cause an exponential decrease of Z_0. With such an arrangement, we have at first a rather rugged structure as well as a means for obtaining very large impedance transformations, which can be made to yield on one side very low Z_0 values. The exponential taper of the surge impedance could also be affected by keeping the area of both flat conductors for the go and the return the same but causing a suitable spread toward the length direction. The practical design would then be more difficult. Besides the wind pressure would be more severe, since larger areas are used as well as "wind pockets" provided.

65. Excitation of Dipoles.—Suppose we have two dipoles in one plane as shown in Fig. 110. The respective feeder gaps 1-1' and 2-2' of the dipoles A-A' and B-B' are taken just large enough to allow the supply of power that excites the respective dipoles and to prevent mutual contact. We can cause half-wave excitations I_1 and I_2, which have generally unequal amplitudes at terminals 1-1' and terminals 2-2' as well as unequal phases ψ_1 and ψ_2. The relative time phase is then generally $\psi = \psi_1 - \psi_2$. The electric fields $\mathcal{E}_1$ and $\mathcal{E}_2$ due to the respective dipoles are proportional to the dipole current distributions. If the two dipoles make any given space angle θ with each other, instead of 90 space degrees as indicated in Fig. 110, we have

$$\left.\begin{array}{l} \mathcal{E}_1 = kI_1 \sin{(\Omega t)} \sin{\psi_1} \\ \mathcal{E}_2 = kI_2 \sin{(\Omega t - \theta)} \sin{\psi_2} \end{array}\right\} \qquad (199)$$

where the exciting frequency $F = \Omega/6.28$ is the same and the respective dipoles are exactly alike.   Since

$$\sin \alpha \sin \beta = 0.5[\cos (\alpha - \beta) - \cos (\alpha + \beta)],$$

the resultant field becomes

$$\left.\begin{aligned}\mathcal{E} = \mathcal{E}_1 + \mathcal{E}_2 = 0.5kI_1[\cos (\Omega t - \psi_1) - \cos (\Omega t + \psi_1] \\ + 0.5kI_2[\cos (\Omega t - \theta - \psi_2) - \cos (\Omega t - \theta + \psi_1]\end{aligned}\right\} \tag{200}$$

When the amplitudes are made equal so that $I_1 = I_2 = I$ and

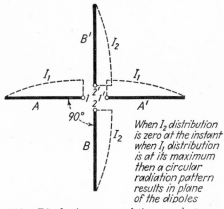

When I_2 distribution is zero at the instant when I_1 distribution is at its maximum then a circular radiation pattern results in plane of the dipoles

Fig. 110.—Dipoles in space and time quadrature.

the relative time phase ψ is 90 deg, as well as $\theta = 90$ space degrees as in Fig. 110, we have the component fields

$$\left.\begin{aligned}\mathcal{E}_1 = kI \sin \Omega t \sin \psi \\ \mathcal{E}_2 = kI \cos \Omega t \cos \psi\end{aligned}\right\} \tag{201}$$

which also, because $\cos \alpha \cos \beta = 0.5[\cos (\alpha + \beta) + \cos (\alpha - \beta)]$, yields the solution

$$\mathcal{E} = \mathcal{E}_1 + \mathcal{E}_2 = kI \cos (\Omega t - \psi) \tag{202}$$

This is the equation of a circle.   Figure 111 shows the horizontal radiation pattern when the two dipoles are in a horizontal plane. In Fig. 111a the amplitudes I_1 and I_2 are kept equal, but the relative time phase ψ is different for different horizontal radiation patterns.   In Fig. 111b, the relative time phase is ± 90 time degrees for all patterns indicated, but patterns for unequal current amplitudes are compared with the pattern for equal amplitudes.

66. Transmitter Antennas.—In order to cover a large service area, a horizontal circular radiation pattern is required. A vertical half-wave dipole will give such a pattern. In FM transmission it is also necessary to have such an FM power transfer from the last power stage toward the antenna array as to avoid as much as possible phase distortion and amplitude modulation.

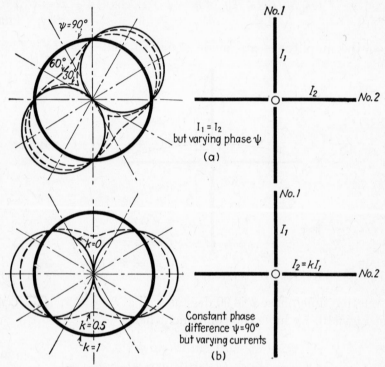

Fig. 111.—Radiation patterns in crossed dipole plane.

The former would cause equivalent parasitic frequency modulation. Such effects can be kept down if the antenna array has a sufficiently broad input impedance with respect to the maximum peak-to-peak frequency swing.

In order to obtain a large horizontal field gain, it is also necessary that the transmitter aerial array *concentrate* the high-angle radiation toward the horizontal service plane. Half-wave dipoles, as indicated in Figs. 112a and 113, satisfy such conditions. The vertical dipole array, also known as the Franklin antenna, has inherently a circular horizontal radiation pattern like all single half-wave radiators in planes perpendicular to the conductor axis.

By phasing the vertical half-wave radiators, distributions as indicated are obtained and high-angle radiation is also diverted toward the horizontal service plane. The height h of such a vertical cascading of dipoles is equal to the total number of half-wave radiators multiplied by the length l required for one fundamental half-wave resonance. The phasing as well as the mounting of such an antenna array is not exactly an easy engineering task

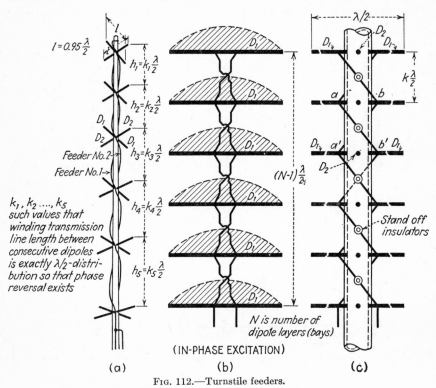

FIG. 112.—Turnstile feeders.

Inherently, horizontal half-wave radiators have the well-known figure-eight horizontal radiation pattern, which is, therefore, not the desired circular pattern. Even though several horizontal half-wave radiators, cascaded as in Fig. 112*b*, give pronounced horizontal energy concentration and easy equal phasing by means of transposed parallel-wire feeders, which terminate into a trapezoidal shunt feed of individual half-wave radiators, we still do not have a circular horizontal radiation pattern. But when, as in Fig. 112*a*, two sets of half-wave radiators are employed in each bay or radiator layer and the two half-wave radiators in the same horizontal layer or bay cross under 90 space degrees, we can obtain a circular pattern. To accomplish this, all D_1 dipoles are excited in time quadrature with respect to all D_2 dipoles. Figure 113 shows that this pattern is a maximum in the horizontal plane while the vertically polarized component vanishes in this plane.

From Fig. 112a we also note that there is no difficulty at all in feeding a turnstile antenna as originally suggested and developed

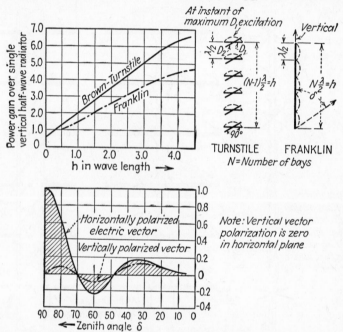

Fig. 113.—Comparison of horizontal dipole bays with vertical half-wave radiators.

by G. H. Brown. A common source, which is the output of the last power stage of an FM transmitter, then supplies the output power to a feeder system, as is described in connection with Fig. 109. The two lengths l_1 and $l_1 + 0.95\lambda/4$ bring about time quadrature, *i.e.*, a phase difference of 90 deg. The connections A-B and A'-B' of Fig. 109 then are the connection points on the lowest dipole D_1 and the lowest dipole D_2 of Fig. 112a. All other dipoles are then connected by the respective dipole interfeeders 1 and 2, where feeder 1 feeds all D_1 half-wave radiators and feeder 2 supplies power to all D_2 half-wave radiators.

Figure 112c shows how simply this can be done. The D_1 dipoles are then in the plane of the paper and the D_2 dipoles are perpendicular to this plane. The center pole is, for instance, a hollow steel flagpole. For a six-bay turnstile four brass rods are screwed into the flagpole for each of the six horizontal dipole layers. The total length of each brass rod is $0.95 \times 0.25\lambda$, where λ denotes the operating wave length in empty space. The feeder line for one set of dipoles, for instance, the D_1 dipoles, then makes the connections a-b' and a'-b, using a standoff insulator, as indicated in Fig. 112c. In a similar way the other D_2 dipoles are being fed by the current which is 90 time degrees out of phase. Bare copper hard-drawn No. 8 wire can be used for the feeder wires. It should be noted that the bays are separated by a vertical distance that must be somewhat less than 0.5λ, otherwise equal phase for each set of dipoles would not exist because the feeders wind around the central pole and the feeder interdistance should not be differing in length from $0.95 \times 0.5\lambda$, in order exactly to reverse the polarity of the exciting current flowing to the following half-wave radiator. If the lines shown in Fig. 109 have a surge impedance $Z_0 = 500$ ohms, we have about the following dimensions: $k_2 = k_3 = 0.085$; $k_6 = 0.355$; l_1 can be any suitable length but should be short in order to reduce unnecessary feeder attenuation; $k_5 = 0.15$, and $k_4 = 0.4$. The No. 8 feeder wires connect to the respective half-wave radiators at places along the dipole that are a distance 0.05λ from the surface of the central supporting pole.

TABLE V

Number of bays	Field (ε) gain	Power (P) gain
1	0.707	0.5
2	1.12	1.24
3	1.414	1.995
4	1.64	2.69
5	1.87	3.5
6	2.07	4.28
7	2.24	5.02
8	2.38	5.67
9	2.5	6.25
10	2.6	6.76

Moreover, Fig. 113a shows that the height h of a turnstile antenna is smaller than the height for a Franklin antenna since we have only $0.5(N - 1)\lambda$ for the height in case of N bays. Table V and Fig. 113 show the gains of turnstile arrays, as well as that of a Franklin antenna, over the value that would be obtained in case of a single half-wave radiator.   Hence, for a six-bay turnstile, a 2.5-kw transmitter would act as though a $2.5 \times 4.28 = 10.7$ kw supply were used in comparison to a single dipole transmitter antenna.

The turnstile of the General Electric Company contains only three bays spaced vertically about 270 electrical degrees apart instead of 180 deg.   The radiation elements are also shunt-excited from a concentric line by a conductor connected through a series capacitor a short distance from the pole.   Also here the correct phase relation and current distribution between the various antenna elements is obtained by an appropriate phasing section of the feeder located below the radiating system of the half-wave radiator array.   An impedance-matching section is used to provide the correct termination for a 150-ohm balanced feeder. The theoretical field intensity ε caused by such an array in the horizontal plane has then an average value of 3.7 db above the radiation from a single half-wave radiator in the direction of maximum radiation.   This is 7.3 db above a single-section turnstile.   The theoretical gain of the General Electric turnstile is about 0.4 db above the four-section turnstile with 180 electrical degrees vertical separation between consecutive bays.   In this system we have also a balanced 150-ohm feeder branching into two single conductor transmission lines of 75 ohms each.

That turnstiles are rugged self-supporting structures can be seen from the fact that in some installations the overturning moment at the base of the tower is in the neighborhood of 48,600 ft-lb.   It is also noteworthy that the lighting connection to the top of the turnstile is completely shielded since the wiring is mounted within the supporting center pole.   It is also possible to mount the turnstile on top of an ordinary broadcast tower as long as this tower can withstand the overturning moment due to abnormal wind pressure and due to the increased height.

67. Quarter-wave-length Feeder Sections.—We have learned on pages 311, 335 that such sections are being used for matching unequal impedances Z_1 and Z_2 by means of the surge impedance $Z_0 = \sqrt{Z_1 Z_2}$ of the matching section.   The "teeter-totter" action given by this square-root relation can exist only when the feeder is exactly 90 electrical degrees long.   If the group velocity c'' of wave propagation along the feeders is the same as the velocity c of light, the physical length l of the matching section would be equal to one-quarter of the operating wave length λ. We have then generally the formula

$$l = \frac{\lambda}{4} = 246 \frac{k}{F} \tag{203}$$

where the length l of an impedance-matching feeder is in feet, the operating frequency F in megacycles per second, and k denotes a factor that expresses the ratio c''/c, *i.e.*, the fraction of the group velocity to the velocity of light. From the discussion given at several places in this text, it is evident that the value of k is closest to unity value when the feeder section is as "open a transmission line" as possible. For this reason customary Lecher wires show a k value in the neighborhood of about 0.96 to 0.98. A concentric line with air as a dielectric shows values of k from 0.87–0.95, where the upper limit holds generally for good lines of this type. Concentric cables with rubber insulation slow down the energy propagation considerably on account of the large dielectric loss and $k = 0.5 - 0.6$. About the same k values hold also for twisted leadins. The accurate values of k can be easily found by experiment.

APPENDIX

This supplementary part gives solutions and tables that were actually used in the discussion of the preceding chapters. The tables are written in such a form that the spectrum distribution of the modulation energy can be directly noted by mere inspection. The arguments are given in terms of radians since this gives actually the numerical value of the ratio $\Delta F/f$ in case of true FM and the value of $\Delta\theta$ in case of true PM. In case of indirect FM, the arguments stand for $k\,\Delta\theta/f$ where k takes care of the modulation efficiency. The tables with the argument β can also be used for finding the decay factors $\epsilon^{-\beta}$ that may be needed in the evaluation of the speed of electrical actions if several circuits transfer desired as well as undesired information. There are also tables on the Si, Ci, and the corresponding integral epsilon functions. They apply to cases where the self- as well as the mutual impedance of radiators and feeders is concerned. Since, by means of such tables in connection with formulas given in the text, it is possible to compute the reactive or the resistive component of a conductor, we can, with the numerical result, also find the Q value of a conductor. At this point it should be again realized that in many systems a high Q value is not at all what is desirable. For instance, when a quarter-wave-length section of a line, as a concentric tank, is used for an interstage coupling in short-wave work, a high impedance is desired; for a concentric tank used as the frequency-determining branch, it is a high Q value that is of interest. It should also be realized that neither a Lecher wire feeder nor a concentric line feeder, even when acting aperiodic, can be considered as being absolutely free from radiation effect, even though the radiation resistance of a concentric line is relatively smallest. Generally, the radiation resistance of a feeder depends on the exciter frequency, on the length of the line in terms of wave length, as well as on the termination. Even though there is the general understanding that a shielded feeder like a concentric line, when terminated into its surge impedance Z_0, does not radiate, it should be noted that it *has* a radiation resistance just the same. As a matter of fact the radiation resistance is equal to the sum of the radiation resistance of the open-ended feeder of the same length as the aperiodic feeder and the radiation resistance with the far end short-circuited. Even though the magnitude of the radiation resistance is small, it can greatly affect the Q value in the upper megacycle range as, for instance, used in FM relay work.

68. Theory of the Spectrum Solution.—There are two places in the literature which date back to the years 1887 and 1862 that have to do with the definition of "instantaneous frequency," which applies to present-day FM even though applied in those years to acoustical problems. Lord Rayleigh in 1887 treated the case where the tension of a string is periodically varied. This is the mechanical case corresponding to the capacitance variation in an oscillatory system. Helmholtz in 1862 solved the difficulty by defining the instantaneous frequency in an acoustic system as

$$\Omega_t = \frac{dF_t}{dt}$$

It is the corresponding integral solution that we employ today in order to include also the integration constant. It is attributable to J. R. Carson who published in 1922, for the first time, a solution for the spectrum distribution when a high-frequency current is modulated in frequency due to a sinusoidal variation in the circuit capacitance.

In 1930, B. van der Pol followed up the contribution of Carson and gave the concept of the modulation index. He also treated the case when a variation of the circuit capacitance is instrumental in causing FM and solved the obtained differential equation by a method leading to the result found by Carson. He gave also a solution for the case of code modulation, *i.e.*, when the value of the circuit capacitance C_t jumps periodically and discontinuously from a value of $C - \Delta C$ to a value of $C + \Delta C$, and vice versa. W. L. Barrow in 1933 discussed the case of direct capacitance modulation, direct frequency variation, and inverse capacitance modulation. The list of references should be consulted for any other details, since the following discussion applies only to the case, as frequency modulation is used to-day, for which the signal frequency f is small compared to the carrier deviation frequency ΔF; the maximum frequency deviation ΔF is also small compared with the center frequency F. The derivaton for the energy distribution in the frequency spectrum is then as follows.

Suppose that we have the case of a reactance modulation where the tank capacitance value is C in absence of modulation, and is affected by an injected parallel capacitance variation of maximum swing ΔC when modulation is present. We have, therefore, to deal with an instantaneous circuit capacitance C_t and a fixed circuit inductance L. Hence, we have no longer an oscillation *constant CL* but an oscillation *factor $C_t L$*, which varies during the modulation cycle of $1/f$ sec. The well-known differential equation then reads

$$L \frac{di}{dt} + e = 0$$

if L denotes the tank inductance, i the instantaneous tank current with an instantaneous condenser voltage e. The effect of the circuit resistance R is ignored since we think in terms of a tube oscillator where the negative resistance action neutralizes the R effect. Besides, the small change of the term $R/(2L)$ is fixed and has nothing to do with the frequency changes due to the modulating current. Since the corresponding charge is $dq = i\,dt$ and $e = q/C_t$, we obtain

$$\frac{d^2q}{dt^2} + \frac{q}{C_t L} = 0 \tag{204}$$

Since

$$\Omega_t = 6.28 F_t = \frac{1}{\sqrt{C_t L}} \tag{205}$$

we can also write

$$\frac{d^2q}{dt^2} + q\Omega_t^2 = 0 \tag{206}$$

Hence Eq. (205) holds for FM while $\Omega = 6.28\,F = 1/\sqrt{CL}$ holds in absence of modulation.

It does not seem possible to solve Eq. (204) generally, as far as practical results are concerned. A solution is, however, feasible when we define C_t or Ω_t. The definition for C_t relates to the case of capacitance variation and the definition of $\Omega_t = 6.28\,F_t$ is the most direct case of frequency modulation. Such definitions actually express what happens in case of present-day direct FM. Suppose a reactance tube injects the variation $C_i = \Delta C \cos \omega t$, then

$$C_t = C + \Delta C \cos \omega t \tag{207}$$

is the required definition. Assuming that $\Delta C < C$, which is always the case in direct FM, we find, by binominal expansion of the instantaneous circuit capacitance C_t, for the reciprocal of the oscillation factor

$$\frac{1}{C_t L} = \Omega^2 - \Omega^4(L\,\Delta C)\cos\omega t + \Omega^6(L\,\Delta C)^2\cos^2\omega t - \cdots + \tag{208}$$

Equation (204) then becomes

$$\frac{d^2q}{dt^2} + q(A_0 + A_1\cos\omega t + A_2\cos 2\omega t + \cdots) = 0 \tag{209}$$

In this expressions A_0, A_1, A_2, etc., are constants obtained after completing the operations contained in Eq. (208) and grouping the terms according to increasing signal frequency angular velocities ωt, $2\omega t$, etc. Assuming $\Delta C \ll C$, Eq. (208) simplifies and the terms with $(\Delta C)^2$ and still higher powers of ΔC may be neglected. We have, therefore,

$$\frac{1}{C_t L} \cong \Omega^2[1 - \Omega^2(L\,\Delta C)\cos\omega t] = \Omega^2\left(1 - \frac{\Delta C}{C}\cos\omega t\right)$$

$$\cong \Omega^2\left(1 + 2\frac{\Delta\Omega}{\Omega}\cos\omega t\right)$$

$$\frac{1}{C_t L} = \Omega^2\left(1 + \frac{2\,\Delta F}{F}\cos\omega t\right) \tag{210}$$

Here ΔF denotes the absolute frequency change, which is the difference between the assigned carrier or center frequency F and $F\sqrt{1 - \Delta C/C}$. The limitation of $\Delta C \ll C$ brings us then to the differential equation

$$\frac{d^2q}{dt^2} + q(\Omega^2 + 2\Omega\,\Delta\Omega\cos\omega t) = 0 \tag{211}$$

This simplified expression of Eq. (209) is the basic relation used by Carson as well as by van der Pol in obtaining the spectrum solution. The limitation of differential equation (211) is, therefore, that the maximum frequency deviation ΔF must be very small compared with the value of the center frequency F. Hence, the spectrum solution (12) is based on such an assumption. This should not be overlooked if, some day, we expect to apply ΔF swings which are not very small with respect to the center frequency F.

If we use the differential equation in the form as expressed by Eq. (206), we have a means for finding out what condition prevails when the frequency $F_t = \Omega_t/6.28$ is directly varied instead of the capacitance of the tank. This is actually the case of true frequency modulation as would happen in an alternator whose speed experiences oscillations, *i.e.*, vibrates about its mean speed. We have then $F_t = F + \Delta F\cos\omega t$ and, when multiplied on each side by 6.28, the case for the corresponding angular velocity at any instant of time. Equation (206) then yields the differential equation

$$\frac{d^2q}{dt^2} + q(\Omega^2 + 0.5\,\Delta\Omega^2 + 2\Omega\,\Delta\Omega\cos\omega t + 0.5\,\Delta\Omega^2\cos 2\omega t) = 0 \tag{212}$$

This expression has *no* limitation and holds for all values of ΔF and F. But when $\Delta F \ll F$, we obtain also here the expression given in Eq. (211). With this limitation we are, therefore, confronted with the solution of the differential equation

$$\frac{d^2q}{dt^2} + \Omega^2\left(1 + 2\frac{\Delta F}{F}\cos\omega t\right)q = 0 \tag{213}$$

This expression, which defines a Mathieu function, is well known in theoretical physics. Hence, if we make the substitution

$$q = \epsilon^{\int x\,dt}$$

we find

$$\frac{dx}{dt} + x^2 + \Omega^2 \left(1 + 2\frac{\Delta F}{F} \cos \omega t\right) = 0 \tag{214}$$

This brings us to a first-order equation of the Riccati type. If we also make the *additional assumption* that $\Delta F/f$ is small, as is the case in present-day FM, besides the assumption that $f \ll F$, we have the approximate solution

$$x_{1,2} = \pm j\Omega \sqrt{1 + 2\frac{\Delta F}{F} \cos \omega t} \cong \pm j(\Omega + \Delta\Omega \cos \omega t) \tag{215}$$

The solution of (213) with such assumptions as are justified is then

$$q = \epsilon^{\int x_1 dt} + \epsilon^{\int x_2 dt} = k \cos \left[\int(\Omega + \Delta\Omega \cos \omega t)dt\right]$$
$$= k \cos \left(\Omega t + \frac{\Delta\Omega}{\omega} \sin \omega t\right) = k \cos \left(\Omega t + \frac{\Delta F}{f} \sin \omega t\right) \tag{216}$$

We note, therefore, that for $f \ll F$ and $\Delta F \ll F$, the cosinoidal modulation function in the C_t variation causes a corresponding sinusoidal frequency variation. This can be explained by the Helmholtz definition for the instantaneous value of Ω_t which yields

$$\Omega_t = \frac{dF_t}{dt} = \frac{d}{dt}\left(\Omega t + \frac{\Delta\Omega}{\omega} \sin \omega t\right) = \Omega + \Delta\Omega \cos \omega t$$

The square of this result yields the approximation

$$\Omega^2 \left(1 + 2\frac{\Delta F}{F} \cos \omega t\right)$$

which checks the second term of Eq. (213).

In the solution of Eq. (216) the arbitrary phase constant has been ignored since it would not contribute anything to the discussion presented here. Putting the amplitude value k of Eq. (216) equal to unity, we can expand this equation and find for $\beta = \Delta F/f$

$$q = \cos (\Omega t + \beta \sin \omega t) = \cos \Omega t \cos (\beta \sin \omega t) - \sin \Omega t \sin (\beta \sin \omega t)$$
$$= \cos y \cos z \qquad\qquad - \sin y \sin z \tag{217}$$

where $z = \beta \sin \omega t$ and $y = \Omega t$. For $\omega t = p$, according to Fourier

$$\cos (\beta \sin p) = J_0(\beta) + 2J_2(\beta) \cos (2p) + 2J_4(\beta) \cos (4p) + 2J_6(\beta) \cos (6p) + \cdots$$
$$\sin (\beta \sin p) = 2J_1(\beta) + 2J_3(\beta) \sin (3p) + 2J_5(\beta) \sin (5p) + 2J_7(\beta) \sin (7p) + \cdots \tag{218}$$

But

$$\cos y \cos z - \sin y \sin z = \cos (y + z) \tag{219}$$

Hence, Eq. (217) yields

$$q = \cos (\Omega t + \beta \sin \omega t)$$
$$= J_0(\beta) \cos \Omega t - J_1(\beta)[\cos (\Omega - \omega)t - \cos (\Omega + \omega)t]$$
$$+ J_2(\beta)[\cos (\Omega - 2\omega)t + \cos (\Omega + 2\omega)t]$$
$$- J_3(\beta)[\cos (\Omega - 3\omega)t - \cos (\Omega + 3\omega)t]$$
$$+ J_4(\beta)[\cos (\Omega - 4\omega)t + \cos (\Omega + 4\omega)t]$$
$$- \quad \cdots \cdots \cdots \cdots \cdots \cdots \tag{220}$$

which is exactly the spectrum solution used in Eq. (12) except that Eq. (12) is expressed in sinus terms, which should not matter as far as the frequencies are concerned. We have, therefore, the Bessel coefficients $J_0(\beta)$, $J_1(\beta)$, $J_2(\beta)$, $J_3(\beta)$, $J_4(\beta)$, etc., of the first type, where for the above derivation the modulation index β stands for $\Delta F/f$ and we have the respective spectrum frequencies F for the center frequency; $F \pm f$ for the first side-current pair; $F \pm 2f$ for the second side-current pair; and $F \pm nf$ for the nth side-current pair.

Table VI gives an extension of the Bessel tables given in the text up to a modulation index $\beta = 24$.

The Bessel function of the first kind $J_n(\beta)$ is, when $n = 0$ or a positive integer, given by the convergent series

$$J_n(\beta) = \frac{\beta^n}{2^n(n!)} \left[1 - \frac{\beta^2}{2(2n+2)} + \frac{\beta^4}{2 \cdot 4(2n+2)(2n+4)} - \frac{\beta^6}{2 \cdot 4 \cdot 6(2n+2)(2n+4)(2n+6)} + \cdots \right] \quad (221)$$

since it satisfies the Bessel[1] differential equation

$$\frac{d^2J_n(\beta)}{d\beta^2} + \frac{1}{\beta}\frac{dJ_n(\beta)}{d\beta} + \left(1 - \frac{n^2}{\beta^2}\right)J_n(\beta) = 0$$

The series for $J_n(\beta)$ becomes essentially useless in case of numerical computations when the modulation factor β is even moderately large. For this reason this function is expressed in another series form which is well adapted for numerical computations for large β values,

$$J_n(\beta) = \sqrt{\frac{2}{\pi\beta}} \left[a_n \cos\left(\beta - \frac{2n+1}{4}\pi\right) - b_n \sin\left(\beta - \frac{2n+1}{4}\pi\right) \right] \quad (222)$$

for

$$\left.\begin{array}{l} a_n = 1 - \dfrac{(4n^2 - 1)(4n^2 - 9)}{2!(8\beta)^2} + \dfrac{(4n^2 - 1)(4n^2 - 9)(4n^2 - 25)(4n^2 - 49)}{4!(8\beta)^4} - \cdots \\[2mm] b_n = \dfrac{4n^2 - 1}{8\beta} - \dfrac{(4n^2 - 1)(4n^2 - 9)(4n^2 - 25)}{3!(8\beta)^3} + \cdots \end{array}\right\} \quad (223)$$

For very large values of β, the functions approximate the values given by

$$J_n(\beta) = \sqrt{\frac{2}{\pi\beta}} \cos\left(\beta - \frac{2n+1}{4}\pi\right) \quad (224)$$

[1] Generally Bessel functions of the first kind $J_n(\beta)$ and $I_n(\beta)$ are given by the expression of $J_n(\beta)$ as given in Eq. (221) and

$$I_n(\beta) = \frac{\beta^n}{2^n(n!)} \left[1 + \frac{\beta^2}{2(2n+2)} + \frac{\beta^4}{2 \cdot 4(2n+2)(2n+4)} + \frac{\beta^6}{2 \cdot 4 \cdot 6(2n+2)(2n+4)(2n+6)} + \cdots \right].$$

This function then satisfies

$$\frac{d^2I_n(\beta)}{d\beta^2} + \frac{1}{\beta}\frac{dI_n(\beta)}{d\beta} - \left(1 + \frac{n^2}{\beta^2}\right)I_n(\beta) = 0$$

The following interrelation then holds

$$I_n(\beta) = j^{-n}J_n(\beta)$$
$$I_{-n}(\beta) = j^nJ_{-n}(\beta)$$

TABLE VI.—INCREASE IN THE NUMBER OF SIGNIFICANT SIDE-CURRENT PAIRS WITH THE VALUE OF THE MODULATION INDEX $\beta = \dfrac{\Delta F}{f} = \Delta\theta$

$$I_t = I_m \{J_0(\beta)\sin\Omega t + J_1(\beta)[\sin(\Omega+\omega)t - \sin(\Omega-\omega)t] + J_2(\beta)[\sin(\Omega+2\omega)t + \sin(\Omega-2\omega)t]$$
$$+ J_3(\beta)[\sin(\Omega+3\omega)t - \sin(\Omega-3\omega)t] + J_4(\beta)[\sin(\Omega+4\omega)t + \sin(\Omega-4\omega)t] \cdots$$
$$+ J_n(\beta)[\sin(\Omega+n\omega)t + (-1)^n\sin(\Omega-n\omega)t]\}$$

Spectrum equation (12) of the text for the resultant instantaneous current value I_t

Modulation index $\beta = \Delta F/f$ or $\beta = \Delta\theta$

Order n of spectrum current	$\beta=1$ $J_n(1)$	$\beta=2$ $J_n(2)$	$\beta=3$ $J_n(3)$	$\beta=4$ $J_n(4)$	$\beta=5$ $J_n(5)$	$\beta=6$ $J_n(6)$	$\beta=7$ $J_n(7)$	$\beta=8$ $J_n(8)$	$\beta=9$ $J_n(9)$	$\beta=10$ $J_n(10)$	$\beta=11$ $J_n(11)$	$\beta=12$ $J_n(12)$
0 (center freq.)	0.7652	0.2239	-0.2601	-0.3071	-0.1776	0.1506	0.3001	0.1717	-0.09033	-0.2459	-0.1712	0.04769
1 (for F ± f)	0.4401	0.5767	0.3391	-0.06604	-0.3276	-0.2767	-0.004683	0.2346	0.2453	0.04347	-0.1768	-0.2234
2 (for F ± 2f)	0.1149	0.3528	0.4861	0.3641	0.04657	-0.2429	-0.3014	-0.1130	0.1448	0.2546	0.1390	-0.08493
3 (for F ± 3f)	0.01956	0.1289	0.3091	0.4302	0.3648	0.1148	-0.1676	-0.2911	-0.1809	0.05838	0.2273	0.1951
4 (for F ± 4f)	0.00248	0.034	0.1320	0.2811	0.3912	0.3576	+0.1578	-0.1054	-0.2655	-0.2196	-0.01504	0.1825
5		0.00704	0.04303	0.1321	0.2611	0.3621	0.3479	0.1858	-0.05504	-0.2341	-0.2383	-0.07347
6		0.001202	0.01139	0.04909	0.131	0.2458	0.3392	0.3376	0.2043	-0.01446	-0.2016	-0.2437
7			0.00285	0.01518	0.05338	0.1296	0.2336	0.3206	0.3275	0.2167	0.01838	-0.1703
8				0.004029	0.01841	0.05653	0.1280	0.2235	0.3051	0.3179	0.2250	0.04510
9					0.00552	0.02117	0.05892	0.1263	0.2149	0.2919	0.3089	0.2304
10					0.001468	0.006964	0.02354	0.06077	0.1247	0.2075	0.2804	0.3005
11						0.002048	0.008335	0.02560	0.06222	0.1231	0.2010	0.2704
12							0.002656	0.009624	0.02739	0.06337	0.1216	0.1953
13							0.0007702	0.003275	0.01083	0.02897	0.06429	0.1201
14								0.001019	0.003895	0.01196	0.03037	0.06504
15								0.0002926	0.001286	0.004508	0.01301	0.03161
16									0.0003933	0.001567	0.005110	0.01399
17										0.0005056	0.001856	0.005698
18											0.000628	0.002152
19												0.000759
20												
22												
24												
25												
26												
27												
28												
29												
30												
31												
32												
33												
34 (for F ± 34f)												

TABLE VI.—INCREASE IN THE NUMBER OF SIGNIFICANT SIDE-CURRENT PAIRS WITH THE VALUE OF THE MODULATION INDEX $\beta = \begin{cases} \dfrac{\Delta F}{f} \\ \Delta\theta \end{cases}$

(Continued)

Modulation index $\beta = \Delta F/f$ or $\beta = \Delta\theta$

Order n of spectrum current	$\beta=13$ $J_n(13)$	$\beta=14$ $J_n(14)$	$\beta=15$ $J_n(15)$	$\beta=16$ $J_n(16)$	$\beta=17$ $J_n(17)$	$\beta=18$ $J_n(18)$	$\beta=19$ $J_n(19)$	$\beta=20$ $J_n(20)$	$\beta=21$ $J_n(21)$	$\beta=22$ $J_n(22)$	$\beta=23$ $J_n(23)$	$\beta=24$ $J_n(24)$
0 (center freq.)	0.2069	0.1711	-0.01422	-0.1749	-0.1699	-0.01336	0.1466	0.1670	0.03658	-0.1207	-0.1624	-0.05623
1 (for F ± f)	-0.07032	0.1334	0.2051	0.09040	-0.09767	-0.1880	-0.1057	0.06683	0.1711	0.1172	0.03952	-0.1540
2 (for F ± 2f)	-0.2177	-0.1520	0.04157	0.1862	0.1584	-0.007533	-0.1578	-0.1603	-0.02028	0.1313	0.1590	0.04339
3 (for F ± 3f)	0.00332	-0.01768	-0.1192	-0.04385	0.1349	0.1863	0.07249	-0.09890	-0.1750	-0.09330	0.06717	0.1613
4 (for F ± 4f)	0.2193	0.07624	0.1305	-0.2026	-0.1107	0.06964	0.1806	0.1307	-0.02971	-0.1568	-0.1164	0.003076
5	0.1316	0.2204	0.2061	-0.05747	-0.1870	-0.1554	0.003572	0.1512	0.1637	0.03630	-0.09086	-0.1623
6	-0.1180	0.08117	0.03446	0.1667	0.0007153	-0.1560	-0.1788	-0.05509	0.1076	0.1733	0.1638	-0.06455
7	-0.2406	-0.1508	-0.1740	0.1825	0.1875	0.05140	-0.1165	-0.1842	-0.1022	0.05820	0.008829	0.1300
8	-0.1410	-0.2320	-0.2200	-0.007021	0.1537	0.1959	0.09294	-0.07387	-0.1757	-0.1362	-0.1576	0.1404
9	0.06698	-0.1143	-0.09007	-0.1895	-0.04286	0.1228	0.1947	0.1251	-0.03175	-0.1573	-0.1322	-0.03643
10	0.2338	0.08501	0.09995	-0.2062	-0.1991	-0.07317	0.09155	0.1865	0.1485	0.007547	0.04268	-0.1677
11	0.2927	0.2357	0.2367	-0.06822	-0.1914	-0.2041	-0.09837	0.06136	0.1732	0.1641	0.1730	-0.1033
12	0.2615	0.2855	0.2787	0.1124	-0.04857	-0.1762	-0.2055	-0.1190	0.03293	0.1566	0.1379	0.07299
13	0.1901	0.2536	0.2464	0.2368	0.1228	-0.03092	-0.1612	-0.2041	-0.1356	0.006688	-0.01718	0.1763
14	0.1188	0.1855	0.1813	0.2724	0.2364	0.1316	-0.01507	-0.1464	-0.2008	-0.1487	-0.1588	0.1180
15	0.05564	0.1174	0.1162	0.2399	0.2666	0.2356	0.1389	-0.008121	-0.1321	-0.1959	-0.1899	-0.03863
16	0.03272	0.06613	0.06653	0.1775	0.2340	0.2611	0.2345	0.1452	0.01202	-0.1185	-0.1055	-0.1663
17	0.01491	0.03372	0.03463	0.1150	0.1739	0.2286	0.2559	0.2331	0.1505	0.02358	0.03402	-0.1831
18	0.006269	0.01577	0.01657	0.06685	0.1138	0.1706	0.2235	0.2511	0.2316	0.1549	0.1587	-0.09311
19	0.002452	0.006824	0.007360	0.03544	0.06710	0.1127	0.1676	0.2189	0.2465	0.2299	0.2282	0.04345
20	0.0008971	0.002753	0.003054	0.01733	0.03619	0.06731	0.1116	0.1647	0.2145	0.2422	0.2381	0.1619
21	0.0003087	0.001041	0.001190	0.007879	0.01804	0.03636	0.06746	0.1106	0.1621	0.2105	0.2067	0.2264
22		0.0003711	0.0004379	0.003354	0.008380	0.01871	0.03748	0.06758	0.1097	0.1596	0.1573	0.2343
23		0.0001251	0.0001527	0.001343	0.003651	0.008864	0.01934	0.03805	0.06767	0.1087	0.1078	0.2031
24				0.0005087	0.001500	0.003946	0.009331	0.01993	0.03857	0.06773	0.06777	0.1550
25				0.0001828	0.0005831	0.001658	0.004237	0.00978	0.02049	0.03905	0.03949	0.1070
26					0.0002154	0.0006607	0.001819	0.004524	0.01022	0.02102	0.02152	0.06778
27						0.0002504	0.0007412	0.001981	0.00481	0.01064	0.01104	0.03990
28							0.0002877	0.0008242	0.002143	0.005084	0.005357	0.02200
29								0.0003827	0.0009094	0.002307	0.00247	0.01143
30								0.000124	0.0003682	0.0009965	0.001085	0.005626
31									0.0001427	0.0004113	0.0004561	0.002633
32										0.0001626	0.0001837	0.001176
33												0.0005024
34 (for ± = 34f)												0.0002060

TABLE VII

x	$Si(x)$	$Ci(x)$	$Ei(x)$	$Ei(-x)$	x	$Si(x)$	$Ci(x)$	$Ei(x)$	$Ei(-x)$
0.00	0	$-\infty$	$-\infty$	$-\infty$	1.7	1.4496	0.4670	3.9210	-0.07465
0.01	0.00999	-4.02798	-4.0179	-4.0379	1.8	1.5058	0.4568	4.2499	-0.06471
0.02	0.019999	-3.3349	-3.3147	-3.3547	1.9	1.5578	0.4419	4.5937	-0.05620
0.03	0.02999	-2.9296	-2.8991	-2.9591	2.0	1.6054	0.4230	4.9542	-0.04890
0.04	0.03999	-2.6421	-2.6013	-2.6813	2.1	1.6487	0.4005	5.3332	-0.04261
0.05	0.04999	-2.4191	-2.3679	-2.4679	2.2	1.6876	0.3751	5.7326	-0.03719
0.06	0.05999	-2.2371	-2.1753	-2.2953	2.3	1.7222	0.3472	6.1544	-0.0325
0.07	0.06998	-2.0833	-2.0108	-2.1508	2.4	1.7525	0.3173	6.6007	-0.02844
0.08	0.07997	-1.9501	-1.8669	-2.0269	2.5	1.7785	0.2859	7.0738	-0.02491
0.09	0.08996	-1.8327	-1.7387	-1.9187	2.6	1.8004	0.2533	7.5761	-0.02185
0.1	0.0994	-1.7279	-1.6228	-1.8229	2.7	1.8182	0.2201	8.1103	-0.01918
0.15	0.1498	-1.3255	-1.1641	-1.4645	2.8	1.8321	0.1865	8.6793	-0.01686
0.2	0.2000	-1.0422	-0.8218	-1.2227	2.9	1.8422	0.1529	9.2860	-0.01482
0.25	0.2491	-0.8247	-0.5425	-1.0443	3.0	1.8487	0.1196	9.9338	-0.01304
0.3	0.2985	-0.6492	-0.3027	-0.9057	3.1	1.8517	0.08699	10.6263	-0.0149
0.35	0.3476	-0.5031	-0.08943	-0.7942	3.2	1.8514	0.05526	11.3673	-0.01013
0.4	0.3965	-0.3788	0.1048	-0.7024	3.3	1.8481	0.02468	12.161	-0.00894
0.45	0.4450	-0.2715	0.2849	-0.6253	3.4	1.8419	0.00452	13.0121	-0.00789
0.5	0.4931	-0.1778	0.4542	-0.5598	3.5	1.8331	0.03213	13.9254	-0.00697
0.55	0.5408	-0.0953	0.6153	-0.5034	3.6	1.8219	-0.05797	14.9063	-0.00616
0.6	0.5881	-0.02227	0.7699	-0.4544	3.7	1.8086	-0.0819	15.9606	-0.00545
0.65	0.6349	0.04265	0.9194	-0.4115	3.8	1.7934	-0.1038	17.0948	-0.00482
0.7	0.6812	0.1005	1.0649	-0.3738	3.9	1.7765	-0.1235	18.3157	-0.004267
0.75	0.7270	0.1522	1.2073	-0.3403	4.0	1.7582	-0.1410	19.6309	-0.003779
0.8	0.7721	0.1983	1.3474	-0.3106	4.1	1.7387	-0.1562	21.0485	-0.00335
0.85	0.8166	0.2394	1.4857	-0.2840	4.2	1.7184	-0.1690	22.5774	-0.002969
0.9	0.8605	0.2761	1.6228	-0.2601	4.3	1.6973	-0.1795	24.2274	-0.002633
0.95	0.9036	0.3086	1.7591	-0.2387	4.4	1.6758	-0.1877	26.009	-0.00234
1.0	0.9461	0.3374	1.8951	-0.2194	4.5	1.6541	-0.1935	27.9337	-0.002073
1.1	1.0287	0.3849	2.1674	-0.1864	4.6	1.6325	-0.1970	30.0141	-0.001841
1.2	1.1080	0.4205	2.4421	-0.1584	4.7	1.611	-0.1984	32.2639	-0.001635
1.3	1.1840	0.4457	2.7214	-0.1355	4.8	1.59	-0.1976	34.6979	-0.001453
1.4	1.2562	0.4620	3.0072	-0.1162	4.9	1.5696	-0.1948	37.3325	-0.001291
1.5	1.3247	0.4704	3.3013	-0.1000	5.0	1.5499	-0.19	40.1853	-0.001148
1.6	1.3892	0.4717	3.6053	-0.08631					

Moreover, we also have

$$\frac{d[J_n(\beta)]}{d\beta} = \frac{n}{\beta} J_n(\beta) - J_{n+1}(\beta) = -\frac{n}{\beta} J_n(\beta) + J_{n-1}(\beta)$$

$$J_{n+1}(\beta) - \frac{2n}{\beta} J_n(\beta) + J_{n-1}(\beta) = 0 \left.\begin{array}{c} \\ \\ \\ \end{array}\right\} \quad (225)$$

$$\frac{d[J_0(\beta)]}{d\beta} = -J_1(\beta)$$

Applying this to the direct Bessel series as given by Eq. (221) we have for the Bessel factor of center frequency F, where $n = 0$

$$J_0(\beta) = 1 - \frac{(0.5\beta)^2}{(1!)^2} + \frac{(0.5\beta)^4}{(2!)^2} - \frac{(0.5\beta)^6}{(3!)^2} + \cdots \quad (226)$$

and for the Bessel factor belonging to either frequency $F - f$ or frequency $F + f$ the substitution $n = 1$ and

$$J_1(\beta) = 0.5\beta \left[1 - \frac{(0.5\beta)^2}{1!2!} + \frac{(0.5\beta)^4}{2!3!} - \frac{(0.5\beta)^6}{3!4!} + \cdots \right] = - \frac{d[J_0(\beta)]}{d\beta} \quad (227)$$

This result explains why in Fig. 9 the $J_0(\beta)$ curve starts out with a maximum value equal to unity and the $J_1(\beta)$ curve must start with a zero value. Inasmuch as the Bessel factors $J_n(\beta)$ are the respective factors by means of which the unmodulated carrier-current level I_m has to be multiplied in order to give the level of the particular spectrum current, we note that at places where the $J_0(\beta)$ curve intersects the β axis there can be no current of frequency F center.

In connection with the derivations in the text, the following trigonometric relations were often used:

$$\left.\begin{array}{l} (\sin x)(\sin y) = 0.5[\cos (x - y) - \cos (x + y)] \\ (\sin x)(\cos y) = 0.5[\sin (x + y) + \sin (x - y)] \\ (\cos x)(\sin y) = 0.5[\sin (x + y) - \sin (x - y)] \\ (\cos x)(\cos y) = 0.5[\cos (x + y) + \cos (x - y)] \end{array}\right\} \quad (228)$$

as well as the forms

$$\left.\begin{array}{l} \sin (x + y) = \sin x \cos y + \cos x \sin y \\ \cos (x + y) = \cos x \cos y - \sin x \sin y \\ \sin (x - y) = \sin x \cos y - \cos x \sin y \\ \cos (x - y) = \cos x \cos y + \sin x \sin y \end{array}\right\} \quad (229)$$

TABLE VIII

x	$Si(x)$	$Ci(x)$	$Ei(x)$	$Ei(-x)$	x	$Si(x)$	$Ci(x)$
1	0.9461	0.3374	1.8951	−0.2194	20	1.5482	0.04442
2	1.6054	0.423	4.9542	−0.0489	25	1.5315	−0.00685
3	1.8487	0.1196	9.9338	−0.01304	30	1.5668	−0.03303
4	1.7582	−0.141	19.6309	−0.00378	35	1.5969	−0.01148
5	1.5499	−0.19	40.1853	−0.001148	40	1.587	0.1902
6	1.4247	−0.06806	85.9898	−0.0003601	50	1.5587	0.1863
7	1.4546	0.0767	191.505	−0.0001155	60	1.5867	−0.0481
8	1.5742	0.1224	440.38	−0.00003767	70	1.5616	0.1092
9	1.665	0.05535	1037.88	−0.00001245	80	1.5723	−0.0124
10	1.6583	−0.04546	2492.23	−0.000004157	90	1.5757	0.009986
11	1.5783	−0.08956	6071.41		100	1.5622	−0.005149
12	1.505	−0.04978	14959.5				
13	1.4994	0.02676	37197.7				
14	1.5562	0.0694	93192.5				
15	1.6182	0.04628	234956				

69. Effective Input Impedance and Q Value of Feeders.—In connection with the dipole theory and the analysis of feeders we have learned that the input impedance depends on the termination as well as on the electrical length. We have also seen that a concentric line (Fig. 97) requires a ratio $D/d = 3.44$ in order to yield a surge impedance $Z_0 = 74$ ohms, which can match the radiation resistance of 74 ohms of a dipole. An axial copper wire AWG No. 4 and a ¾-in.-outside-diameter copper tubing whose wall is $\frac{1}{32}$ in. thick would meet this requirement. It can be shown that optimum Q value obtains for a concentric feeder as shown in Fig. 97, when $D/d = 4.22$. For such a diameter ratio, the ratio of the reactance to the resistance of the feeder becomes a maximum. Optimum Q is also obtained for the Lecher wires of Fig. 97, when the ratio of the spacing between the centers of the parallel conductors to the diameter of either conductor is 3.093. If such feeders are used between two tube stages, it is of interest to have high impedance termination. The impedance Z_1 looking into the line then is a maximum for the concentric feeder when $D/d = 14.3$. For the parallel-wire system, an optimum value occurs when the ratio of wire spacing to the diameter of either parallel wire is 10.48. These requirements are in some ways conflicting with the ratio requirement for a definite surge impedance value Z_0. In many practical applications it will be found, however, that when a line is used for a high Q tank, or if it is used for a high impedance termination, the requirement as far as the value of Z_0 is concerned is of only secondary importance. The above ratio values for optimum Q and optimum input impedance take the radiation resistance of the line into account as well as the proximity effect in case of the parallel-wire system.

TABLE IX

β		Circular functions			Hyperbolic functions			Epsilon functions	
Radians	Degrees	$\sin \beta$	$\cos \beta$	$\tan \beta$	$\sinh \beta$	$\cosh \beta$	$\tanh \beta$	ϵ^{β}	$\epsilon^{-\beta}$
0.5	28.65	0.4794	0.8776	0.5463	0.5211	1.1276	0.4621	1.6487	0.6065
1.0	57.3	0.8415	0.5403	1.5574	1.1752	1.5431	0.7616	2.7183	0.3679
1.5	85.94	0.9975	0.0707	14.101	2.1293	2.3524	0.9052	4.4817	0.2231
2	114.59	0.9093	−0.4161	−2.1850	3.6269	3.7622	0.9640	7.3891	0.1353
2.5	143.24	0.5985	−0.8011	−0.7470	6.0502	6.1323	0.9866	12.182	0.0821
3.0	171.89	0.1411	−0.9900	−0.1426	10.018	10.068	0.9951	20.086	0.0498
3.5	200.54	−0.3508	−0.9365	0.3746	16.543	16.573	0.9982	33.115	0.0302
4.0	229.18	−0.7568	−0.6536	1.1578	27.290	27.308	0.9993	54.598	0.0183
4.5	257.83	−0.9775	−0.2108	4.6373	45.003	45.014	0.9998	90.017	0.0111
5.0	286.48	−0.9589	0.2837	−3.3805	74.203	74.210	0.9999	148.41	0.0067
5.5	315.13°	−0.7055	0.7087	−0.9956	122.34	122.35	1.0000	244.69	0.0041
6.0	343.77°	−0.2794	0.9602	−0.2910	201.71	201.72	1.0000	403.43	0.0025

Another important relation is the ratio $4Q/\pi$ which is the step-up ratio of an open-ended quarter-wave-length feeder. For instance, at 300 Mc, an open-ended concentric line which is $\lambda/4$ long gives a voltage step-up of 5,810. Since for any line

$$Q = \frac{\text{reactance}}{\text{resistance}} = \frac{\Omega L}{R} = \frac{2\pi c L}{R\lambda} = \frac{2\pi L}{\lambda R \sqrt{CL}}$$

We have generally the Q value

$$Q = \frac{6.28 Z_0}{R\lambda} \tag{230}$$

where R, L, C are the line constants per unit length (per centimeter length since $c = 3 \times 10^{10}$ cm/sec and λ is in centimeters).

TABLE X

β		Circular functions, circular radians			Hyperbolic functions, hyperbolic radians			Epsilon functions	
Radians	Degrees	sin β	cos β	tan β	sinh β	cosh β	tanh β	ϵ^β	$\epsilon^{-\beta}$
0.00	0	0.0	1.0	0.0000	0.0	1.0	0.0	1.000	1.000
0.01	0.57	0.0100	1.0	0.0100	0.0100	1.0001	0.0100	1.0101	0.9900
0.02	1.15	0.0200	0.9998	0.0200	0.0200	1.0002	0.0200	1.0202	0.9802
0.03	1.72	0.0300	0.9996	0.0300	0.0300	1.0005	0.0300	1.0305	0.9704
0.04	2.29	0.0400	0.9992	0.0400	0.0400	1.0008	0.0400	1.0408	0.9608
0.05	2.86	0.0500	0.9988	0.0500	0.0500	1.0013	0.0500	1.0513	0.9512
0.06	3.44	0.0600	0.9982	0.0601	0.0600	1.0018	0.0599	1.0618	0.9418
0.07	4.01	0.0699	0.9976	0.0701	0.0701	1.0025	0.0699	1.0725	0.9324
0.08	4.58	0.0799	0.9968	0.0802	0.0801	1.0032	0.0798	1.0833	0.9231
0.09	5.16	0.0899	0.9960	0.0902	0.0901	1.0041	0.0898	1.0942	0.9139
0.10	5.73	0.0998	0.9950	0.1003	0.1002	1.0050	0.0997	1.1052	0.9048
0.11	6.30	0.1098	0.9940	0.1104	0.1102	1.0061	0.1096	1.1163	0.8958
0.12	6.88	0.1197	0.9928	0.1206	0.1203	1.0072	0.1194	1.1275	0.8869
0.13	7.45	0.1296	0.9916	0.1307	0.1304	1.0085	0.1293	1.1388	0.8781
0.14	8.02	0.1395	0.9902	0.1409	0.1405	1.0098	0.1391	1.1503	0.8694
0.15	8.59	0.1494	0.9888	0.1511	0.1506	1.0113	0.1489	1.1618	0.8607
0.16	9.17	0.1593	0.9872	0.1614	0.1607	1.0128	0.1587	1.1735	0.8521
0.17	9.74	0.1692	0.9856	0.1717	0.1708	1.0145	0.1684	1.1853	0.8437
0.18	10.31	0.1790	0.9838	0.1820	0.1810	1.0162	0.1781	1.1972	0.8353
0.19	10.89	0.1889	0.9820	0.1923	0.1912	1.0181	0.1878	1.2093	0.8270
0.20	11.46	0.1987	0.9801	0.2027	0.2013	1.0201	0.1974	1.2214	0.8187
0.21	12.03	0.2085	0.9780	0.2131	0.2116	1.0221	0.2070	1.2337	0.8106
0.22	12.61	0.2182	0.9759	0.2236	0.2218	1.0243	0.2165	1.2461	0.8025
0.23	13.18	0.2280	0.9737	0.2341	0.2320	1.0266	0.2260	1.2586	0.7945
0.24	13.75	0.2377	0.9713	0.2447	0.2423	1.0289	0.2355	1.2712	0.7866
0.25	14.32	0.2474	0.9689	0.2553	0.2526	1.0314	0.2449	1.2840	0.7788
0.26	14.90	0.2571	0.9664	0.2660	0.2629	1.0340	0.2543	1.2969	0.7711
0.27	15.47	0.2667	0.9638	0.2768	0.2733	1.0367	0.2636	1.3100	0.7634
0.28	16.04	0.2764	0.9611	0.2876	0.2837	1.0395	0.2729	1.3231	0.7558
0.29	16.62	0.2860	0.9582	0.2984	0.2941	1.0424	0.2821	1.3364	0.7483
0.30	17.19	0.2955	0.9553	0.3093	0.3045	1.0453	0.2913	1.3499	0.7408
0.31	17.76	0.3051	0.9523	0.3203	0.3150	1.0484	0.3004	1.3634	0.7334
0.32	18.33	0.3146	0.9492	0.3314	0.3255	1.0516	0.3095	1.3771	0.7261
0.33	18.91	0.3240	0.9460	0.3425	0.3360	1.0550	0.3185	1.3910	0.7189
0.34	19.48	0.3335	0.9428	0.3537	0.3466	1.0584	0.3275	1.4049	0.7118

β		Circular functions, circular radians			Hyperbolic functions, hyperbolic radians			Epsilon functions	
Radians	Degrees	sin β	cos β	tan β	sinh β	cosh β	tanh β	ϵ^β	$\epsilon^{-\beta}$
0.35	20.05	0.3429	0.9394	0.3650	0.3572	1.0619	0.3364	1.4191	0.7047
0.36	20.63	0.3523	0.9359	0.3764	0.3678	1.0655	0.3452	1.4333	0.6977
0.37	21.20	0.3616	0.9323	0.3879	0.3785	1.0692	0.3540	1.4477	0.6907
0.38	21.77	0.3709	0.9287	0.3994	0.3892	1.0731	0.3627	1.4623	0.6839
0.39	22.35	0.3802	0.9249	0.4111	0.4000	1.0770	0.3714	1.4770	0.6771
0.40	22.92	0.3894	0.9211	0.4228	0.4108	1.0811	0.3800	1.4918	0.6703
0.41	23.49	0.3986	0.9171	0.4346	0.4216	1.0852	0.3885	1.5068	0.6637
0.42	24.06	0.4078	0.9131	0.4466	0.4325	1.0895	0.3969	1.5220	0.6570
0.43	24.64	0.4169	0.9090	0.4586	0.4434	1.0939	0.4053	1.5373	0.6505
0.44	25.21	0.4259	0.9048	0.4708	0.4543	1.0984	0.4136	1.5527	0.6440
0.45	25.78	0.4350	0.9005	0.4831	0.4653	1.1030	0.4219	1.5683	0.6376
0.46	26.36	0.4440	0.8961	0.4954	0.4764	1.1077	0.4301	1.5841	0.6313
0.47	26.93	0.4529	0.8916	0.5080	0.4875	1.1125	0.4382	1.6000	0.6250
0.48	27.50	0.4618	0.8870	0.5206	0.4987	1.1174	0.4462	1.6161	0.6188
0.49	28.07	0.4706	0.8823	0.5334	0.5098	1.1225	0.4542	1.6323	0.6126
0.50	28.65	0.4794	0.8776	0.5463	0.5211	1.1276	0.4621	1.6487	0.6065
0.51	29.22	0.4882	0.8727	0.5594	0.5324	1.1329	0.4700	1.6653	0.6005
0.52	29.79	0.4969	0.8678	0.5726	0.5438	1.1383	0.4777	1.6820	0.5945
0.53	30.37	0.5055	0.8628	0.5859	0.5552	1.1438	0.4854	1.6989	0.5886
0.54	30.94	0.5141	0.8577	0.5994	0.5666	1.1494	0.4930	1.7160	0.5827
0.55	31.51	0.5227	0.8525	0.6131	0.5782	1.1551	0.5005	1.7333	0.5769
0.56	32.09	0.5312	0.8473	0.6269	0.5897	1.1609	0.5080	1.7507	0.5712
0.57	32.66	0.5396	0.8419	0.6410	0.6014	1.1669	0.5154	1.7683	0.5655
0.58	33.23	0.5480	0.8365	0.6552	0.6131	1.1730	0.5227	1.7860	0.5599
0.59	33.80	0.5564	0.8309	0.6696	0.6248	1.1792	0.5299	1.8040	0.5543
0.60	34.38	0.5646	0.8253	0.6841	0.6367	1.1855	0.5371	1.8221	0.5488
0.61	34.95	0.5729	0.8197	0.6989	0.6485	1.1919	0.5441	1.8404	0.5434
0.62	35.52	0.5810	0.8139	0.7139	0.6605	1.1984	0.5511	1.8589	0.5379
0.63	36.10	0.5891	0.8080	0.7291	0.6725	1.2051	0.5581	1.8776	0.5326
0.64	36.67	0.5972	0.8021	0.7445	0.6846	1.2119	0.5649	1.8965	0.5273
0.65	37.24	0.6052	0.7961	0.7602	0.6969	1.2188	0.5717	1.9155	0.5220
0.66	37.82	0.6131	0.7900	0.7761	0.7090	1.2258	0.5784	1.9348	0.5169
0.67	38.39	0.6210	0.7838	0.7923	0.7213	1.2330	0.5850	1.9542	0.5117
0.68	38.96	0.6288	0.7776	0.8087	0.7336	1.2403	0.5915	1.9739	0.5066
0.69	39.53	0.6365	0.7713	0.8253	0.7461	1.2477	0.5980	1.9937	0.5016
0.70	40.11	0.6442	0.7648	0.8423	0.7586	1.2552	0.6044	2.0138	0.4966

It can be shown that for an open-ended feeder shorter than $\lambda/4$ the line behaves like a condenser of quality

$$Q = \frac{Z_0 \sin (2\delta l)}{lR} \tag{231}$$

where l is the actual length of the line in centimeters and δ is the phase constant $2\pi/\lambda$. In a similar way a feeder short-circuited at the far end and shorter than $\lambda/4$ acts at the input side like a coil with a quality

$$Q = \frac{Z_0 \sin (2\delta l)}{lR} \tag{232}$$

It can be shown that the input impedance Z_1 for a length l which is almost any integer multiple of $\lambda/2$ such as $\lambda/2$, λ, $3\lambda/2$, etc., and open at the far end is

$$Z_1 = \frac{2Z_0^2}{lR} \frac{1}{1 + j\dfrac{2\pi Z_0}{\lambda R}\left(\dfrac{F}{F_r} - \dfrac{F_r}{F}\right)} \tag{233}$$

where F_r is the frequency that would cause exact line resonance and F is the operating frequency that produces almost line resonance for $\lambda/2$ distributions. Hence, when we deal with *exact* line resonance conditions, as with tank feeders (feeder acting as a tank), we have $F = F_r$ and $Z_1 = Z_r$, or

$$\left.\begin{array}{l} Z_r = \dfrac{2Z_0^2}{lR} \\[2mm] Q_r = \dfrac{2\pi Z_0}{\lambda R} \end{array}\right\} \tag{234}$$

For the case of an open-ended line whose length l is almost any odd multiple of $\lambda/4$, we have the input impedance

$$Z_1 = \frac{lR}{2}\left[1 + j\frac{2\pi Z_0}{R\lambda}\left(\frac{F}{F_r} - \frac{F_r}{F}\right)\right] \tag{235}$$

We have, therefore, the case similar to a series resonance circuit. Equation (235) holds not only for an open-ended line almost any odd multiple of $\lambda/4$ long but also for any short-circuited line nearly any integer multiple of $\lambda/2$.

70. Magnitudes of Important Factors.

In empty space
$$\begin{cases} \text{Permeability } \mu = 4\pi \times 10^{-7} \text{ henrys/m} \\[2mm] \text{Dielectric constant } \kappa = \dfrac{10^{-9}}{36\pi} \text{ farads/m} \\[2mm] \text{Velocity of propagation } c = \dfrac{1}{\sqrt{\mu\kappa}} = \dfrac{1}{\sqrt{1.257 \times 10^{-6} \times 8.854 \times 10^{-12}}} \\ \hspace{10cm} = 2.998 \text{ m/sec} \\[2mm] \text{Natural impedance } Z_0 = \sqrt{\dfrac{\mu}{\kappa}} = 376.7 \text{ ohms} \end{cases}$$

In salt water (ocean)
$$\begin{cases} \mu_s = \mu \\ \kappa_s = 80\kappa \\ c_s = \dfrac{c}{\sqrt{80}} = \dfrac{2.998}{\sqrt{80}} \text{ m/sec} \\[2mm] \text{Natural impedance } Z_s = \sqrt{\dfrac{\mu}{80\kappa}} = \dfrac{z_0}{\sqrt{80}} = \dfrac{376.7}{\sqrt{80}} = 37.6 \text{ ohms} \end{cases}$$

With respect to Fig. 36a the ratio of the field strength of refracted wave to incident wave (Υ coefficient of refraction) depends on angles φ. We have

$$\Upsilon = \frac{2 \cos \varphi \cdot \sin \gamma}{\sin (\varphi + \gamma) \cdot \cos (\varphi - \gamma)}$$

$$\frac{\sin \varphi}{\sin \gamma} = \sqrt{\kappa - \frac{2j\sigma}{F}}$$

REFERENCES

In order to eliminate certain references in which the reader may not be interested, the following are grouped according to their topics. The first group deals, for instance, only with publications having a bearing on the spectrum solution.

Publications on the Theory of the Distribution of the Modulation Energy in the Frequency Spectrum

VON HELMHOLTZ, H. L. F., On Sound Sensations ("Lehre von den Tonempfindungen"), 1862 (Latest edi., 1913, Braunschweig, p. 649–650, 1913).

RAYLEIGH, LORD JOHN WILLIAM STRUTT, Scientific Papers, Vol. 3, p. 1, 1887; Vol. 2, p. 88, 1883.

MATHIEU, E., Jour. de math. pures et appliguées, 13, p. 137, 1868.

WHITTAKER, E. T., Proc. Edinburgh Math. Soc., 33: p. 22, 1914; 32, p. 75, 1914.

CARSON, J. R., Proc. IRE, 10, p. 57, 1922.

INCE, E. L., Proc. London Math. Soc., 23, (2), 56, 1925; Proc. Roy. Soc. (Edinburgh), 45, 106, 1925; Proc. London Math. Soc. 25, (2), 53, 1926.

POL, B. VAN DER, Exp. Wireless, 1926; Proc. IRE, 18, 1194, 1930.

POL, B. VAN DER, and M. J. O. STRUTT, Phil. Mag., 5, 18, 1928.

STRUTT, M. J. O., Zeit. f. Phys., 69, 597, 1931; "Lamésche-Mathieusche-, und verwandte Funktionen in Physik und Technik," Ergeb. der Math., Band I, Hirschwaldsche Buchhandlung, Berlin, 1932.

HUMBERT, "Fonctions de Lamé et fonctions de Mathieu," Mémorial des Sc. Math., Vol. 10, Paris, 1926.

WINTER-GUENTER, H., Jahrb. der drahtl., 34, 1, 1929; 37, 172, 1931.

SALINGER, H. ENT, 6, 294, 1929.

BARROW, W. L., Ann. der Phys., 11, 147, 1931; Proc. IRE, 20, 1626, 1932.

POINCARÉ, H., "Mécanique Céleste II," p. 253.

WHITAKER and WATSON, Modern Analysis, Chap. IX.

Publications on the Theory of Wave Propagation in the FM Range of Carrier Frequencies

BEVERAGE, H. H., H. O. PETERSON, and C. W. HANSELL, Application of Frequencies above 30,000 Kilocycles to Communication Problems, Proc. IRE, 19, 1313, 1931.

ECKERSLEY, T. L., Short-wave Wireless Telegraphy, J.I.E.E. (London), 65, 600, 1927; Ultra-short Wave Refraction and Diffraction, J.I.E.E. (London), 80, 286, 1937.

JONES, L. F., A Study of the propagation of wave Lengths between Three and Eight Meters, Proc. IRE, 21, 349, 1933.

TREVOR, BERTRAM, and P. S. CARTER, Notes of Propagation of Waves below Ten Meters in Length, Proc. IRE, 21, 387, 1933.

SCHELLENG, J. C., C. R. BURROWS, and E. B. FERRELL, Ultra-short-wave Propagation, Proc. IRE, 21, 427, 1933.

ENGLUND, CARL R., ARTHUR B. CRAWFORD, and WILLIAM W. MUMFORD, Some Results of a Study of Ultra-short-wave Transmission Phenomena, Proc. IRE, 21, 464, 1933.

SMITH-ROSE, R. L., and J. S. McPETRIE, Proc. Phys. Soc. (London), 43, Part 5, No. 240, 592, 1931.

MUNRO, G. H., *J.I.E.E.* (*London*), **71**, No. 426, 135, 1932.

FELDMAN, C. B., The Optical Behavior of the Ground for Short Waves. *Proc. IRE*, **21**, 764, 1933.

BURROWS, C. R., A. DECINO, and L. E. HUNT, *Elec. Eng.*, **54**, 115, 1935; *Proc. IRE*, **23**, 1507, 1935.

VAN DER POL, B., and H. BREMMER, *Phil. Mag.*, **24**, 141, 826, 1937; *Hochfrequenztechnik und Elektroakustik*, **51**, 181, 1938; Report of Committee on Radio Wave Propagation, *Proc. IRE*, **26**, 1193, 1938.

BURROWS, C. R., Radio Propagation over Plane Earth-field Strength Curves, *Bell System Tech. J.*, **16**, 45, 1937.

PETERSON, H. O., Ultra-high-frequency Propagation Formulas, *RCA Rev.*, **4**, 162, 1939.

CROSBY, MURRAY G., Frequency-modulation Propagation Characteristics, *Proc. IRE*, **24**, June, 1936; The Service Range of Frequency Modulation, *RCA Rev.* **4**, 349, 1940.

BEVERAGE, H. H., Some Notes on Ultra-high-frequency Propagation, *RCA Rev.*, **1**, January, 1937.

MACLEAN, K. G., and G. S. WICKIZER, Notes on the Random Fading of 50-megacycle Signals over Nonoptical Paths, *Proc. IRE*, **27**, August, 1939.

WEIR, I. R., Comparative Field Tests of Frequency-modulation and Amplitude-modulation Transmitters, *Proc. RCA*, **16**, July, 1939.

NORTON, K. A., Ground Wave Propagation, *FCC*, Fourth Annual Broadcast Engineering Conference, February 10–21, 1941, No. 47475; Report No. 48466 of FCC, Report prepared by K. A. Norton on the Effect of Frequency on the Signal Range of an Ultra-high Frequency Radio Station.

CROSBY, M. G., Observations of Frequency Modulated Propagation on 26 Megacycles, *Proc. IRE*, **29**, 398, 1941.

EASTMAN, A. V., and J. R. WOODWARD, Binaural Transmission on a Single Channel, *Electronics*, **14**, February, 1941.

GUY, R. F., and R. M. MORRIS, NBC Frequency Modulation Field Test, *Radio Eng.*, **255**, 12–31, 136, January, 1941; *Electronics, Reference Issue*, June, 1941 (contains a very clear exposition for the entire field of FM in Sec. 3 consult also footnotes, p. 132).

BURROWS, HUNT, and DECINO, Ultra-short-wave Propagation: Mobile Urban Transmission Characteristics, *Bell System Tech. J.*, 1935.

HANDEL, P. V., and WOLFGANG PFISTER, Ultra-short Wave Propagation along the Curved Earth's Surface, *Hochfrequenctezhnik und Elektroakustik*, **47**, June, 1936.

HULL, ROSS, Air-mass Conditions and the Bending of Ultra-high-frequency Waves, *QST*, June, 1935, p. 13.

HOLMES, R. S., and A. H. TURNER, An Urban Field Strength Survey, at Thirty and One Hundred Megacycles, *Proc. IRE*, May, 1936.

BURROWS, C. R., The Propagation of Short Radio Waves over the North Atlantic, *Proc. IRE*, Sept., 1931.

CARTER, P. S., and G. S. WICKIZER, Ultra High Frequency Transmission between the RCA Building and the Empire State Building in New York City, *Proc. IRE*, August, 1936.

BEVERAGE, H. H., Some Notes on Ultra-high Frequency Propagation, *RCA Television*, Vol. II, October, 1937, p. 98 (a reprint from *RCA Rev.*, January, 1937).

Publications on Dipoles, other Antenna Systems and Feeders Employed in FM Work

CARTER, P. S., Circuit Relations in Radiating Systems and Applications to Antenna Problems. *Proc. IRE*, **20**, 1004, 1932; see also footnotes on p. 285.

BROWN, G. H., Directional Antennas, *Proc. IRE*, **25**, 78, 1937; The Turnstile Antenna, *Electronics*, **9, 14**, April, 1936.

ACEVES, J. G., Antennas for FM—reception, **14**, 42, September, 1941.

LINDENBLAD, N. E., Antennas and Transmission Lines at the Empire State Television Station, *Communications*, **21**, 10, April, 1941.

HARRIS, C. C., Losses in Twisted Pair Transmission Lines at Radio Frequencies, *Proc. IRE*, **24**, 425, 1936.

WHEELER, HAROLD A., and V. E. WHITMAN, The Design of Doublet Antenna Systems, *Proc. IRE*, **24**, 1257, 1936.

EASTMAN, A. V., and E. D. SCOTT, Transmission Lines as Frequency Modulators, *Proc. IRE*, **22**, 878, 1934.

RAKSKIT, H., Recent Technical Development in Wireless and Broadcasting in Great Britain, *Science and Culture*, **6**, November–December, 1940.

KRAUS, JOHN D., Multiwire Dipole Antennas, *Electronics*, January, 1940, p. 26.

BARBER, ALFRED W., Television Receiving Antennas and Transmission Lines, *Communications*, February, 1940, p. 15.

RODER, HANS, Graphical Methods for Problems Involving Radio-frequency Transmission Lines, *Proc. IRE*, February, 1933, pp. 290–302.

WHITMER, ROBERT, Radiation Resistance of Concentric Conductor Transmission Lines, *Proc. IRE*, September, 1933, pp. 1343–1353.

GOLDMAN, S., Dipoles and Reflectors, *Electronics*, May, 1940, p. 20.

BROWN, G. H., Vertical vs. Horizontal Polarization, *Electronics*, October, 1940, p. 20 (consult also: C. J. Young, *Proc. IRE*, **22**, 1290, November, 1934, and C. N. Anderson and I. E. Lattimer, *Proc. IRE*, **20**, 415, March, 1932); *Electronics*, *Reference Issue*, **14**, June, 1941.

NERGAARD, L. S., and B. SALZBERG, Resonant Impedance of Transmission Lines, *Proc. IRE*, **27**, 579, 1939.

SALZBERG, B., On the Optimum Length for Transmission Lines Used as Circuit Elements, *Proc. IRE*, **25**, 1564, 1937.

LEEDS, L. A., Concentric Narrow-band-elimination Filter, *Proc. IRE*, **26**, 576, 1938.

EVERITT, W. L., "Communication Engineering," McGraw-Hill Book Company, Inc., New York.

STERBA, E. J., and C. B. FELDMAN, Transmission Lines for Short-wave Radio Systems, *Proc. IRE*, **20**, 1163, 1932.

BROWN, G. H., and J. EPSTEIN, An Ultra-high Frequency Antenna of Simple Construction, *Communications*, **20**, 3, July, 1940.

WINLUND, E. S., FM Engineering Considerations (Contains "Economics of Antenna Design"), *FM*, July, 1941, p. 23.

Publications on Noise and Interference Due to Noise

CARSON, JOHN R., Selective Circuits and Static Interference, *Bell System Tech. J.* **4**, (2) April, 1925; also in *Electrical Communication*, **3** (4) April, 1925; Reduction of Atmospheric Disturbances, *Proc. IRE*, July, 1928, p. 967.

ARMSTRONG, E. H., A Method of Reducing Disturbances in Radio Signalling by a System of Frequency Modulation, *Proc. IRE*, May, 1936, p. 689.

LANDON, V. D., A Study of Noise Characteristics, *Proc. IRE*, November, 1936, p. 1514.

CROSBY, M. G., Frequency-modulation Noise Characteristics, *Proc. IRE*, April, 1937, p. 472.

RODER, H., Noise in Frequency Modulation, Electronics, May, 1937, p. 22.

PLUMP, E. H., Reduction of Interference by Frequency Modulation, *Hochfrequenz-tecknik und Elektroakustik*, September, 1938, p. 73.

FYLER, G. W., and J. A. WORCESTER, A Noise-free Receiver for the Reception of Frequency-modulated Ultrashort Waves, *Gen. Elec. Rev.*, July, 1939, p. 307.

SEELEY, S. W., Frequency Modulation, *RCA Rev.*, **5**, 472–474, 1941.

GOLDMAN, S., Noise and Interference in Frequency Modulation. *Electronics*, **14**, 37–42, August, 1941.

KEALL, O. E., Interference in Relation to Amplitude, Phase and Frequency Modulated Systems, *Wireless Eng.*, **18**, 6–17, 56–63, January–February, 1941.

LANDON, V. D., Impulse Noise in FM Reception, *Electronics*, **14**, 26–30, 73–76, February, 1941; Noise in Frequency Modulation Receivers, *Wireless World*, **47**, 156–158, June, 1941; *Electronics, Reference Issue*, **14**, 46–49, June, 1941.

REICH, H. J., Interference Suppression in AM and FM Systems, *Communications*, August, 1942, p. 7.

Publications on Fundamentals on FM, PM, and AM

AIKEN, C. B., The Detection of Two Modulated Waves Which Differ Slightly in Carrier Frequency, *Proc. IRE*, **19**, 120, 1931.

CARSON, J. R., Notes on the Theory of Modulation, *Proc. IRE*, **10**, 57, 1922; *Proc. IRE*, **7**, 187, 1929.

COOLEBROOK, F. M., The Physical Reality of Side Bands, *Exp. Wireless and Wireless Eng.*, **8**, 4, 1930.

ECKERSLEY, P. P., On the Simultaneous Operation of Different Broadcast Stations on the Same Channel, *Proc. IRE*, **19**, 175, 1931.

ECKERSLEY, T. L., Frequency Modulation and Distortion, *Exp. Wireless and Wireless Eng.*, **7**, 482, 1920.

GERTH, F., and W. HAHNEMANN, "Einige Betrachtungen zum Problem des Gleich-wellenrundfunks (Discussion of broadcast stations on same channel), *ENT*, **7**, 226, 1930.

HEILMANN, A., Einige Betrachtungen zum Problem der Frequenzmodulation (perhaps the first contribution to explain the features of FM and PM as compared with AM), *ENT*, **7**, 217, 1930.

HOWE, G. W. O., An Interesting Side Band Problem, *Exp. Wireless and Wireless Eng.* **7**, 651, 1930.

LADNER, A. W., The Phase of Carrier to Side Bands and Its Relation to A Synchronous Fading Phenomenon, *Marconi Rev.*, **25**, August, 1930.

LOEST, W., Phasen Modulation, *Z. f. Hochfrequenztechnik und Elektroakustik*, **36**, 188, 1930.

POL, B. VAN DER, Frequency Modulation, *Proc. IRE*, **18**, 1194, 1930 (the clearest exposition for the distribution of the modulation energy in the early days of FM).

POTTER, R. K., Transmission Characteristics of a Short-wave Telephone Circuit, *Proc. IRE*, **18**, 581, 1930.

RODER, H., Ueber Frequenzmodulation (on frequency modulation), *Telefunkenzeitung*, **53**, 48, 1929; Amplitude, Phase, and Frequency Modulation, *Proc. IRE*, **19**, 2145, 1931; Effects of Tuned Circuits Upon a Frequency Modulated Signal, *Proc. IRE*, **25**, 1617, 1937; Wide Band Frequency Modulation, *Electronics*, **10**, 22–64, May, 1937.

BEATTY, R. T., Apparent Demodulation of a Weak Station by a Stronger One, *Exp. Wireless and Wireless Eng.*, **5**, 300, June, 1928.

BUTTERWORTH, S., Apparent Demodulation of a Weak Station by a Stronger One, *Exp. Wireless and Wireless Eng.*, **6**, 619, November, 1929.

COLEBROOK, F. M., A Further Note on Apparent Demodulation, *Exp. Wireless and Wireless Eng.*, **8**, 409, August, 1931.

HOWE, G. W. O., Mutual Demodulation and Allied Problems, *Exp. Wireless and Wireless Eng.*, **8**, 405, August, 1931.

ARMSTRONG, E. H., Method of Reducing Disturbances in Radio Signaling by a System of Frequency Modulation (an unusual nonmathematical description of the Armstrong indirect FM system, describing many of the auxiliary apparatus employed), *Proc. IRE*, **24**, 689–740, May, 1936.

RUNGE, W., Ueber Modulation, Senderbreite, und Demodulation (on modulation, band width, and demodulation), *Telefunkenzeitung*, **55**, 28, 1930; Ueber die Moeglichkeit, Sender zu trennen, deren Seitenbaender sich ueberlappen (on the separation of two waves whose side bands overlap), *Telefunkenzeitung*, **55**, 34 1930; Untersuchungen an amplituden—und frequenz—modulierten Sendern, (experiments on AM and FM transmitters), (deals with AM, PM, and FM and is perhaps the first contribution on experimental methods for determining frequency deviation and phase deviation when AM is also present), *ENT*, **7**, 488, 1930.

SALINGER, H., Zur Theorie der Frequenzanalyse mittels Suchtons (on the theory of frequency analysis with a search current), *ENT*, **6**, 293, 1929.

SMITH, C. H., Note on the Relationships Existing between Radio Waves Modulated in Frequency and in Amplitude, *Exp. Wireless and Wireless Eng.*, **7**, 609, 1930.

SCOTT, EARL, and JOHN WOODYARD, Side Bands in FM, *Bull.* 68, *Eng. Esp. Station*, University of Washington, Seattle.

AIKEN, C. B., and H. S. LOH, An Experimental Single-sideband Transmitter, *Communications*, **19**, 10, February, 1939.

JAFFE, D. L., Armstrong's Frequency Modulator (tells in simple mathematical language how the Armstrong transmitter functions. It also shows what condition has to be satisfied to demodulate an FM-current. At the end of this paper is a discussion on harmonic distortion), *Proc. IRE*, **26**, 475, 1938.

CROSBY, M. G., Communication by Phase Modulation (a very clear exposition of networks and principles involved in the generation of PM currents and their demodulation), *Proc. IRE*, **27**, 126, 1939.

BRAINERD, J. G., Note on Modulation, *Proc. IRE*, **28**, 136, 1940.

BLACK, L. J., and H. J. SCOTT, Modulation Limits in FM, *Electronics*, September, 1940, p. 30.

SCOTT, H. J., Frequency vs. Phase Modulation *Communications*, **20**, 10, August, 1940.

SABAROFF, S., System of Phase and Frequency Modulation, *Communications*, **20**, 11, October, 1940.

SEELEY, S. W., Frequency Modulation (an unusually clear and nonmathematical presentation of FM), *RCA Rev.*, **5**, April, 1941.

CROSBY, M. G., Band Width and Readability in Frequency Modulation, *RCA Rev.*, **5**, January, 1941.

ARTZT, M., and D. E. FOSTER, Duplex Transmission of Frequency-modulated Sound and Facsimile, *RCA Rev.*, **6**, July, 1941.

SABAROFF, S., New System of Frequency Modulation, *Communications*, **21**, 8, September, 1941.

HOLLAND, L. N., and L. J. GIACOLETTO, Frequency Deviation Measurements, *Electronics*, October, 1941, p. 51.

THOMAS, H. P., FM-measurements, *Electronics*, July, 1941, p. 36.

DEAN, C. E., Bandwidth Factors for Cascade Tuned Circuits, *Electronics*, July, 1941, p. 41.

STONG, C. L., Limits FM Frequency Swing, FM, May, 1941, p. 37.

THOMAS, H. P., FM-transmitter Measurements, *Electronics*, May, 1941, p. 23.

WINLUND, E. S., Drift Analysis of the Crosby Frequency-modulated Transmitter Circuit, *Proc. IRE*, **29**, 390, 1941.

ARMSTRONG, E. H., Evolution of Frequency Modulation, *Elec. Eng.*, **59**, 485, December, 1940.

CARSON, J. R., Amplitude, Frequency, and Phase Angle Modulation, *Wireless Eng.*, **17**, 477, November, 1940.

HUDEO, E., The Transmission of Pictures by Frequency Modulation, *ENT*, **18**, 12, January–February, 1941.

HOWE, G. W. O., Frequency versus Amplitude Modulation, *Wireless Eng.*, **18**, 1, January, 1941.

NORTON, L., Why Not Narrow Band FM for General Amateur Use?, *Radio*, 88–92, 152–153, 159, January, 1941.

SPRAYBERRY, F. L., Principles of Frequency Modulation Part II, *Radio and Telev.*, **11**, 744, April, 1941.

WEISS, W., Detection in Frequency Modulation Receivers, *Communications*, **21**, 16, 18, March, 1941; Amplitude, Frequency and Phase Modulation, Letter to Editor, *Wireless Eng.*, **17**, 441, October, 1940.

WHEELER, H. A., Two-signal Cross Modulation in a Frequency Modulation Receiver, *Proc. IRE*, **28**, 537, December, 1940.

BARROW, W. L., A New Electrical Method of Frequency Analysis and Its Application to FM, *Proc. IRE*, **20**, 1626, 1932.

CHAFFEE, J. G., The Application of Negative Feedback to FM Systems, *Bell System Tech. J.* 404, October, 1937; *Proc. IRE*, 317, May, 1939.

YOCUM, C. H., Frequency Modulated Transmitters, *Communications*, November, 1939, p. 5; *Electronics*, November, 1939, p. 20.

FINK, D. G., Phase-frequency Modulation, *Electronics*, November, 1935, p. 431.

CARSON and FRY, Variable-frequency Electric Circuit Theory with Application to the Theory of FM, *Bell System Tech. J.*, October, 1937, p. 513.

WOODYARD, J. R., Application of the Autosynchronized Oscillator to Frequency Demodulation, *Proc. IRE*, May, 1937, p. 612.

WEIR, I. R., Wide Band FM vs. AM for Aircraft, *Electronics*, November, 1940, p. 34; Synchronized Frequency Modulation, *Communications*, **20**, 12, August, 1940.

CROSBY, M. G., A Method of Measuring Frequency Deviation, *RCA Rev.*, **4**, 473, April, 1940.

Publications on Apparatus Employed in FM Transmitters and Receivers

DAY, J. R., A Receiver for FM, *Electronics*, June, 1939, p. 32.

BARBER, A. W., Frequency Modulated Generators, *Radio Eng.*, November, 1936, p. 14.

EASTMAN, A. V., and E. D. SCOTT, Transmission Lines as Frequency Modulators, *Proc. IRE*, July, 1934, p. 878.

TRAVIS, CHARLES, Automatic Frequency Control, *Proc. IRE*, **23**, 1125, 1935.

MILLER, R. L., Fractional-frequency Generators Utilizing Regenerative Modulation, *Proc. IRE*, **27**, 446, 1939.

NYQUIST, H., Regeneration Theory, *Bell System Tech. J.*, **11**, 236, 1932.

HORTON, J. W., U. S. Patent, No. 1690299.

STERKY, H., Frequency Multiplication and Division, *Proc. IRE*, **25**, 1153, 1937.

GROSZKOWSKI, J., Frequency Division, *Proc. IRE*, **18**, 1960, 1930.

KOGA, I., A New Frequency Transformer or Frequency Changer, *Proc. IRE*, **15**, 669, 1927.

RODER, H., Theory of the Discriminator Circuit for Automatic Frequency Control, *Proc. IRE*, **26**, 590, 1938.

FOSTER, D. E., and S. W. SEELEY, Automatic Tuning, Simplified Circuits and Design Practice, *Proc. IRE*, **25**, 289, 1937.

RODER, H., Some Notes on Demodulation, *Proc. IRE*, **20**, 1946, 1932.

SHEAFFER, C. F., Frequency Modulator, *Proc. IRE*, **28**, 66, February, 1940.

PIERACCI, ROGER J., A Frequency-modulation Monitoring System, *Proc. IRE*, **28**, 374, 1940.

NOBLE, D. E., A State-wide FM Police System, *Electronics*, November, 1940, p. 18 December, 1940, p. 28.

DAVID, W. R., FM Broadcast Transmitters, *Communications*, **20**, 8, October, 1940.

HOBBS, M., FM Receivers—Design and Performance, *Electronics*, August, 1940, p. 22

SHEA, R. F., Frequency Modulation Receiver Design, *Communications*, **20**, 17, June, 1940.

CROSBY, M. G., Reactance Tube Frequency Modulators, *RCA Rev.*, **5**, 89, July, 1940.

BUDELMAN, F. T., 2-way Link FM Data (circuit analysis of 25-UFM transmitter and 11-UF receiver), *FM*, June, 1941, p. 24.

BROWNING, GLENN H., FM Service Instruments and Alignment Procedure, *FM*, June, 1941, p. 29.

LEVY, M. L., FM-AM Engineering Data (explaining the circuit design details and performance of the Stromberg-Carlson model 535 three-unit FM-AM receiver), *FM*, March, 1941, p. 8.

JAHNS, EDWARD, New Pilot A-FM Features, *FM*, July, 1941, p. 30.

THOMAS, H. P., and R. H. WILLIAMSON, A Commercial 50-kilowatt Frequency-modulation Broadcast Transmitting Station, *Proc. IRE*, **29**, 537, October, 1941.

MORRISON, J. F., A New Broadcast Transmitter Design for Frequency Modulation, *Proc. IRE*, June, 1940. Also, a reprint by the Western Electric Company.

FOSTER, D. E., and JOHN A. RANKIN, Intermediate-frequency Values for Frequency Modulated-wave Receivers, *Proc. IRE*, **29**, 546, October, 1941.

RICE, HARRY E., Factory Alignment Equipment for Frequency-modulation Receivers, *Proc. IRE*, **29**, 551, October, 1941.

MONTGOMERY, BRUCE E., Air Inductively Coupled Frequency Modulator, *Proc. IRE*, **29**, 559, October, 1941.

HALL, E. L., 30 to 340 Mc-wavemeter, *Electronics*, May, 1941, p. 37.

WEIR, I. R., Operating Problems in Frequency-modulation Transmitters, *Communications*, **21**, 5, May, 1941.

DAVID, W. R., G.E. Perfects FM Station Monitor, *FM*, 43, April, 1941; A Review of the Current A-FM Receiving Sets, *FM*, 12, May, 1941.

THOMAS, H. P., FM Measurements (outlines methods of measuring performance of FM transmitters and of making determinations of field strength), *Electronics*, July, 1941, p. 36.

HOBBS, M., A Demonstration System for Frequency Modulation, *Electronics*, **20**, January, 1941.

WEIR, I. R., Operating Problems in Frequency-modulated Transmitters, *Communications*, **21**, 7, June, 1941.

LEVY, M. L., Frequency-modulation Receivers, *Communications*, **21**, 5, March, 1941. Frequency-modulation Transmitters, *Communications*, **21**, 8, March, 1941.

TAYLOR, S. GORDON, AM/FM Broadcast Tuner, *Communications*, **21**, 10, March, 1941.

WING, A. K., and J. E. YOUNG, A Transmitter for Frequency-modulated Broadcast Service Using a New Ultra-high-frequency Tetrode, *RCA Rev.*, **5**, 327, January, 1941.

THOMAS, H. E., The Development of a Frequency Modulated Police Receiver for Ultra-high-frequency Use, *RCA Rev.*, **6**, 222, October, 1941.

HALLER, CECIL E., The Design and Development of Three New Ultra-high-frequency Transmitting Tubes, *Proc. IRE*, **30**, 20, January, 1942.

BARBER, A. W., C. J. Franks, and A. G. RICHARDSON, A Frequency Modulated Low Signal Generator, *Electronics*, 36–38, 92–95, April, 1941.

CROSBY, M. G., Tuned Filter for Frequency Modulation Defection, *Electronics and Telev. and Short Wave World*, **13**, 486, November, 1940.

GUY, R. F., and R. M. MORRIS, NBC Frequency Modulation Field Test, *Radio*, 12–31, 136, January, 1941.

MUNIZ, R., D. OESTREICHER, and W. OESTREICHER, A pull-swing Frequency Modulation System for the Amateur, *Radio and Telev.*, **11**, 598, February, 1941; **12**, 96, June, 1941.

SPRAYBERRY, F. L., Frequency Modulation Receivers, *Radio and Telev.*, **12**, 294, September, 1941.

THOMPSON, R. T., An 8-tube Converter for FM Reception, *Radio*, 9, 70, 72, 74, March, 1941.

TOOMBS, A., The Radio Battle of 1941, FM vs. AM, *Radio News*, **24**, 43, March, 1941.

INDEX

A

Accentuation (audio frequency), 11, 76, 121, 128, 219, 221, 236
Actions, in amplitude limiter, 105 (Fig. 28), 91, 209, 259, 276
    in accentuator, 96, 121, 128, 219, 221, 236
    in Armstrong system, 1, 3, 7, 36, 38, 44, 45, 77, 81, 121, 188, 231
    in deaccentuator, 96, 210, 219, 221, 256, 265
    in discriminator, 78, 193, 207
    in frequency demodulation, 78, 193
    in frequency modulation, 3, 14, 155
    in phase demodulation, 78, 193, 225
    in phase modulation, 3, 9, 225
Advance of phase, 2, 6, 9, 12, 45, 108, 111
Aerials (*see* antennas)
Alignment, of converter, 253, 264
    of discriminator, 207
    of FM receiver, 264
    of h-f stages, 266, 268
    of i-f stages, 266, 268, 271
AM + FM, 40, 63
AM + PM, 55
AM + PM + FM, 42, 69
Amplitude, carrier, 2, 3, 7
    instantaneous value, 2, 3, 7, 8
    limiter, 7, 63, 83, 92, 105
    modulation, 3, 7
    swing (deviation), 3, 9
Allocations of FM stations, 131, 249
Angle, of line, 309, 311, 313
    of phase, 2, 3, 6, 9, 12, 45, 108, 111
    of reflection, 133, 138, 143, 358
Angular velocity, of carrier, 2
    of deviation, 2
    of signal, 2
Antennas, receiver, 278, 294
    reflector, 295
    transmitter, 278, 334, 339
    turnstile, 341

B

Apparent PM, 1, 45
Armstrong system, 1, 3, 7, 36, 38, 44, 45, 77, 81, 121, 188, 231
Armstrong transmitter, 121, 188, 231
Ascending electromagnetic ray, 133, 138, 143
Assignments, frequency of, 131, 249
Attenuation, line, 307, 315, 321, 328
Audio-frequency accentuation (pre-emphasis), 96, 221
    deaccentuation (de-emphasis), 96, 221
Automatic Bessel current suppression, 23, 41, 86
    carrier suppression, 23, 86, 151, 153
    center-frequency control, 127, 128, 205, 236, 239, 242
    lower side-current suppression, 41

B

Backfeed, for center-frequency control, 128, 236
    for regenerative modulation, 154, 155
Balanced amplitude modulator, 1, 150, 183, 185, 187
    frequency modulator, 153, 175, 179
    tube circuits, 151
Band-restriction filter, 90
Band width, 25, 48, 88, 99
    comparison with deviation, 31, 32
    design, 28, 33, 93, 203
Beat frequency, 93, 101
Beat interference, 93, 101
Bessel curves, 23, 25, 32, 86
    distribution, 17, 21, 26, 30, 31, 33, 34, 44, 51, 58, 59, 347
    distribution feature, 51
    formulas, 17, 50, 56, 57, 61, 65, 70, 347–355
    functions, 17, 19, 23, 25, 32, 352, 353
    tables, 19, 20, 24, 33, 353
    theorem, 347–355
Bridge circuits, 150, 151, 153, 155

369